The Stereochemistry
of Macromolecules (*In Three Volumes*)

VOLUME 3

"*Nearly all great technological advances depend upon discoveries so unexpected as to be unplannable. Nature in her own time reveals her secrets to the patient questioner, and the plain fact is that nature is infinitely cleverer than man.*"

SIR CYRIL HINSHELWOOD, *The Listener*, Sept. 2, 1965.

The Stereochemistry
of Macromolecules *(In Three Volumes)*

Volume 3

Edited by A. D. ⌊KETLEY

W. R. GRACE & CO.
WASHINGTON RESEARCH CENTER
CLARKSVILLE, MARYLAND

1968

MARCEL DEKKER, INC., NEW YORK

Introduction to the Series

Most synthetic polymers contain either asymmetric atoms or double bonds which can give rise to geometrical isomers. As long as thirty years ago, the problem of stereoisomerism in polymer chains was discussed. However, the field lay dormant since, at that time, it was not possible either to synthesize polymers which were highly stereoregular or to measure the degree of regularity in the chains of those polymers which were known.

In the late 1940's, Schildknecht obtained indications that some steric control could be exerted by the catalyst in the polymerization of vinyl ethers and Morton developed catalysts which enabled him to influence the geometrical isomerism in diene polymers. However, it was not until Natta showed that transition-metal-based catalysts could exert a very high degree of steric control in the polymerization of simple olefins and a wide variety of other monomers that this field became a major area of research.

To some extent, the excitement surrounding the synthesis of highly stereoregular crystalline polymers has overshadowed another recent development of almost equal scientific significance—the enormous increase in our knowledge of the stereochemistry of polymers whose chains do not possess a high degree of stereoregularity. Undoubtedly the most important contribution to this latter problem has come from the application of nuclear magnetic resonance spectroscopy.

In Volume 1 of this three-volume series, we have attempted to bring together the latest knowledge of Ziegler-Natta polymerization. In Volume 2, we are concerned mainly with the stereospecific polymerization of monomers by catalysts other than the Ziegler-Natta type. In both volumes an attempt has been made to emphasize the mechanism of these reactions. In general there is very little real understanding of the way in which the stereochemistry of the growing chain is controlled, and even the starting point for any discussion, the structure of the catalyst, has not, in most cases, been elucidated. Many of the mechanisms which have been proposed in the literature are pure speculation and are not based on any experimental facts or accurate chemical knowledge. Consequently, the authors were asked not to impartially present ideas of this kind but to critically evaluate them and emphasize those which seem most sound. In this respect, we have given a special place to the ideas of Cossee and Arlman on Ziegler-Natta catalysis, not because, as these authors themselves would agree, they represent a definitive mechanism and all controversy has now ceased, but because the ideas are most in keeping with current knowledge and their approach seems to be one which could be most fruitfully followed to plan further research.

In Volume 3, the ways in which the steric structure of polymers may be determined are discussed, together with the way such structural features influence the physical, mechanical, and chemical properties of polymers.* We have also chosen to include in this volume some discussion of the effects of stereochemistry in processes involving biological macromolecules. This, obviously, is a topic which is too huge in scope to receive comprehensive treatment in a book mainly concerned with synthetic polymers. On the other hand, it is far too important to neglect. We have, consequently, aimed at including some material which might stimulate polymer chemists to work at the interface between their own field and biochemistry. We feel strongly that this kind of interaction is of enormous importance. The direct study of biological systems is made difficult by their overwhelming complexity. Small molecules are often, on the other hand, too far removed as realistic models for meaningful extrapolation to biological systems to be made. Synthetic polymers, in many cases, may be the best compromise between reality and simplicity.

Perhaps because polymer chemistry has such great industrial importance, chemists and physicists working in other areas have, it seems, sometimes regarded it as a relatively uninteresting field for research. We hope that these volumes will help to show that polymer chemistry is, in fact, an area of almost infinite fascination. The problems are often tremendously complex but the rewards for solving them are correspondingly great.

Acknowledgments

To the following, our sincere thanks: Above all, to the authors who gave their time and also to their long-suffering wives, one of whom threatened to send me a bowl of poisoned fruit; to W. R. Grace & Co.

* It is assumed that most of the readers of Volumes 1 and 2 will be acquainted with the nomenclature used to describe steric arrangements in polymers. For any who are not, this nomenclature is described in Chapter 1 of Volume 3 and in *Die Makromolekulare Chemie*, **82**, 1 (1965).

and in particular to Dr. F. X. Werber and Dr. T. R. Steadman for their encouragement in this project and for putting the facilities of the Washington Research Center at my disposal; to Blanche White and Gabriella Schwarzman for their assistance in searching the literature and in a thousand other ways; to Doris Gardner and Lois deCheubel for being unflagging, loyal typists; and to Jennie Touchette for drawing and redrawing figures at short notice when she would rather have been skiing or sunning on the beach.

A. D. K.

August, 1967

Contributors to Volume 1

M. COMPOSTELLA, Istituto Ricerche Polymer S.p.A., Terni, Italy

P. COSSEE, Koninklijke/Shell-Laboratorium (Shell Research N.V.), Amsterdam, The Netherlands

DONALD F. HOEG, Borg-Warner Corporation, Ingersoll Research Center, Des Plaines, Illinois

D. O. JORDAN, University of Adelaide, Adelaide, South Australia

WALTER MARCONI, SNAM-Laboratori Riuniti Studi e Ricerche, S. Donato, Milan, Italy

ITALO PASQUON, Istituto di Chimica Industriale del Politecnico, Milan, Italy

GUIDO SARTORI, ESSO Research, Brussels, Belgium

ALBERTO VALVASSORI, Istituto Ricerche G. Donegani, Montecatini-Edison, S.p.A., Milan, Italy

Contributors to Volume 2

J. N. BAPTIST, Brandenton, Florida

M. BINAGHI, Istituto di Ricerche G. Donegani, Montecatini-Edison, S.p.A., Milan, Italy

DIETRICH BRAUN, Deutsches Kunststoff-Institut, Darmstadt, Germany

W. COOPER, Dunlop Research Centre, Birmingham, England

A. D. KETLEY, W. R. Grace & Co., Washington Research Center, Clarksville, Maryland

N. MARANS, W. R. Grace & Co., Washington Research Center, Clarksville, Maryland

G. F. PREGAGLIA, Istituto di Ricerche G. Donegani, Montecatini-Edison, S.p.A., Milan, Italy

TEIJI TSURUTA, University of Tokyo, Tokyo, Japan

Contributors to Volume 3

GIANCARLO BRESSAN, Istituto di Ricerche G. Donegani, Montecatini-Edison, S.p.A., Milano, Italy

P. CORRADINI, Istituto Chimico, Università di Napoli, Napoli, Italy

V. CRESCENZI, Istituto Chimico, Università di Napoli, Napoli, Italy

MARIO FARINA, Istituto di Chimica Industriale del Politecnico, Milano, Italy

H. H. G. JELLINEK, Department of Chemistry, Clarkson Institute of Technology, Potsdam, New York

JULIAN F. JOHNSON, Chevron Research Company, Richmond, California

A. M. LIQUORI, Centro Nazionale di Chimica delle Macromolecole del C.N.R., Sez. III, Istituto Chimico, Università di Roma, Rome, Italy

TATSUO MIYAZAWA, Institute for Protein Research, Osaka University, Osaka, Japan

H. H. PATTEE, Biophysics Laboratory, Stanford University, Stanford, California

ROGER S. PORTER, University of Massachusetts, Polymer Science and Engineering Program, Amherst, Massachusetts

J. C. WOODBREY, Monsanto Chemical Center, St. Louis, Missouri

M. M. VAN BEYLEN, University of Louvain, Louvain, Belgium

Contents

xi

CHAPTER 1

Chain Conformation and Crystallinity

P. Corradini

ISTITUTO CHIMICO
UNIVERSITÁ DI NAPOLI
NAPLES, ITALY

I. CONFIGURATION OF STEREOREGULAR POLYMERS

A. Definitions

The constitution of a compound specifies which atoms in the molecule are bound to one another and with what type of bonds, without regard to

1

their spatial arrangement (*1*). A polymer is said to be regular when its constitution is regular; that is, its constitution is described by the enchainment of conventional base units all of the same type, in a head-to-tail sequence (*2*).

The configuration of a compound specifies the spatial arrangement of bonds in a molecule (of a given constitution) without regard to the multiplicity of spatial arrangements that may arise by rotation about single bonds. The configuration of a polymer is regular, and the polymer is said to be stereoregular, when its constitution is regular, and the law of succession of configurations of successive base units is assigned (*3*).

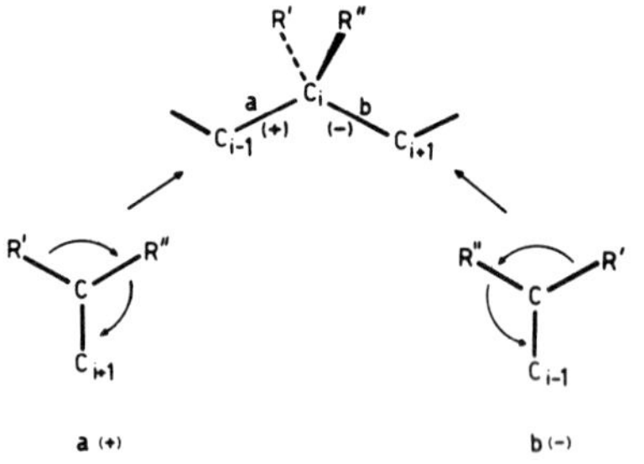

Fig. 1. Tetrahedral stereoisomeric centers. Definition of (+) and (−) bonds.

Different configurations of a regular polymer arise from the existence of stereoisomeric centers. The more important stereoisomeric centers that are found along the chain of a polymer are as follows:

1. Double bonds, which can have a *cis* or *trans* configuration
2. Tetrahedral stereoisomeric centers, that is, carbon atoms along the chain, bonded to two different substituents R' and R''

As regards the second type of stereoisomeric center, it is important to note that the two bonds of the chain adjacent to the carbon atom constituting the stereoisomeric center can be distinguished from a configurational viewpoint as (+) or (−) bonds (Fig. 1). This is also true where the carbon atom is not optically active. We shall designate by the (+) sign, with respect to the stereoisomeric center C_i, a bond adjacent to C_i along a chain

such that, as we look down the C_{i-1}—C_i bond (a) or the C_{i+1}—C_i bond (b), we see that the substituents C_{i+1}, R', and R'' or C_{i-1}, R', and R'' succeed each other by a clockwise rotation. R' is conventionally defined as being bulkier than R″ (4). We can define a (−) bond in an analogous manner. It is clear that, if (a) is (+) with respect to the stereoisomeric center C_i, (b) must be (−), and vice versa; bonds astride a tetrahedral stereoisomeric center are always opposite in sign by definition.

Two monomeric units are identical, from the configurational viewpoint, when corresponding bonds are characterized by the same set of (+) and (−) signs; they are configurationally enantiomorphous if corresponding bonds are characterized by opposite signs. Hence, insofar as the chain

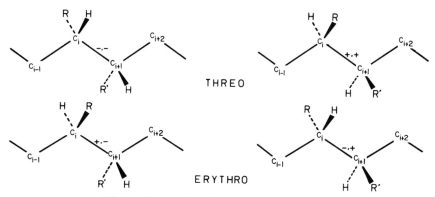

Fig. 2. *Threo* and *erythro* relative configurations.

atoms are concerned, enantiomorphous configurations of a monomeric unit can be obtained simply by changing all the configurational signs in an orderly manner.

As regards polymers having tetrahedral stereoisomeric centers, we call a polymer "isotactic" if it is formed from monomeric units with regular enchainment which are configurationally identical for long sequences of the chain and "syndiotactic" if it is formed from monomeric units with regular enchainment, alternately enantiomorphous from a configurational viewpoint. Isotaxy and syndiotaxy are the only two possibilities of stereoregular enchainment of order 1.

Whenever a monomeric unit contains more than one tetrahedral stereoisomeric center, it is necessary to define the relative configuration of the centers. In the case of two adjacent stereoisomeric centers, for instance, —CHR— and —CHR′—, the bond connecting them can be assigned two configurational signs (Fig. 2). The pairs (−,−) or (+,+) define a relative configuration *threo*, whereas the pairs (−,+) or (+,−) define a relative configuration *erythro*.

B. Examples

1. The conventional base unit of a vinyl polymer is:

$$-CH_2-CH-$$
$$\underset{R}{|}$$

Two stereoregular head-to-tail enchainments are possible (Fig. 3) with stereoregularity of order 1 [each monomeric unit equivalent to the preceding one (5)]:

(A) Isotactic:

$$---CH_2\overset{(+)}{----}CH\overset{(-)}{----}CH_2\overset{(+)}{----}CH\overset{(-)}{----}CH_2\overset{(+)}{----}CH\cdots$$
$$\qquad\qquad\underset{R}{|}\qquad\qquad\underset{R}{|}\qquad\qquad\underset{R}{|}$$

(B) Syndiotactic:

$$---CH_2\overset{(+)}{----}CH\overset{(-)}{----}CH_2\overset{(-)}{----}CH\overset{(+)}{----}CH_2\overset{(+)}{----}CH\overset{(-)}{----}CH_2\overset{(-)}{----}CH\overset{+)}{----}\cdots$$
$$\qquad\qquad\underset{R}{|}\qquad\qquad\underset{R}{|}\qquad\qquad\underset{R}{|}\qquad\qquad\underset{R}{|}$$

It is possible to prove that an isotactic chain of a vinyl polymer cannot be optically active as long as the two ends of the chain are indistinguishable or as long as the chain can be assumed to have infinite length.

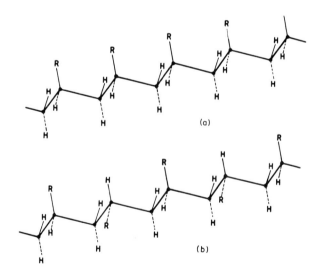

Fig. 3. Model of (a) isotactic and (b) syndiotactic polyolefin configurations with planar zigzag chains (5). (Reproduced with permission of Wiley-Interscience.)

The enantiomorphous configuration of (A) should be written:

(A') $\overset{(-)}{—CH_2}\overset{(+)}{—CH—}\overset{(-)}{CH_2}\overset{(+)}{—CH—}\overset{(-)}{CH_2}—CH—$
       with R substituents below each CH

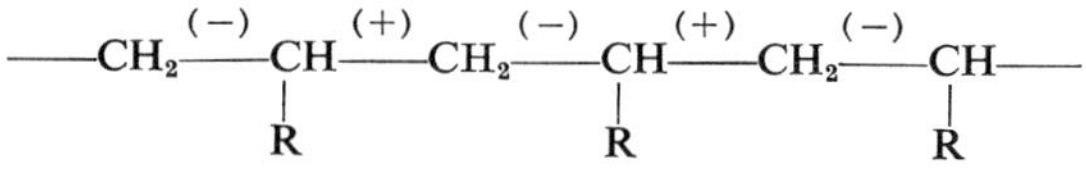

Configuration (A') can also be obtained by writing (A) in reverse; hence (A') is identical with (A) under the above conditions.

In nonstereoregular vinyl polymers we can find, more or less at random, an irregular head-to-tail succession of monomeric units having the configurations:

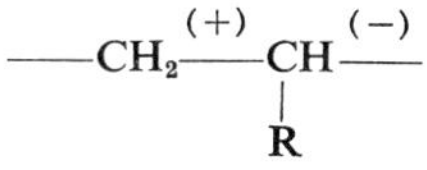

$\overset{(+)}{——CH_2}\overset{(-)}{—CH——}$ $\overset{(-)}{——CH_2}\overset{(+)}{—CH——}$
with R below CH   with R below CH

(a) 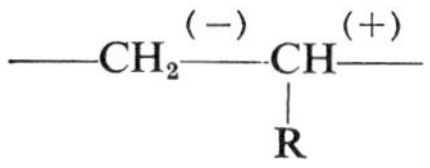   (b)

An isotactic pair is defined as a pair of configurations (aa) or (bb), for instance,

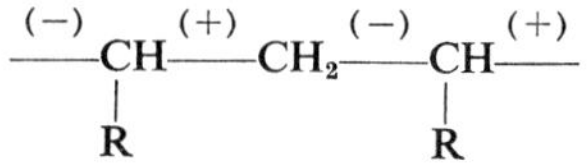

$\overset{(-)}{——CH}\overset{(+)}{——CH_2}\overset{(-)}{—CH}\overset{(+)}{—}$
with R below each CH

A syndiotactic pair is defined as a pair of configurations (ab) or (ba), for instance,

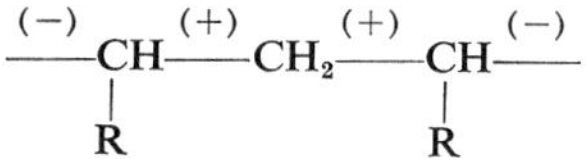

$\overset{(-)}{——CH}\overset{(+)}{——CH_2}\overset{(+)}{—CH}\overset{(-)}{—}$
with R below each CH

Introducing higher order correlations, an isotactic placement is defined as a triplet of configurations (aaa) or (bbb); a syndiotactic placement as a triplet (aba) or (bab); a heterotactic placement as a triplet (aab), (bba), (baa), or (abb) (6). The above definitions are particularly useful in the analysis of taxis in polymers which are not completely stereoregular.

The configurational regularity relationships holding for vinyl polymers also apply to polymers of aldehydes (7), dienes with 1,2 head-to-tail enchainment (5,8), and methyl methacrylate (9).

Isotactic polyaldehydes have the configuration:

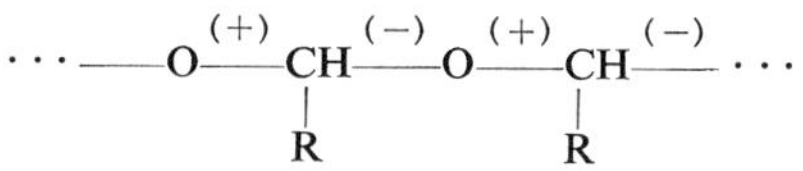

$\cdots \overset{(+)}{——O}\overset{(-)}{—CH}\overset{(+)}{——O}\overset{(-)}{—CH}— \cdots$
with R below each CH

Isotactic 1,2-polybutadiene has the configuration:

$$\cdots -\!\!-CH_2\overset{(+)}{-\!\!-}\underset{\underset{CH=CH_2}{|}}{CH}\overset{(-)}{-\!\!-}CH_2\overset{(+)}{-\!\!-}\underset{\underset{CH=CH_2}{|}}{CH}\overset{(-)}{-\!\!-}\cdots$$

Syndiotactic 1,2-polybutadiene has the configuration:

$$\cdots -\!\!-CH_2\overset{(+)}{-\!\!-}\underset{\underset{CH=CH_2}{|}}{CH}\overset{(-)}{-\!\!-}CH_2\overset{(-)}{-\!\!-}\underset{\underset{CH=CH_2}{|}}{CH}\overset{(+)}{-\!\!-}CH_2\overset{(+)}{-\!\!-}\underset{\underset{CH=CH_2}{|}}{CH}\overset{(-)}{-\!\!-}\cdots$$

Isotactic poly(methyl methacrylate) has the configuration:

$$\cdots -\!\!-CH_2\overset{(-)}{-\!\!}\underset{\underset{COOCH_3}{|}}{\overset{\overset{CH_3}{|}}{C}}\overset{(+)}{-\!\!}CH_2\overset{(-)}{-\!\!}\underset{\underset{COOCH_3}{|}}{\overset{\overset{CH_3}{|}}{C}}\overset{(+)}{-\!\!}CH_2\overset{(-)}{-\!\!}\underset{\underset{COOCH_3}{|}}{\overset{\overset{CH_3}{|}}{C}}\overset{(+)}{-\!\!}\cdots$$

Syndiotactic poly(methyl methacrylate) has the configuration:

$$\cdots -\!\!-CH_2\overset{(-)}{-\!\!}\underset{\underset{COOCH_3}{|}}{\overset{\overset{CH_3}{|}}{C}}\overset{(+)}{-\!\!}CH_2\overset{(+)}{-\!\!}\underset{\underset{COOCH_3}{|}}{\overset{\overset{CH_3}{|}}{C}}\overset{(-)}{-\!\!}CH_2\overset{(-)}{-\!\!}\underset{\underset{COOCH_3}{|}}{\overset{\overset{CH_3}{|}}{C}}\overset{(+)}{-\!\!}\cdots$$

2. The conventional base unit of a propylene oxide polymer (*10*) is:

$$-CH_2-\underset{\underset{CH_3}{|}}{CH}-O-$$

and contains one stereoisomeric center.

For the isotactic polymer, there are two enantiomorphous nonidentical configurations, as expected because of the asymmetry of the tertiary carbon atoms:

$$\cdots -\!\!-CH_2\overset{(+)}{-\!\!-}\underset{\underset{CH_3}{|}}{CH}\overset{(-)}{-\!\!-}O-\!\!-CH_2\overset{(+)}{-\!\!-}\underset{\underset{CH_3}{|}}{CH}\overset{(-)}{-\!\!-}O-\!\!-\cdots$$

$$\cdots -\!\!-CH_2\overset{(-)}{-\!\!-}\underset{\underset{CH_3}{|}}{CH}\overset{(+)}{-\!\!-}O-\!\!-CH_2\overset{(-)}{-\!\!-}\underset{\underset{CH_3}{|}}{CH}\overset{(+)}{-\!\!-}O-\!\!-\cdots$$

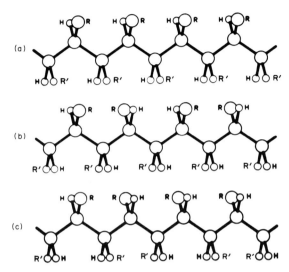

Fig. 4. Model of (a) *threo* diisotactic, (b) *erythro* diisotactic, and (c) disyndiotactic configurations with planar zigzag chains (*11*). (Reproduced with permission of Accademia Nazionale dei Lincei.)

3. Stereoregular polymers having the conventional base unit (—CHR—CHR'—), for instance, polychloro-*n*-butoxyethylene, are ditactic [(*11*); Fig. 4]. The possible stereoregular configurations are:

$$\cdots \text{——CH} \overset{(+,+)}{\text{——}} \text{CH} \overset{(-,-)}{\text{——}} \text{CH} \overset{(+,+)}{\text{——}} \text{CH} \overset{(-,-)}{\text{——}} \cdots$$
$$\qquad\quad | \qquad\quad | \qquad\quad | \qquad\quad |$$
$$\qquad\quad \text{R} \qquad\quad \text{R}' \qquad\quad \text{R} \qquad\quad \text{R}'$$

threo isotactic

$$\cdots \text{——CH} \overset{(+,-)}{\text{——}} \text{CH} \overset{(+,-)}{\text{——}} \text{CH} \overset{(+,-)}{\text{——}} \text{CH} \overset{(+,-)}{\text{——}} \cdots$$
$$\qquad\quad | \qquad\quad | \qquad\quad | \qquad\quad |$$
$$\qquad\quad \text{R} \qquad\quad \text{R}' \qquad\quad \text{R} \qquad\quad \text{R}'$$

erythro isotactic

$$\cdots \text{——CH} \overset{(-,-)}{\text{——}} \text{CH} \overset{(+,-)}{\text{——}} \text{CH} \overset{(+,+)}{\text{——}} \text{CH} \overset{(-,\,|\,)}{\text{——}} \text{CH} \overset{(\,,\,)}{\text{——}} \text{CH} \overset{(+,-)}{\text{——}} \cdots$$
$$\qquad\quad | \qquad\quad | \qquad\quad | \qquad\quad | \qquad\quad | \qquad\quad |$$
$$\qquad\quad \text{R} \qquad\quad \text{R}' \qquad\quad \text{R} \qquad\quad \text{R}' \qquad\quad \text{R} \qquad\quad \text{R}'$$

syndiotactic

4. The 1,4 polymers of 1,3-dienes contain a double bond along the chain as a stereoisomeric center and may contain up to two stereoisomeric

tetrahedral centers. Some typical examples are:

$$\begin{array}{c} \overset{cis}{\text{CH}=\text{CH}} \\ \end{array}$$

—CH₂ $\diagdown$ CH=CH (cis) $\diagdown$ CH₂—CH₂ $\diagup$ CH=CH (cis) $\diagdown$ CH₂—

1,4-*cis*-polybutadiene (*12*)

—CH₂—CH
     $\overset{trans}{\diagdown}$ CH—CH₂—CH₂—CH
                $\overset{trans}{\diagdown}$ CH—CH₂—

1,4-*trans*-polybutadiene (*13*)

CH₃
  $\diagup$ C=CH
—CH₂ $\overset{cis}{}$ CH₂—CH₂
          CH₃
            $\diagup$ C=CH
             $\overset{cis}{}$ CH₂—

1,4-*cis*-polyisoprene (*12*)

CH₃
  $\diagup$
—CH₂—C
     $\overset{trans}{\diagdown}$ CH—CH₂—CH₂—C
                              CH₃
                               $\diagup$
                      $\overset{trans}{\diagdown}$ CH—CH₂—CH₂—

1,4-*trans*-polyisoprene (*13*)

$$\overset{(+)}{—\text{CH}}\!\!—\overset{(-)}{\text{CH}}\overset{cis}{=\!\!=}\text{CH}—\text{CH}_2—\overset{(+)}{\text{CH}}—\overset{(-)}{\text{CH}}\overset{cis}{=\!\!=}\text{CH}—\text{CH}_2—\overset{(+)}{}$$
| |
CH₃   CH₃

isotactic 1,4-*cis*-polypentadiene (*14*)
(two enantiomorphous configurations)

$$\overset{(+)}{—\text{CH}}\!\!—\overset{(-)}{\text{CH}}\overset{cis}{=\!\!=}\text{CH}—\text{CH}_2—\overset{(-)}{\text{CH}}—\overset{(+)}{\text{CH}}\overset{cis}{=\!\!=}\text{CH}—\text{CH}_2—\overset{(+)}{}$$
| |
CH₃   CH₃

syndiotactic 1,4-*cis*-polypentadiene (*15*)

$$\overset{(+)}{—\text{CH}}\!\!—\overset{(-)}{\text{CH}}\overset{trans}{=\!\!=}\text{CH}—\text{CH}_2—\overset{(+)}{\text{CH}}—\overset{(-)}{\text{CH}}\overset{trans}{=\!\!=}\text{CH}—\text{CH}_2—\overset{(+)}{}$$
| |
CH₃   CH₃

isotactic 1,4-*trans*-polypentadiene (*16*) (two enantiomorphous configurations)

$$\overset{(+)}{—\text{CH}}\!\!—\overset{(-)}{\text{CH}}\overset{trans}{=\!\!=}\text{CH}—\text{CH}_2—\overset{(-)}{\text{CH}}—\overset{(+)}{\text{CH}}\overset{trans}{=\!\!=}\text{CH}—\text{CH}_2—\overset{(+)}{}$$
| |
CH₃   CH₃

syndiotactic 1,4-*trans*-polypentadiene

$$—\text{CH}\overset{trans}{=\!\!=}\text{CH}—\overset{(+)}{\text{CH}}—\overset{(-,+)}{\text{CH}}—\overset{(-)}{\text{CH}}—\text{CH}\overset{trans}{=\!\!=}\text{CH}—\overset{(+)}{\text{CH}}—\overset{(-,+)}{\text{CH}}—\overset{(-)}{\text{CH}}—$$
| | | |
OR   COOR'   OR   COOR'

erythro isotactic 1,4-*trans*-polycarboalkoxybutadienes (*17*)
(two enantiomorphous configurations)

The stereoregular polymers of carboalkoxybutadienes are tritactic.

5. The alternating copolymer between ethylene and *cis*-butene-2 has the conventional base unit —CH$_2$—CHCH$_3$—CHCH$_3$—CH$_2$—, corresponding to two propylene units in a head-to-head, tail-to-tail enchainment. Stereoregular polymers of order 1 are:

$$\begin{array}{ccccccccc}
^{(+)} & & ^{(-,+)} & & ^{(-)} & & & & \\
\text{—CH—} & & \text{—CH—} & & \text{—CH}_2\text{—} & & \text{—CH}_2\text{—} & \\
| & & | & & & & & \\
\text{CH}_3 & & \text{CH}_3 & & & &
\end{array}$$

—CH————CH————CH$_2$———CH$_2$———CH————CH————CH$_2$———CH$_2$—
 (+)   (−,+)   (−)   (+)   (−,+)   (−)
|CH$_3$ |CH$_3$ |CH$_3$ |CH$_3$

erythro isotactic (*18*)

—CH————CH————CH$_2$———CH$_2$———CH————CH————CH$_2$———CH$_2$—
 (−)   (+,+)   (−)   (−)   (+,+)   (−)
|CH$_3$ |CH$_3$ |CH$_3$ |CH$_3$

threo isotactic (two enantiomorphous configurations)

—CH————CH————CH$_2$———CH$_2$———CH————CH————CH$_2$———CH$_2$—
 (+)   (−,+)   (−)   (−)   (+,−)   (+)
|CH$_3$ |CH$_3$ |CH$_3$ |CH$_3$

erythro syndiotactic

—CH————CH————CH$_2$———CH$_2$———CH————CH—
 (−)   (+,+)   (−)   (+)   (−,−)   (+)
|CH$_3$ |CH$_3$ |CH$_3$ |CH$_3$

threo syndiotactic

II. CHAIN CONFORMATION OF STEREOREGULAR POLYMERS

A. Introduction

We accept the viewpoint that the conformations of a molecule are the different spatial arrangements of the atoms in a molecule of a given constitution and configuration that may arise by rotation about single bonds (*1*).

Thus, the assignment of the conformation to a macromolecule in the crystalline state corresponds to the specification of the internal rotation angles which characterize its molecular structure. (The molecular structure is established by the specification of the complete ensemble of internal coordinates, but since bond lengths and bond angles of the same nature are fairly constant in different compounds, it is often said, perhaps improperly, that the shape of a macromolecule is determined by its internal rotation angles.)

We shall use the convention of measuring the internal rotation angles in the following way [(*7*); Fig. 5]: calling the three successive bonds along the chain L_1, L_2, and L_3, we establish that the σ angle between the L_1L_2

and L_2L_3 planes (i.e., the angle of internal rotation σ_2, referring to L_2) is smaller than 180° if, looking parallel to L_2 from L_3, L_3 must be rotated clockwise by an angle smaller than 180° in order to superpose it on L_1; or (which is the same) if, looking parallel to L_2 from L_1, L_1 must be rotated clockwise by an angle smaller than 180° in order to superpose it on L_3.†

The conformation of a macromolecule satisfies two principles established in successive steps by Huggins (19), Bunn (20), Pauling (21) and Natta and Corradini (22).

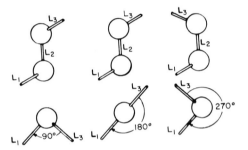

Fig. 5. Convention used to measure the internal rotation angles (7). (Reproduced with permission of Wiley-Interscience.)

a. *Equivalence Principle.* The conformation of the chain in the crystalline state is defined by a succession of equivalent structural units. The structural unit coincides in general with 1 monomeric unit (m.u.) or $\frac{1}{2}$ m.u.; in exceptional cases it corresponds to 2 m.u. (23). Successive structural units occupy geometrically (not necessarily crystallographically) equivalent positions with respect to a crystallographic axis of repetition.

b. *Principle of Minimum Internal Conformational Energy.* The conformation of a chain in a crystal approaches one of minimum internal conformational energy which would be taken by an isolated chain subjected to the restrictions imposed by the equivalence postulate.

B. Line Repetition Groups (24)

The crystalline state implies three-dimensional order. Hence, in the case of crystalline polymers, one of the translations of the lattice must relate atoms belonging to the same macromolecule.

† We use the convention in which $\sigma = 180°$ for *trans* conformations.

With the exception of a case to be treated later, where isomorphism of monomeric units is present (see Sect. IIIF), the regularity and the stereoregularity in the succession of the conventional base units is a necessary condition for a polymer to be crystallizable.

Besides the translation, other symmetry elements are possible for the conformation of a linear macromolecule, provided they are compatible with the chemical constitution and configuration. Of course, they must be such as to leave the chain axis c unchanged. For instance, a threefold rotation axis perpendicular to c is not a possible symmetry operator of the conformation of a macromolecule.

Of the symmetry operators which leave the chain axis unchanged, rotations r around the chain have to be taken into consideration only in extremely rare cases.

If we exclude rotations r around the chain axis, the symmetry elements compatible with the chain repetition are: t, translation along the chain axis; i, symmetry center; m or d, symmetry planes perpendicular or parallel to the c axis, respectively; c, glide plane, with a translation equal to half of the repetition axis c; 2, twofold axis perpendicular to the chain axis. A rotation $2\pi(N/M)$ around the chain axis can be combined with a translation c/M giving rise to the screw symmetry operator $s(M/N)$, involving the repetition of M structural units in N pitches ($2M$ if twofold axes perpendicular to the chain axis are also present). The conformation of a polymer for which $M/N \neq 1$ is called helicoidal (Fig. 6).

The screw operator s cannot combine with the operators i, m, d, and c, which would change the sense of the screw, except in the case that $M/N = 1$ or $M/N = 2$.

By combining the symmetry elements listed above in the appropriate way, it is possible to establish the so-called chain repetition groups. There are thirteen of them in all and they are listed in Table 1, together with examples of polymers having the corresponding symmetry. The symbol which characterizes each group is formed as follows: the first letter, s or t, indicates whether the repetition along the axis is helicoidal (translation plus rotation) or translatory (simple translation). Finally, there are the symmetry elements sufficient to specify the full symmetry of the chain.

Table 2 lists the cylindrical coordinates of the structural units for some of the chain repetition groups (the axis z being coincident with the chain axis). Structural units related by one change of sign in ϕ or z are enantiomorphous; structural units related by no change of sign or by two changes of sign in ϕ and z are isomorphous; structural units related by no change

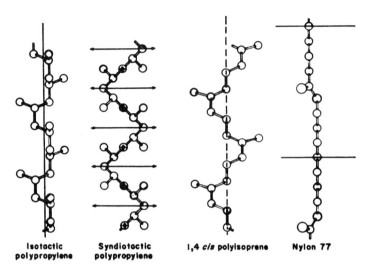

Isotactic   Syndiotactic   1,4 *cis* polyisoprene   Nylon 77
polypropylene   polypropylene

Fig. 6. Examples of different types of chain conformation: isotactic polypropylene $s(3/1)1$; syndiotactic polypropylene $s(2/1)2$; 1,4-*cis*-polyisoprene tc; and nylon 77 tm (*26*). (Reproduced with permission of Wiley-Interscience.)

TABLE 1

Possible Chain Repetition Groups

$s(M/N)1$, subgroup $t1$	Isotactic polypropylene	$s(3/1)1$
$s(M/N)2$, subgroup $t2$	Syndiotactic polypropylene	$s(2/1)2$
tm	Nylon 77	
td	—	
tc	1,4-*cis*-polyisoprene	
ti	Ethylene-butene-2 (*cis–erythro*) isotactic alternating copolymer	
$s(2/1)m$	*trans*-polypentenamer	
$s(2/1)d$	Nylon 6	
tdm	—	
tid	Nylon 66	
tcm	Syndiotactic 1,2-polybutadiene	
tic	*cis*-1,4-polybutadiene	
$s(2/1)dm$	Polymethylene	

TABLE 2

Line repetition groups	Cylindrical coordinates of equivalent structural units			
$s(M/N)1$	ρ, ϕ, z	$\rho, \phi + 2\pi(N/M), z + c/N \cdots$		
$s(M/N)2$ (2 in $z = 0, \phi = 0$)	ρ, ϕ, z	$\rho, \phi + 2\pi(N/M), z + c/N$	$\rho, -\phi, -z$	$\rho, -\phi + 2\pi(N/M), -z + c/N \cdots$
tm	ρ, ϕ, z	$\rho, -\phi, -z$	$\rho, \phi, z + c \cdots$	
td	ρ, ϕ, z	$\rho, -\phi, z$	$\rho, \phi, z + c \cdots$	
tc	ρ, ϕ, z	$\rho, -\phi, z + (c/2)$	$\rho, \phi, z + c \cdots$	
ti	ρ, ϕ, z	$\rho, \phi + \pi, -z$	$\rho, \phi, z + c \cdots$	
$s(2/1)m$	ρ, ϕ, z	$\rho, \phi + \pi, z + (c/2)$	$\rho, \phi, -z$	$\rho, \phi + \pi, -z + (c/2)$
$s(2/1)d$	ρ, ϕ, z	$\rho, \phi + \pi, z + (c/2)$	$\rho, -\phi, z$	$\rho, -\phi + \pi, z + (c/2)$
tdm	ρ, ϕ, z	$\rho, -\phi, z$	$\rho, \phi, -z; \quad \rho, -\phi, -z$	
tcd	ρ, ϕ, z	$\rho, \phi + \pi, z + (c/2)$	$\rho, -\phi, z$	$\rho, -\phi + \pi, z + (c/2)$
tcm	ρ, ϕ, z	$\rho, -\phi, z + (c/2)$	$\rho, \phi, -z$	$\rho, -\phi, -z$
tic	ρ, ϕ, z	$\rho, \phi + \pi, -z$	$\rho, -\phi, z + (c/2)$	$\rho, -\phi + \pi, -z + (c/2)$
$s(2/1)dm$	ρ, ϕ, z	$\rho, \phi + \pi, z + (c/2)$	$\rho, -\phi, z$	$\rho, -\phi + \pi, z + (c/2)$
	$\rho, \phi, -z$	$\rho, \phi + \pi, -z + (c/2)$	$\rho, -\phi, -z$	$\rho, -\phi + \pi, -z + (c/2)$

13

of sign in z are isoclined; structural units related by a change of sign in z are anticlined [(25); Fig. 7].

The compatibility relationships between configuration and possible line repetition groups (possible chain symmetries) have been established for a number of polymers. We shall examine some examples of them.

Head-to-tail polymers in which the two directions of the chain are intrinsically nonequivalent, such as polyamino acids, polyisoprene, etc., may have as line repetition groups only those which allow the repetition of all isoclined structural units ($s(M/N)1$, $t1$, etc.). For example, in a

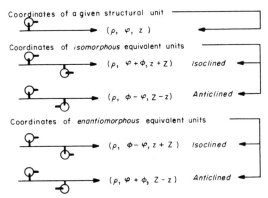

Fig. 7. Cylindrical coordinates of various structural units (26). (Reproduced with permission of Wiley-Interscience.)

polyamino acid, $s(M/N)2$ would change a NH—CO group into a CO—NH group as we proceed along a given chain, contrary to the chemical constitution.

As first recognized by Pauling (21), if a polyamino acid contains asymmetric α-carbon atoms, it must necessarily have a helicoidal structure in the crystal state. The symmetry element c must be immediately withdrawn because of the fact that it would repeat a carbon atom $-l$ into the enantiomorphous $-d$ form.

The chain of a vinyl polymer cannot have symmetry operators such as d or i because of the chemical constitution. It may be easily seen (26) that the only chain symmetries which are possible for a vinyl polymer are $s(M/N)2$, tc, and $s(M/N)1$. The chain symmetries $s(M/N)2$ and tc are compatible only with a syndiotactic configuration,

$$-\overset{(+)}{CH}-\overset{(+)}{CH_2}-\overset{(-)}{CH}-\overset{(-)}{CH_2}-\overset{(-)}{CH}-$$
$$\quad\ \ |\qquad\qquad\ \ |\qquad\qquad\ \ |$$
$$\quad CH_3\qquad\quad CH_3\qquad\quad CH_3$$

because the twofold axis 2 must pass through the methylene carbon atom, leaving the (+) or (−) nature of symmetry-related bonds unchanged, whereas the glide plane c changes a (+,+) pair into a succeeding (−,−) one. The chain symmetry $s(M/N)1$ is compatible only with an isotactic configuration where the structural unit is coincident with a monomeric unit.

The symmetry element m could also be allowed for a vinyl polymer in the case of a planar or nearly planar zigzag chain.

C. Principle of Minimum Conformational Internal Energy

This principle is taken into account to a greater or lesser extent in all the recent work on the interpretation of polymer structures. As plainly discussed by Bunn and Holmes (27), the energetic factors which determine the conformations of polymer chains are as follows:

1. A bond orientation effect which favors staggered bond conformations in saturated molecules, as found, for example, in the zigzag polyethylene and poly(vinyl chloride) chains or in isotactic polypropylene. Bunn proposed a nomenclature which describes A as a *trans* staggered bond along the chain and B(C) as a *gauche* right-handed (left-handed) staggered bond along the chain. In the following we shall, however, call T a *trans* staggered bond and G_+ and G_- the *gauche* bonds with $\sigma = +60°$, and $\sigma = -60°$, respectively. In single bonds adjacent to double bonds, skew (S_+, S_- with $\sigma = \pm120°$) and *cis* (C with $\sigma = 0°$) conformations are favored instead.

2. Intramolecular interactions between neighboring substituents or between substituents and chain atoms. These may eventually lead to deviations from staggered conformations in overcrowded molecules, as occurs, for example, in isotactic vinyl polymers with bulky side groups.

3. Packing effects, which may influence the choice between conformations of nearly equal energy for the isolated chain. If the energy differences between different conformations are greater than a few hundred calories per mole of chain atom, the choice of conformation is not likely to be influenced by the possible energy differences associated with packing efficiency.

Careful consideration of the above principles are sufficient to justify the $(TG_+)_3$ or $(G_-T)_3$ equivalent conformations found in the crystal state for isotactic polypropylene (28)

$$\left(-CH\overset{(-)}{\underset{\underset{CH_3}{|}}{-}}CH_2\overset{(+)}{-}\right)_n$$

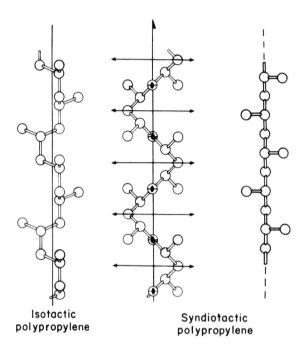

Fig. 8. Different conformations of polypropylene chains: isotactic $(TG_+)_3$ and syndiotactic $(G_+G_+TT)_2$ and (TTTT).

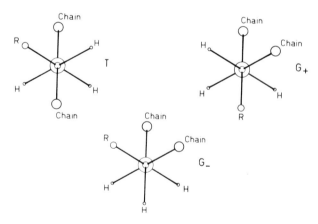

Fig. 9. The conformations T and G_+ are preferred for a (+) bond.

and the (TTG_G_) or (G$_+$G$_+$TT) equivalent conformations found in the crystal state for syndiotactic polypropylene (*29*)

$$\left(-\overset{(+)}{\underset{\underset{CH_3}{|}}{CH}}-\overset{(+)}{CH_2}-\overset{(-)}{\underset{\underset{CH_3}{|}}{CH}}-\overset{(-)}{CH_2}-\right)_n$$

For syndiotactic polypropylene also, a (TTTT) conformation has been found in a crystalline polymorph [(*30*); Fig. 8].

As a general rule (Fig. 9), it can be shown in fact (*31*) that (a) (+) bonds tend to assume only G$_+$ or T conformations, whereas (−) bonds tend to

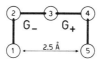

Fig. 10. Steric hindrance of a G$_+$G$_-$ sequence of bonds.

assume only G$_-$ or T conformations. Further conditions restricting the possible conformations arise from the fact that (b) G$_+$ cannot be followed by G$_-$ (Fig. 10) and from the fact that (c) the pair of internal rotation angles around the chain bonds lying between two

$$-\underset{\underset{CH_3}{|}}{CH}-$$

groups cannot be TT for an isotactic pair

$$-\overset{\overset{(-)}{(+)}}{\underset{\underset{CH_3}{|}}{CH}}-\overset{\overset{(+)}{(-)}}{CH_2}-\underset{\underset{CH_3}{|}}{CH}-$$

nor TG or GT for a syndiotactic one

$$-\overset{\overset{(-)}{(+)}}{\underset{\underset{CH_3}{|}}{CH}}-\overset{\overset{(-)}{(+)}}{CH_2}-\underset{\underset{CH_3}{|}}{CH}-$$

(Fig. 11). As an example, for the pair of chain bonds of isotactic polypropylene lying between the two tertiary carbon atoms

$$-\underset{\underset{CH_3}{|}}{CH}-\overset{(+)}{CH_2}-\overset{(-)}{\underset{\underset{CH_3}{|}}{CH}}-$$

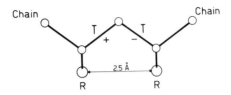

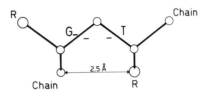

Fig. 11. Steric hindrance of a TT conformation of the bonds between two CH—R groups in isotactic polymers and of a GT conformation in syndiotactic polymers.

staggered conformations like (G_T), (G_G+), (G_G_), (G+G+), and (TG+) are prohibited through (a) and (b) and the conformation (TT) is prohibited through (c). The only conformations which are left are G+T and TG_, which can be followed only by G+T and TG_, respectively, giving rise to the well-known helical conformation.

D. Attempts to Calculate the Conformational Internal Energy of a Polymer Chain as a Function of Internal Rotation Angles

On the basis of the principles outlined above, various attempts have been made in the last few years to calculate the conformational internal energy of a polymer chain as a function of internal rotation angles. The first attempt by Liquori (*32*) for one-atom helices was based largely on the Mason and Kreevoy (*33*) data for the van der Waals contributions to the internal energy. Bunn and Holmes (*27*) pointed out that van der Waals' interactions alone are not sufficient to explain the barriers to internal rotation, since bond orientation effects must be taken into account as well. Barriers to internal rotation analogous to those found in low molecular weight compounds together with van der Waals' energy–distance data given by Mason and Kreevoy for the interaction between methyl and methylene groups separated by four or more bonds have since been used by Natta, Corradini, and Ganis in an approximate calculation of the conformational internal energy of a polypropylene chain, both in the crystal state (26) and as an isolated chain (34),† as a function of the internal rotation angles.

Solely on the basis of the equivalence postulate, the chain of the isotactic polymer should have a conformation in the crystal state with a succession of internal rotation angles of the type $\sigma_1, \sigma_2, \sigma_1, \sigma_2 \ldots$, whereas the chain of a syndiotactic polymer should have a conformation in the

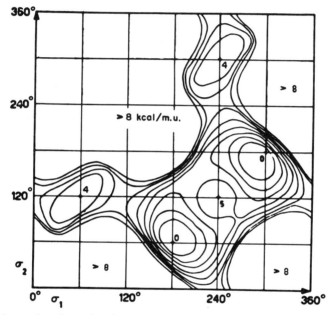

Fig. 12. Internal conformational energy of an isotactic polypropylene chain for different helicoidal conformations (26). (Reproduced with permission of Wiley-Interscience.)

crystal state of the type $\sigma_1, \sigma_1, \sigma_2, \sigma_2 \cdots$ or of the type $\sigma_1 = 180°, \sigma_2, -\sigma_1 = 180°, -\sigma_2 \ldots$. Consequently, contour plots of the internal energy E as a function of two parameters (σ_1 and σ_2) are sufficient to establish the conformation or conformations of minimum conformational internal energy content. The results are shown in Figs. 12 and 13.

For isotactic polypropylene, two minima are present and correspond to the chain conformations $(TG_+)_3$ and $(G_-T)_3$ found in the crystal state. All known isotactic vinyl polymer conformations are very close to the minimum energy values of the $E(\sigma_1, \sigma_2)$ plot of polypropylene (35).

† That is, when restraints imposed on its shape by factors influencing the efficiency of packing in the crystal lattice are eliminated, as in a dilute solution.

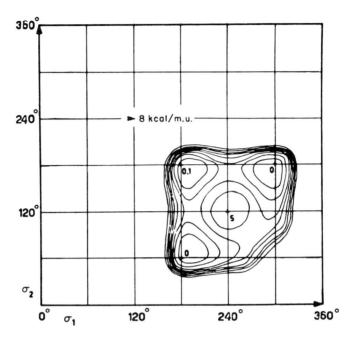

Fig. 13. Internal conformational energy of a syndiotactic polypropylene chain for different helicoidal conformations (*26*). (Reproduced with permission of Wiley-Interscience.)

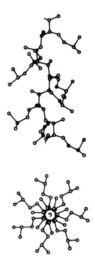

Fig. 14. Model of the chain of poly-*trans*(methylisobutoxy)ethylene. Projected parallel and perpendicular to the chain axis (*11*). (Reproduced with permission of Accademia Nazionale dei Lincei.)

For syndiotactic polypropylene, three minima of nearly equal depth are found, as expected. Two of them correspond to the chain conformations $(TTG_-G_-)_2$ and $(G_+G_+TT)_2$, respectively, having symmetry $s(2/1)2$ (Fig. 8). The third one corresponds to the (TTTT) conformation of a polymorph of syndiotactic polypropylene (Fig. 8) and is also found for syndiotactic polybutadiene and syndiotactic poly(vinyl chloride).

Calculations of the type shown above have also been used to supplement data on the configurational assignment of polymers, such as *erythro* and *threo* diisotactic polymers, whose chain conformation was already known from an interpretation of fiber diagrams [(*36*); Fig. 14].

E. Unperturbed Chain Conformations

It may be of interest at this point to give an idea of how it is possible to apply the above energetic considerations to the calculation of the chain conformation of a polymer under conditions where the chain conformation is not bound to contain a translation, for instance, in dilute solution. It is clear that in such a case the equivalence principle does not hold and the possible chain conformations are more near those of minimum free energy of the isolated chain.

An approximate calculation has been done for polypropylene by Corradini et al. (*37*), taking into account only interactions between neighboring atoms, depending on not more than two internal rotation angles. Analogous calculations have been performed subsequently by Flory et al. (*38*). The results can be applied to head-to-tail polypropylenes with any specified sequence of $(+)$ and $(-)$ bonds. It is possible to construct graphs $E(\sigma_i, \sigma_{i+1})$ showing the internal conformational energy relating to the hindered rotation around the l_{i+1} bond and to the repulsion between atoms that are not directly linked, which are a function of the internal rotation angles σ_i and σ_{i+1} alone.

If we order the bonds of the chain in the following way:

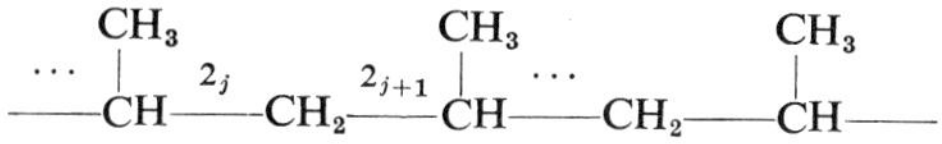

$$
\begin{array}{ccccc}
\text{CH}_3 & & \text{CH}_3 & & \text{CH}_3 \\
| & 2j & | & 2j+1 & | \\
\cdots \quad \text{CH} & \text{CH}_2 & \text{CH} & \text{CH}_2 & \text{CH} \\
\end{array}
$$

it is easy to see that two main types of graphs arise, $E(\sigma_{2j}, \sigma_{2j+1})$ and $E(\sigma_{2j+1}, \sigma_{2j+2})$.

The pair $\sigma_{2j}, \sigma_{2j+1}$ may correspond, from a configurational viewpoint, to a $(+,-)$, $(-,+)$, $(+,+)$ pair [Fig. 15, (a)–(d)]; whereas the couple $\sigma_{2j+1}, \sigma_{2j+2}$ may correspond, from a configurational viewpoint, to a $(-,+)$ or $(+,-)$ pair [Fig. 16(a) and (b)].

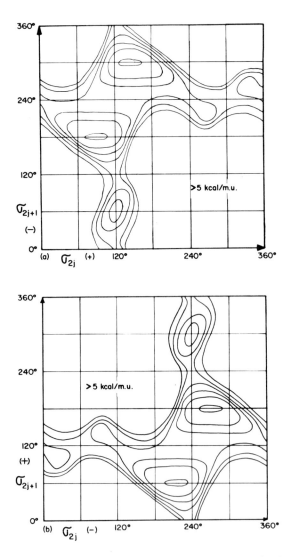

Fig. 15. Graphs of the internal conformational energies of interaction between neighboring bonds of polypropylene chain. Bonds 2_j and 2_{j+1} are comprised between two CH—R groups.

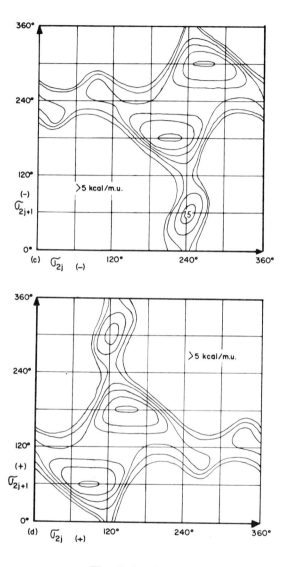

Fig. 15 (continued)

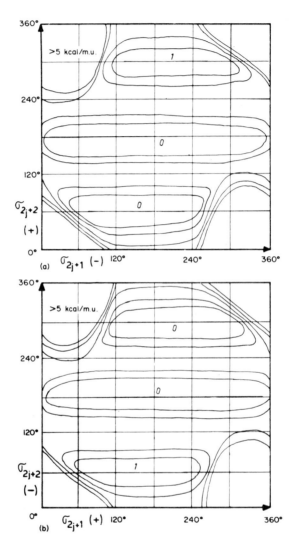

Fig. 16. Graphs of the internal conformational energies of interaction between neighboring bonds of a polypropylene chain. Bonds 2_{j+1} and 2_{j+2} are astride a CH—R group.

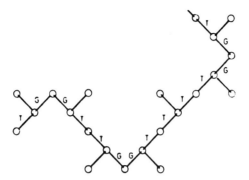

Fig. 17. Chain model of syndiotactic polypropylene in solution (*34*). (Reproduced with permission of Accedemia Nazionale dei Lincei.)

As an example, for a syndiotactic polymer, it is possible to verify that possible isoenergetic sequences are as follows:

	CH_3		CH_3		CH_3		CH_3
	|		|		|		|
	—CH——	—CH$_2$—	—CH——	—CH$_2$——	—CH—	—CH$_2$-	—CH——
Configuration:	(+)	(+)	(−)	(−)	(+)	(+)	
See Figure:		15(d)	16(b)	15(c)	16(a)	15(d)	16(b)
Minimum energy	···180°	180°	180°	180°	180°	180° ···	
conformations:	···180°	180°	180°	180°	60°	60° ···	
	···180°	180°	300°	300°	180°	180° ···	
	···60°	60°	180°	180°	180°	180° ···	
	···60°	60°	180°	180°	60°	60° ···	

that is, the conformation of syndiotactic polypropylene tends to correspond to a succession of *trans* bond pairs separated by pairs of *gauche* bonds, which must always be separated by at least one pair of *trans* bonds (Fig. 17).

The conformation of the macromolecules of isotactic vinyl polymers in unperturbed solutions corresponds to an alternation of helical chain segments with different senses of spiralization. The junction between right- and left-handed spirals may be of the type underlined:

	—CH$_2$—	—CH—	—CH$_2$—	—CH——	—CH$_2$—	—CH—	—CH$_2$—	
		(+) | (−)		(+) | (−)		(+) | (−)		
		CH_3		CH_3		CH_3		
$(180°, 300°)_m$	180°	300°	180°	180°	60°	180°	$(60°, 180°)_n$	

which requires no extra energy with respect to the *trans–gauche* (TG) conformation, alternating with the type:

$$—CH_2—CH—CH_2—CH—CH_2—CH—CH_2—$$
$$(+) \mid (-) \quad (+) \mid (-) \quad (+) \mid (-)$$
$$CH_3 \qquad CH_3 \qquad CH_3$$

$$(60°, 180°)_n \quad 60° \quad 180° \quad 120° \quad 300° \quad 180° \quad 300° \quad (180°, 300°)_m$$
$$\text{or}$$
$$60° \quad 240°$$

which can be realized at the cost of some extra energy.

Thus, the model of isotactic polymer chains can be represented by sequences of the following general type:

$$\cdots (G_+T)_p(G'_+G'_-)(TG_-)_q(TT)(G_+T)_r(G'_+G'_-)(TG_-)_s \cdots$$

each pair being astride a CHR group (Fig. 18).

For syndiotactic polymers, adopting the foregoing conventions, the chain model is of the type:

$$\cdots (G_-G_-)(TT)_{2n+1}(G_-G_-)(TT)_{2p}(G_+G_+)(TT)_{2p+1}(G_+G_+) \cdots$$

with $E(G_-G_-) = E(G_+G_+) = E(TT)$.

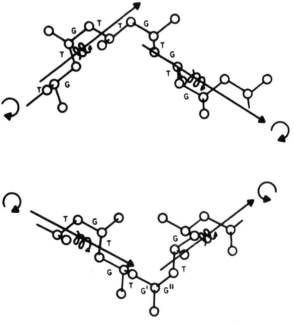

Fig. 18. Model of the inversions of helical sense of isotactic polypropylene in solution (*34*). (Reproduced with permission of Accademia Nazionale dei Lincei.)

The pairs indicated in the case of syndiotactic polymers—unlike the previous case—relate to bonds included between two CH—R groups.

F. Determination of the Geometry of Polymer Chains from X-ray Data

In the case of polymers, the parameters which can be directly determined from the X-ray fiber spectra are the identity period (c) and the number of monomeric units (M) which repeat within the identity period. In the case of polymers with complex helicoidal chain structures $[s(M/N)1]$, we can determine from X-ray spectra the identity period per monomeric unit $(p = c/M)$ and the period P of each turn of the helix $(P = c/N)$.

Fig. 19. Parameters determining the chain conformation of an isotactic polyolefin.

These two parameters depend on the ensemble of internal coordinates, which characterize the structural unit, and, in particular, on the ensemble of internal rotation angles which characterize the macromolecular conformation.

Various papers have been published (39) concerning the relationships which relate the above parameters p and P (or c and M) with the internal coordinates q_i of the chain atoms. For instance, in the case of isotactic vinyl polymers, the geometry of the chain is determined by the values assumed by $b_1, b_2, \phi_1, \phi_2, \sigma_1, \sigma_2$ (Fig. 19) and by the fact that $b_i = b_{i+2}$, $\phi_i = \phi_{i+2}$, and $\sigma_i = \sigma_{i+2}$, as imposed by the helicoidal symmetry. The relationships which can be deduced are:

$$d = \frac{\begin{aligned} &b_1(\cos \phi_1 \cos \phi_2 - \cos \Theta - \sin \phi_1 \sin \phi_2 \cos \sigma_1)^{1/2} \\ &- b_2(\cos \phi_1 \cos \phi_2 - \cos \Theta - \sin \phi_1 \sin \phi_2 \cos \sigma_2)^{1/2} \end{aligned}}{2^{1/2} \sin (\Theta/2)}$$

$$1 + 2 \cos \Theta = \cos \phi_1 \cos \phi_2(1 + \cos \sigma_1 \cos \sigma_2) - \sin \phi_1 \sin \phi_2$$
$$\times (\cos \sigma_1 + \cos \sigma_2) - (\cos \phi_1 + \cos \phi_2) \sin \sigma_1 \sin \sigma_2$$
$$+ \cos \sigma_1 \cos \sigma_2$$

In the case of isotactic polypropylene, assuming $b_1 = b_2 = 1.54$ Å, $\phi_1 = \phi_2 = 114°$, $\sigma_1 = 60°$, and $\sigma_2 = 180°$, we have $d = 2.17$ Å and $\Theta = 2\pi(N/M) = 120°$ (helix $s(3/1)1$).

In the case of a stereoregular polymer fulfilling the tc symmetry (40), the number of monomeric units n which repeat within the identity period is 2; the geometry of the chain is again determined by the assumed internal coordinates $b_1, b_2, \phi_1, \phi_2, \sigma_1, \sigma_2$ under the conditions $b_i = b_{i+2}$, $\phi_i = \phi_{i+2}$, and $\sigma_i = -\sigma_{i+2}$ (imposed by the glide plane symmetry).

In the case where $\phi_1 = \phi_2 = \phi$ and $b_1 = b_2 = r$, we obtain

$$p = 2r \sin (\phi/2)[\sin^2 (\phi/2) + \cos (\phi/2) \sin^2 (\sigma_2/2)]^{1/2}$$

with $\sigma_1 = 180°$.

In the case of a stereoregular vinyl polymer fulfilling the $s(M/N)2$ symmetry (40), the internal coordinates of the structural unit are $b_1, b_2, \phi_1, \phi_2, \sigma_1, \sigma_2$. A twofold axis crosses each CH_2 group.

Assuming that $\phi_1 = \phi_2 = \phi$ and $b_1 = b_2 = r$,

$$d = \frac{r \sin^2 \phi[tg^2(\phi/2) \sin (\sigma_1 + \sigma_2) - \sin \sigma_1 - \sin \sigma_2]}{2 \sin \Theta}$$

$$\cos \theta = \cos^2 (\phi/2) - \tfrac{1}{2} \sin^2 \phi(1 + \cos \sigma_1)(1 + \cos \sigma_2)$$
$$+ \sin^2 (\phi/2) \cos (\sigma_1 + \sigma_2)$$

Assuming that d and θ are equal to the experimental value (1.85 Å) and $\pi/2$, respectively, we find in the case of syndiotactic polypropylene with tetrahedral bond angles and $r = 1.54$ Å that $\sigma_1 = 64°$ and $\sigma_2 = 184°$.

G. Experimental Determination of the Period and Number of Monomeric Units within the Period of a Crystalline Polymer (41)

Whereas in the case of crystalline polymers it is not easy to get single crystals and X-ray spectra thereof, it is possible in many instances to obtain oriented fibers in which the very small polymer crystallites are all oriented with their chain axis (which is coincident with a crystallographic axis) in a direction parallel or close to parallel to the fiber axis. The X-ray diffraction pattern which can be obtained from such fibers is completely equivalent to the X-ray pattern given by a single crystal rotating along one of its crystallographic axes. The X-ray pattern given by an oriented fiber of isotactic poly-α-butene (42) is shown as an example in Fig. 20. Reflections with indices $hk0$ appear along the equator of the film; for such reflections, the angle of diffraction θ can be read directly on the film and

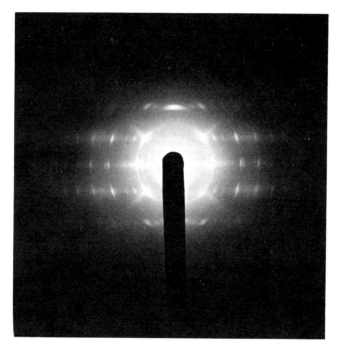

Fig. 20. Oriented fiber spectrum of isotactic poly-1-butene (*42*). (Reproduced with permission of Nicola Zanichelli.)

is connected to the corresponding lattice distances through the well-known Bragg relation:

$$\lambda = 2d_{hk0} \sin \theta_{hk0} \qquad (1)$$

The length of the crystallographic axis parallel to the fiber axis can be obtained directly from the spacing between the layer lines on the spectrum through the relationship:

$$c = \frac{s\lambda}{\sin tg^{-1}(Y_s/R)} = sd_s \qquad (2)$$

where Y_s is the distance between the 0th (equatorial) and the sth layer line and R is the radius of the camera.

The identity period c equals 6.5 ± 0.1 Å and the Bragg distances d_{hk0} appear in the ratio $1:1/\sqrt{3}:\frac{1}{2}:\ldots$, pointing to a hexagonal or rhombohedral lattice which can be further confirmed through a more detailed analysis of the whole spectrum.

The identity period per monomeric unit p, which is a whole fraction of c, can be readily deduced from the Bragg distances of the equatorial reflections taken from a fiber rotating with the fiber axis perpendicular to the rotation axis; it can be shown that the appearance of the spectrum of poly-α-butene taken in this way with a strong reflection having $d = 2.16$ Å is indicative of an identity period per monomeric unit $p = 6.5$ Å/3. This is consistent with a chain conformation having a threefold helix symmetry.

A slightly more sophisticated procedure is required to interpret fiber spectra of polymers having complicated helical structures. When the helix is nonintegral, the parameter P/p (number of monomeric units per pitch) seems to be more suitable than other parameters such as c/P or c/p for describing the helix. Moreover, the number s which appears in Eq. (2) is not easily determined, or may not even be determinable.

From the X-ray experiment we can get $d_s = c/s$ and p directly. To each layer line we can associate a given value ζ_s of the ratio p/d_s. The intensity distributed along the layer lines ζ_s is simply related to the value of P/p. It is beyond the scope of this review to go into further details (*43*).

TABLE 3

Polymer	Ref.	Identity period, Å	Number of m.u. in the period	Chain symmetry	Space group
Polypropylene (form I)	28	6.5	3	$s(3/1)1$	Cc
Polybutene-1 (form I)	42	6.5	3	$s(3/1)1$	$R3c$
Polypentene-1 (form I)	44	6.6	3	$s(3/1)1$	—
Poly-3-methylbutene-1	45	6.8	4	$s(4/1)1$	—
Poly-4-methylpentene-1	46	13.8	7	$s(7/2)1$	$P\bar{4}$
Poly-5-methylhexene-1	47	6.5	3	$s(3/1)1$	—
Polystyrene	48	6.65	3	$s(3/1)1$	$R3c$
Poly-o-methylstyrene	49	8.1	4	$s(4/1)1$	$I4_1cd$
Poly-m-methylstyrene	50	21.7	11	$s(11/3)1$	—
Polyvinylcyclohexane (form I)	51	6.5	4	$s(4/1)1$	$I4_1/a$
Polyvinylcyclohexane (form II)	71	44.6	24	$s(24/7)1$	$I\bar{4}$
Poly(vinyl methyl ether)	52	6.5	3	$s(3/1)1$	Rc
Poly(vinyl isopropyl ether)	53	35.5	17	$s(17/5)1$	—
Poly(vinyl isobutyl ether)	54	6.5	3	$s(3/1)1$	—
Poly(*trans*-β-chlorovinyl ether)	55	6.5	3	$s(3/1)1$	—
Poly(*cis*-β-chlorovinyl ether)	55	8.6	4	$s(4/1)1$	—
Poly-p-fluorostyrene	45	8.1	4	$s(4/1)1$	—
Poly-o-fluorostyrene	56	6.63	3	$s(3/1)1$	$R3c$

H. Some Data Concerning the Chain Conformation of Stereoregular Polymers

a. *Isotactic Polymers.* The chain conformation of isotactic polypropylene $(TG)_3$ corresponding to an identity period of 6.5 Å has been thoroughly discussed in the previous sections. In Table 3 the data concerning the chain conformation of some other isotactic polymers are given. The chain conformation is always helicoidal. The number of monomeric units per pitch ranges in all observed cases between 3.0 and 4.0, and the internal rotation angles do not deviate, in general, more than 20° from the staggered values.

The small deviations from staggered values of the internal angles can be associated in many instances with the bulkiness of the side groups. Thus, for instance, the helices of 3-substituted polyolefins, such as poly-3-methylbutene, have a fourfold helix which can be designated $(T'G')_4$. The identity period lies between 6.5 and 7 Å. Polyolefins which are 4-substituted, such as poly-4-methylpentene, have a helix slightly less deformed than the staggered one, and the repetition is obtained after 7 m.u. in two turns of the helix $(T'G')_{3.5}$ (Fig. 21). However, poly-4-methyl-1,3-pentadiene has an even more complicated helix, containing 3.6 monomeric units per pitch $(T'G')_{3.6}$. Poly-5-methylhexene has the methyl substituent of the side group sufficiently far from the chain atoms to be capable of crystallizing again as a threefold helix.

Reasons related to packing efficiency are probably why poly-*o*-fluorostyrene crystallizes with a threefold helix $(TG)_3$ corresponding to an identity period of 6.6 Å, whereas poly-*p*-fluorostyrene crystallizes with a fourfold helix $(TG')_4$ having an identity period of 8.1 Å.

Polymers of the higher olefins like polyoctedecene-1 also have a chain conformation corresponding to a fourfold helix (*57*), but the whole symmetry of the macromolecule appears to be lower, neighboring side chains being parallel to each other in pairs. This is a case where the "structural unit" is not coincident with 1 m.u. (*23*).

b. *Polymers Containing Double Bonds along the Chain.* The internal rotation angles of single bonds adjacent to double bonds preferentially assume values equal to $\alpha = 120°$ or $-\alpha = -120°$. The internal rotation angles of single bonds not adjacent to double bonds tend to assume staggered conformations (*trans* or possibly *gauche*). The chain configurations and conformations of some typical polymers, containing double bonds along the chain, are reported in Table 4. Figs. 22, 23, 24, 25, and 26 give, respectively, the chain conformations of 1,4-enchained

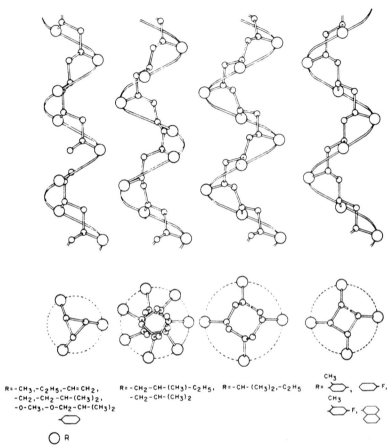

Fig. 21. Chain conformations of various isotactic polymers having different side groups (*45*). (Reproduced with permission of *Gazzetta Chimica Italiana*.)

stereoregular polybutadienes (compared with the 1,2-enchained), poly-pentenamer, *cis*-1,4-poly(2-*t*-butylbutadiene), and *cis*-1,4-polypentadiene (syndiotactic and isotactic).

c. *Polymers Containing Oxygen along the Chain.* The chain conforma-tions of some polymers containing oxygen along the chain are reported in Table 5. The chain conformation of isotactic polyaldehydes is very similar to that of isotactic vinyl polymers (Fig. 27). The internal rotation angles are displaced from the staggered values, being $\sigma_+ = 82.5°$ and $\sigma_- = 225°$ for many polyaldehydes. This displacement has been neatly justified by

TABLE 4

Polymer	Ref.	Identity period, Å	Number of m.u. in the period	Chain symmetry	Space group
1,2-Polybutadiene (syndiotactic)	5	5.1	2	*tcm*	*Pacm*
1,2-Polybutadiene (isotactic)	8	6.5	3	*s(3/1)1*	R3*c*
1,4-Polybutadiene (*trans*)	13	4.9	1	*ti*	—
1,4-Polybutadiene (*cis*)	12	8.6	2	*tci*	C2/*c*
1,4-Polyisoprene (*trans*)	13	4.7	1	*t1*	P2$_1$2$_1$2$_1$
1,4-Polyisoprene (*cis*)	12	8.1	2	*tc*	P*bac*
1,4-Polypentadiene (isotactic, *trans*)	16	4.8	1	*t1*	—
1,4-Polypentadiene (isotactic, *cis*)	14	8.15	2	*s(2/1)1*	—
1,4-Polypentadiene (syndiotactic, *cis*)	15	8.5	2	*tc*	—
1,4-Polyhexadiene (isotactic, *trans*)	58	4.8	1	*t1*	P2$_1$2$_1$2$_1$
Polypentenamer (*trans*)	59	11.9	2	*s(2/1)m*	—
Polyheptenamer (*trans*)	59	17.1	2	*s(2/1)m*	—
Polyoctenamer (*trans*)	59	9.85	1	*ti*	—
Polydodecenamer (*trans*)	59	14.85	1	*ti*	—

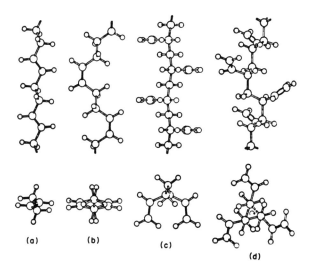

(a)   (b)   (c)   (d)

Fig. 22. Conformations in the crystalline state of the chains of the four known stereo-regular polybutadienes: (a) *trans*; (b) *cis*-1,4; (c) syndiotactic 1,2; (d) isotactic 1,2. [Reproduced from G. Natta and P. Corradini, *Nuovo Cimento Suppl.*, **15**, 111 (1960), with permission of Nicola Zanichelli.]

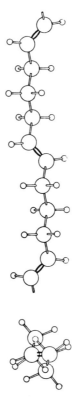

Fig. 23. Model of the chain of *trans*-polypentenamer. [Reproduced from G. Natta and I. W. Bassi, *Rend. Accad. Nazl. Lincei*, **38**, 315 (1965), with permission of Accademia Nazionale dei Lincei.]

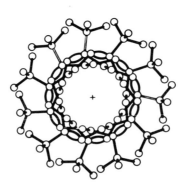

Fig. 24. Projection on the plane perpendicular to the helix of *cis*-1,4-poly(2-*t*-butyl-butadiene). [Reproduced from M. Cesari, *J. Polymer Sci.*, **B2**, 453 (1964), with permission of Wiley-Interscience.]

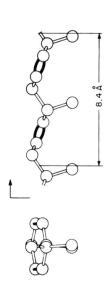

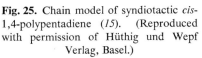

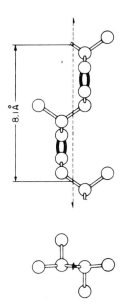

Fig. 25. Chain model of syndiotactic *cis*-1,4-polypentadiene (*15*). (Reproduced with permission of Hüthig und Wepf Verlag, Basel.)

Fig. 26. Chain model of isotactic *cis*-1, 4-polypentadiene (15). (Reproduced with permission of Hüthig und Wepf Verlag, Basel.)

TABLE 5

Polymer	Ref.	Identity period, Å	Number of m.u. in the period	Chain symmetry	Space group
Poly(methylene oxide) (form I)	60	56.0	29	s(29/16)1	P1
Poly(methylene oxide) (form II)	61	3.56	2	s(2/1)1	P2₁2₁2₁
Poly(ethylene oxide)	62	19.5	7	s(7/2)1	—
Poly(propylene oxide) (isotactic)	63	7.0	2	s(2/1)1	P2₁2₁2₁
Polytetrahydrofuran	64	12.2	2	tic	C2/c
Polyacetone	65	10.2	7	s(7/2)1	P4
Polyacetaldehyde (isotactic)	7	4.8	4	s(4/1)1	I4₁/a
Polypropionaldehyde (isotactic)	7	4.8	4	s(4/1)1	I4₁/a
Poly-n-butyraldehyde (isotactic)	7	4.8	4	s(4/1)1	I4₁/a
Polyisobutyraldehyde (isotactic)	7	5.2	4	s(4/1)1	—
Polyisovaleraldehyde (isotactic)	7	5.2	4	s(4/1)1	—

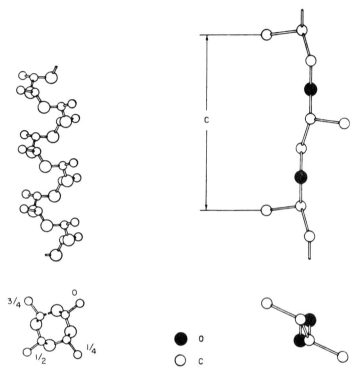

Fig. 27. Chain model of isotactic poly-
acetaldehyde, side and end views (7).
(Reproduced with permission of Wiley-
Interscience.)

Fig. 28. Side and views of the chain conformation of isotactic polypropylene oxide
in the crystalline state (63). (Reproduced
with permission of Hüthig und Wepf
Verlag, Basel.)

Borisova and Birshtein on the basis of the minimum energy postulate (66).
The chain conformation of isotactic poly(propylene oxide) corresponds to
a nearly planar twofold helix, as shown in Fig. 28.

III. MODE OF PACKING AND CRYSTALLINITY
OF STEREOREGULAR POLYMERS

A. Mode of Packing of Polymeric Chains: Principles

Where no strong electrostatic interactions are possible, polymer crystals
are built up according to the close-packing principle. This means that if
the cell and symmetry are given, the packing of macromolecules can be

found from the condition of equality of intermolecular distances of atoms of one kind. It has been shown by Kitajgorodskij (67) that the close-packing principle is a consequence of minimum free energy. The crystal structure of a molecule corresponds to one of the minima of the multi-dimensional surfaces of the energy as calculated for all symmetry-consistent arrangements of the molecules.

The close-packing principle implies that the minima in the multi-dimensional energy surface are close to the minima of the multidimensional volume surface, provided that distances between neighboring atoms of different molecules cannot become lower than some given values, the so-called van der Waals' distances. Together with a trend toward close packing, a molecule in a crystal tends to retain part of its symmetry elements, provided that this retention does not cause a serious loss of density. This tendency may be assumed to be of an entropic nature. As Kitajgorodskij says, it seems natural to assume that in a more symmetric position a molecule has a greater freedom of vibration, that is, the structure occupies a wider potential well on the multidimensional energy surface. We expect that a more symmetric structure will be unstable at low temperatures; however, high barriers of phase transformation may prevent a more stable structure from manifesting itself.

In the case of polymers, the application of the close-packing principle is perhaps easier than in the case of low molecular weight organic compounds. First of all, a simplification arises from the fact that the known chain conformation enables us to determine the structure at least along one of the identity periods of the crystal, namely, the one corresponding to the chain axis. The problem is further simplified if, in addition, as happens in the great majority of cases, the symmetry elements of an isolated chain which are allowed in a crystal (for instance, a fivefold helical symmetry is not allowed in a crystal) are preserved: in other words, if atoms geometrically (but not crystallographically a priori) equivalent, belonging to different structural units of the same chain, can assume equivalent positions with respect to the corresponding atoms of neighboring chains.

Two typical cases, to be discussed in the following sections, appear worthy of illustration. Between these two extreme cases almost all known crystal structures can be fitted.

B. Mode of Packing of Chains with Nearly Cylindrical Encumbrance

In this class we find polymers (a), such as polyethylene (68), 1,4-*trans*-poly-*n*-amers (polybutadiene, polypentenamer) (59), polytetrafluoroethylene (69), polyformaldehyde (60,61), and polyisobutylene (70), for which the form of the chain is, in a first approximation, a cylinder of uniform radius.

In this class we also find those polymers (b), such as many vinyl polymers like poly-4-methylpentene (46), characterized by helices with a fractional ratio M/N. Such chains have an encumbrance similar to that of a cylinder in which hollows and bulges are periodically repeated, or, better, have an encumbrance similar to that of a screw, as shown in Fig. 29.

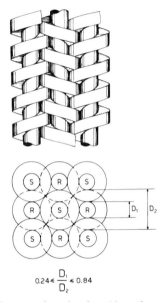

$$0.24 \leqslant \frac{D_1}{D_2} \leqslant 0.84$$

Fig. 29. Tetragonal mode of packing of screws.

Let us consider the possible ways of close packing cylinders of radius r, bearing a periodical helical relief of radius R. If the ratio r/R is near 1.0, the best way to pack the chains side by side is with coordination number 6, and, indeed, this is the case for all the polymers of subclass (a).

If the ratio r/R is near $\sqrt{2} - 1$ (a condition which is similar to that stabilizing the NaCl structure, in the case of ionic compounds) and bulges are able to penetrate into hollows, the best way to pack is that shown in Fig. 30, with coordination number 4, each right-handed helix being surrounded by four left-handed helices and vice versa. As a matter of fact, all polymers of subclass (b), that is, isotactic polymers with complex helices and for which the ratio between the encumbrance radius of the main chain to that of the lateral chains lies between 0.3 and 0.8, have a tetragonal lattice, space group P$\bar{4}$ [I$\bar{4}$ in the case where the helix contains a twofold screw axis; for instance, a 24/7 helix also contains a 2/1 axis (*71*)]. This type of packing is exemplified in Fig. 30 for poly-*m*-methylstyrene, which has a 11/3 helix chain conformation. It occurs very frequently.

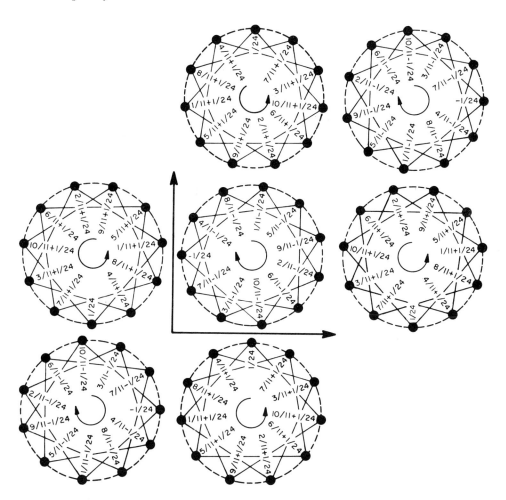

Fig. 30. Mode of packing of poly-*m*-methylstyrene. [Reproduced from P. Corradini and P. Ganis, *J. Polymer Sci.*, **43**, 311 (1960), with permission of Wiley-Interscience.]

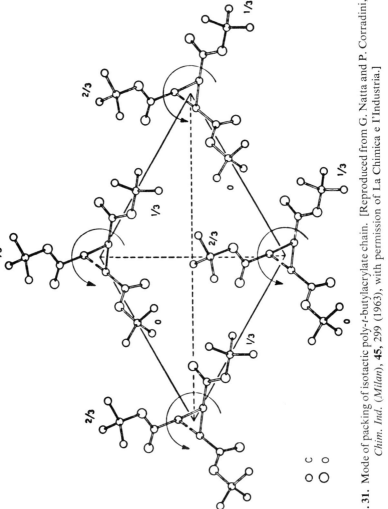

Fig. 31. Mode of packing of isotactic poly-*t*-butylacrylate chain. [Reproduced from G. Natta and P. Corradini, *Chim. Ind. (Milan)*, **45**, 299 (1963), with permission of La Chimica e l'Industria.]

C. Mode of Packing of Chains When Some Symmetry Elements of the Chain Are Maintained in the Lattice

As an example let us first take isotactic polymers with a ternary or quaternary helix conformation. The simplest case is that of a lattice in which the macromolecules are all isomorphous and have all the lateral groups oriented in the same direction with respect to the chain axis (i.e., all chains isoclined each to the other).

The ternary helix type of chain leads always to the $P3_1$ space group (for right-handed helices) or to the $P3_2$ space group (for left-handed helices). The only reasonable way of fitting the side groups is a disposition of them near the three hexagonal axes $(a, b,$ and $-a-b)$ perpendicular to the three-fold axis. Figure 31 shows the simple geometry of poly-t-butylacrylate (72), whose unit cell parameters are strictly regulated by: (1) the threefold helix conformation of the chain along the c axis, and (2) the necessity of bringing the methyl groups to mutual van der Waals' distances of about 4.2 Å with hexagonal axes ab $(b = a)$ of the lowest possible length.

Let us examine the type of lattices occurring when enantiomorphous macromolecules are present in each crystal. We shall distinguish between two cases depending upon the relative orientation of the side groups of enantiomorphous molecules facing each other (isoclined or anticlined).

In the first case (isoclined orientation) the possible symmetry elements able to repeat neighboring molecules are either a symmetry plane or a glide plane parallel to the chain axis. It is well known that good space filling is generally obtained much more easily through a glide plane than through a symmetry plane, particularly with objects having a periodic pattern of bulges and hollows, as in the case of spiralized polymer chains (73).

If the helix is of a ternary type, each right-handed helix will be surrounded, through a glide plane operation, by three left-handed helices and vice versa (Fig. 32). This type of crystal lattice (space group R3c) occurs for isotactic polystyrene (48), polybutene (42), polybutadiene (8), and poly-o-fluorostyrene (56). It does not occur for polypropylene, since it would give rise to a low density lattice, assuming van der Waals' contacts between carbon atoms of neighboring chains of 4.2 Å (28).

If a quaternary helix occurs, each right-handed helix will be surrounded through the glide operation by four left-handed isoclinic helices and vice versa; the only possible space group will therefore be I4$_1cd$ (Fig. 33). This type of lattice occurs for isotactic poly-o-methylstyrene (49) and poly-α-vinylnaphthalene (74).

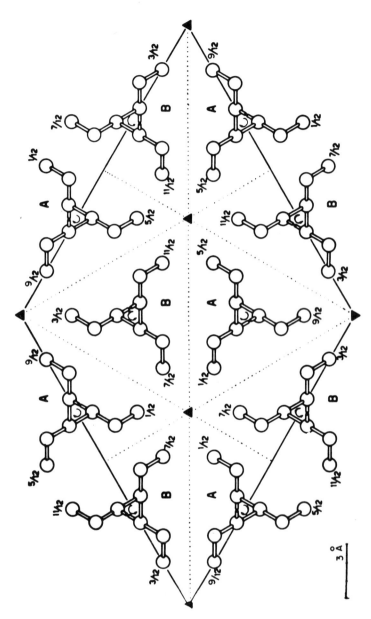

Fig. 32. Mode of packing of left- and right-handed isoclined chains in an isotactic polymer with a threefold helix (polybutene-1). [Reproduced from G. Natta and P. Corradini, *Chim. Ind.* (*Milan*), **45**, 299 (1963), with permission of La Chimica e l'Industria.]

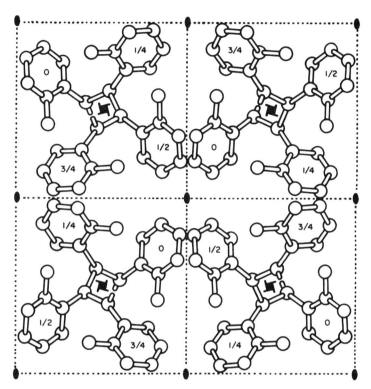

Fig. 33. Right- and left-handed chains in an isotactic polymer with a fourfold helix (poly-o-methylstyrene). [Reproduced from G. Natta and P. Corradini, *Chim. Ind. (Milan)*, **45**, 299 (1963), with permission of La Chimica e l'Industria.]

If the relative orientation of the side groups is anticlined, the only symmetry element able to repeat one chain into a neighboring equivalent one is a symmetry center.

Again for a ternary helix, each right-handed spiral will be surrounded, through three inversions at symmetry centers, at 120° to each other, by three left-handed helices and vice versa; the packed chains will thus be oriented in order to minimize the length of lattice constants perpendicular to the ternary axis, with best possible van der Waals' distances; the space group is therefore $R\bar{3}$ and it occurs, for instance, in poly(vinyl methyl ether) [(52); Fig. 34].

With a quaternary helix, each right-handed spiral will be surrounded by four left-handed helices and vice versa; the space group will be $I4_1/a$ and it occurs for almost all isotactic polyaldehydes [(7); Fig. 35] and for

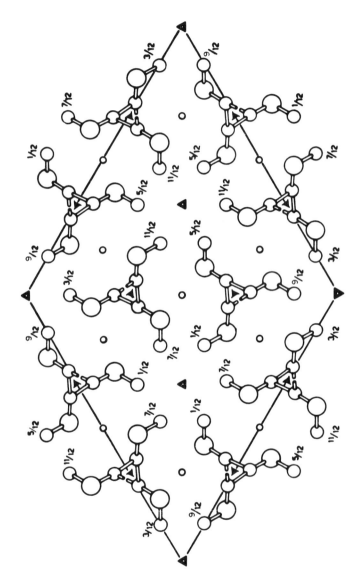

Fig. 34. Mode of packing of chains in the lattice of isotactic poly(vinyl methyl ether). [Reproduced from G. Natta and P. Corradini, *Chim. Ind. (Milan)*, **45**, 299 (1963), with permission of La Chimica e l'Industria.]

polyvinylcyclohexane (*51*). It was shown by Natta et al. (*7*) that from the knowledge of the chain conformation of polyacetaldehyde, which defines the *c* axis, both the *a* constant and the packing are exactly defined by the simple condition that the contacts between side methyl groups all be greater than 4.2 Å.

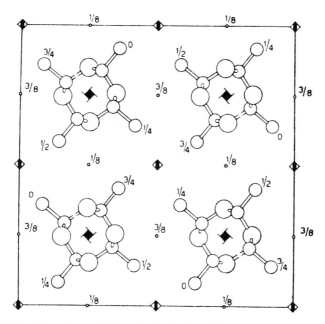

Fig. 35. Mode of packing of chains in the lattice of isotactic polyaldehydes with a fourfold helix (polyacetaldehyde). [Reproduced from G. Natta and P. Corradini, *Chim. Ind. (Milan)*, **45**, 299 (1963), with permission of La Chimica e l'Industria.]

After this necessarily short and incomplete exposition of the crystal lattices of helicoidal isotactic polymers, it is probably worth mentioning polymers with a different chain symmetry. If this symmetry is permitted in a crystal, it will in many instances be preserved. This happens especially for symmetry elements of the glide type, since they permit a good distribution of the bulky substituents of different chains between themselves.

In almost all known structures of polymers showing a chain conformation with a glide plane, this symmetry element is preserved in the crystal lattice. This occurs for 1,4-*cis*-polybutadiene (*12*), natural rubber and its hydrochloride (*75*), 1,2 syndiotactic polybutadiene (*5*), and poly(vinyl chloride) (*76*). Syndiotactic 1,4-*cis*-polypentadiene is an exception [(*15*); Fig. 36].

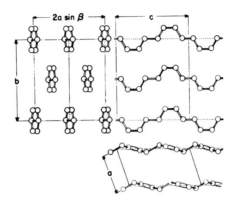

Fig. 36. Model of packing of 1,4-*cis*-polybutadiene. [Reproduced from G. Natta and P. Corradini, *Nuovo Cimento Suppl.*, **15**, 111 (1960), with permission of Nicola Zanichelli.]

In some of the above examples, the complete chain symmetry is preserved in the crystal lattice. For instance, in 1,4-*cis*-polybutadiene the binary axes perpendicular to the chain axis and going through the double bonds, as well as the symmetry centers located on the CH_2—CH_2 bonds, are maintained in the crystal lattice; in 1,2 syndiotactic polybutadiene the binary axes centered on the CH_2 group and the symmetry planes perpendicular to the chain axis are also preserved.

D. Determination of the Degree of Crystallinity

One of the most important characteristics of a given sample of a polymer is its degree of crystallinity, defined as the weight fraction of crystalline material in the sample. The definition is only apparently simple, because various types of more or less ordered structures have been recognized and may coexist in a polymer. It may turn out to be very difficult to classify some of these structures as crystalline and others as amorphous (*77*). Single crystals of polymers have been observed [(*78*); Fig 37]. They appear as thin platelets, having a thickness of the order of 100 Å; the axis of the chain is perpendicular to the plane of the platelet so that the chains must be folded in the crystal (Fig. 38). Thus, even in single crystals, besides defects, vacancies, and dislocations, the material in the bulk of the crystal has a different degree of order than the material at the boundaries of the same crystal. Sometimes, as we shall discuss later, the chain conformation of the polymer is regularly ordered, whereas the chains are

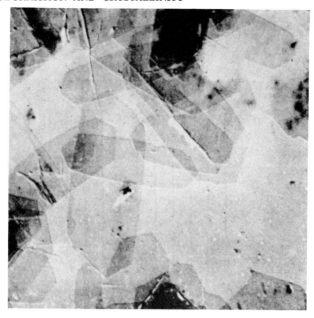

Fig. 37. Electron micrograph of polyethylene single crystals obtained from isoamylacetate at 114°C. Magnification 3900×. [Reproduced from P. G. Orsini, B. Marchese and L. Mazzarella, *J. Polymer Sci.*, **A1**, 1901 (1963), with permission of Wiley-Interscience.]

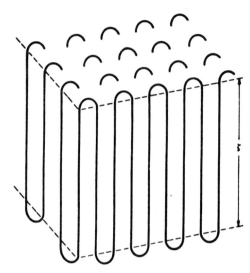

Fig. 38. Schematic diagram of a portion of a lamellar crystallite with the polymer chains in a regularly folded array. [Reproduced from P. J. Flory, *J. Am. Chem. Soc.*, **84**, 2857 (1962), with permission of the Americal Chemical Society.]

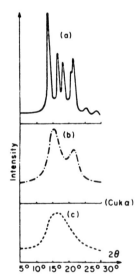

Fig. 39. Comparison between the X-ray Geiger spectra (Cukα) of (a) a sample of crystalline isotactic polypropylene, (b) a sample of a paracrystalline isotactic polypropylene, and (c) a sample of amorphous atactic polypropylene (*90*). (Reproduced with permission of Nicola Zanichelli.)

irregularly displaced with respect to each other (77), as happens in paracrystalline polypropylene. In this case, the X-ray diffraction pattern is intermediate in character between that given by a crystalline and that given by an amorphous polymer [(79); Fig. 39].

Also in amorphous polymers, a certain degree of order in the side-by-side packing of the chains is maintained, as evidenced by the appearance in the X-ray spectrum of several so-called "amorphous haloes," the

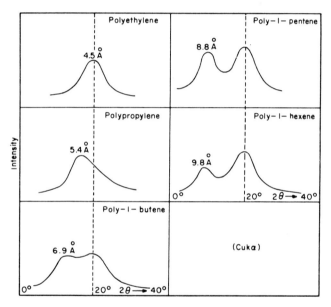

Fig. 40. Typical diffraction diagrams of amorphous polymers (80). (Reproduced with permission of Istituto Lombardo di Scienze e Lettere.)

position of the first of which may be correlated, in the series of poly-*n*-alkenes, to the expected mean distance between the axes of chain segments [(80); Fig. 40].

Despite the above difficulties, in many instances it has been possible to distinguish in the X-ray spectrum of a polymer between the X-ray intensity diffracted from amorphous regions and that diffracted from the crystalline regions. This is the basis of the most popular method of crystallinity determination (81). This method relies upon the assumption that the weight fraction of crystalline polymer is proportional to the energy diffracted from crystalline regions, whereas the weight fraction of amorphous polymer is proportional to the energy diffracted from amorphous regions. The degree of crystallinity is calculated from a comparison of the diffracted energies.

Figure 41 shows, as an example, the Geiger X-ray spectrum of a sample of isotactic polypropylene. The area of the amorphous band (O_{AM}) is proportional to the weight fraction of amorphous material. The total

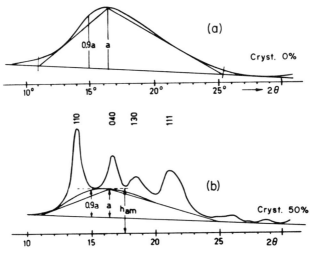

Fig. 41. Diffraction curves of polypropylene: (a) entirely amorphous sample and (b) partially crystalline sample (*82*). (Reproduced with permission of Hüthig und Wepf Verlag, Basel.)

area under the four observed crystalline peaks (O_{CR}) is taken as proportional to the weight fraction of crystalline polymer. The ratio O_{CR}/O_{AM} is related through the regression diagram elaborated by Weidinger and Hermans to the percent crystallinity in the sample [(*82*); Fig. 42].

The dependence of the degree of crystallinity as measured by X-rays on the degree of stereoregularity is qualitatively illustrated in Fig. 43.

The determination of the degree of crystallinity may also be obtained through the IR spectrum (*83*), density measurements (*84*), or differential thermal analysis (*85*).

Whereas crystallinity measurements through density measurements are generally consistent with X-ray values, the presence of paracrystallinity (or isomorphism) phenomena (to be discussed later) may lead to differences

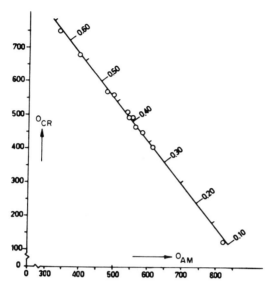

Fig. 42. Regression line of O_{CR} on O_{AM} (polypropylene). Actual position of observed values of O_{CR} and O_{AM} plotted against each other are also indicated. Scale giving the crystalline fraction is indicated along the regression line (82). (Reproduced with permission of Hüthig und Wepf Verlag, Basel.)

between the X-ray and IR values, giving lower (or higher) values for X-ray values as compared to IR values (83).

In the case of density measurements, if we call d_c and d_a, respectively, the density of the crystalline and amorphous regions of a polymer, and d the density of a given sample, the degree of crystallinity is given by:

$$ X = \frac{d_c(d - d_a)}{d(d_c - d_a)} $$

E. Paracrystalline Forms

Many polymers, upon rapid cooling and provided they are not annealed at a temperature slightly lower than the melting point, give rise to structures which can be appropriately called paracrystalline (77). This is shown by the observation of a diffuse X-ray spectrum (see, for instance, Fig. 39, which refers to a rapidly quenched sample of polypropylene (79) as compared with a well-crystallized sample). This spectrum resembles but is in some ways different from that of an atactic or amorphous sample.

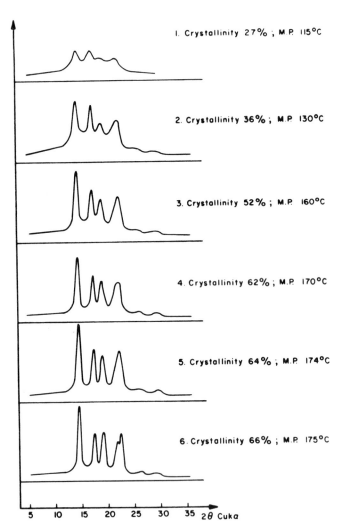

Fig. 43. X-ray Geiger spectra (Cukα) of extracted fractions of polypropylene having increasing melting points and decreasing solubilities (*80*). (Reproduced with permission of Istituto Lombardo di Scienze e Lettere.)

However, the infrared spectrum is typical of a polymer with a regular chain conformation (see, for instance, Fig. 44; the IR spectrum of paracrystalline polypropylene is practically identical with that of a well-crystallized sample, whereas it is completely different from that of an amorphous sample).

The fiber X-ray photographs of paracrystalline polymers show a good layering of diffracted intensity in the reciprocal lattice planes perpendicular to the stretching direction but only a poor resolution of the reflections

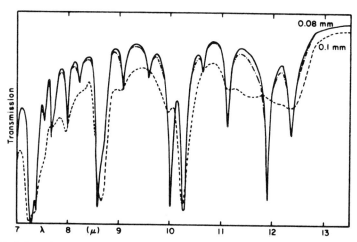

Fig. 44. Infrared spectra of a sample of isotactic polypropylene: ———— , modification I; — · — · — , paracrystalline; — — — — — , melt (79). (Reproduced with permission of Accademia Nazionale dei Lincei.)

within the said reciprocal lattice planes. This shows a high degree of conformational order along the chain direction and strict parallelism of neighboring chains but a more or less disordered structure as regards the lateral packing of the chains among themselves. At high angles the diffuse X-ray spectrum more and more resembles the Fourier transform of an isolated chain. Paracrystalline modifications are shown by isotactic polypropylene, as described above, and by 1,4-*trans* polymers of 1-substituted derivatives of 1,3-butadiene (86).

F. Isomorphism in Polymers

In the case of vinylic (87) and dienic polymers (88) as well as in the case of polyaldehydes (89), it is possible to modify the crystal lattice of the polymer by the presence in the chain of monomeric units of different types without destroying the crystallinity. Instead, this gives rise to continuous and regular variations of some of the crystal lattice parameters and, consequently, of other physical properties (e.g., solubility and melting point).

From this point of view, a very important condition is that the substitution be isosteric so that the shape of the chain backbone will be left approximately unchanged. The maintenance of the macromolecular chain conformation requires, of course, that the configuration also be preserved. In other words, in order to have a crystalline polymer, it is most important to have a tactic (for instance isotactic) order along the chain. Possible differences in the bulkiness of side groups are of secondary importance.

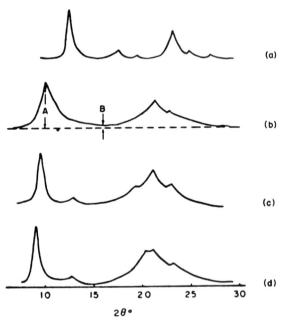

Fig. 45. X-ray powder spectra (Cukα) registered with a Geiger counter; (a) of poly-acetaldehyde; of acetaldehyde-n-butyraldehyde copolymers containing (b) 69.0 and (c) 36.0 mole % of acetaldehyde unit; and (d) of poly-n-butyraldehyde. [Reproduced from A. Tanaka, Y. Hozumi, K. Hatada, S. Endo, and R. Fujishige, *J. Polymer Sci.*, **B2,** 181 (1964), with permission of Wiley-Interscience.]

It is possible to foresee two general types of isomorphous substitution (*90*) in the crystal lattice of a linear macromolecule:

1. Isomorphism of different chains
2. Isomorphism of different monomeric units

The latter type of isomorphism introduces a new concept in physical chemistry, a concept which is entirely peculiar to macromolecules. It defines the possibility of introducing, in a statistical way, monomeric units of different chemical structure along the chain of a crystallizable polymer without preventing the crystallization of the resulting copolymer. Some of the values of the lattice constants of this copolymer will simply be different from those of the homopolymer.

Copolymers of acetaldehyde and *n*-butyraldehyde, which are crystalline over the entire composition range (Fig. 45), have been prepared by Tanaka and co-workers (*88*). The unit cells of these copolymers have the same tetragonal $I4_1/a$ space group with the same identity period ($c = 4.8$ Å) as either homopolymer, while only the lattice constant $a = b$ changes continuously with the copolymer composition (Fig. 46). From these results it is possible to conclude that isomorphism of monomeric units occurs in the case of these copolymers.

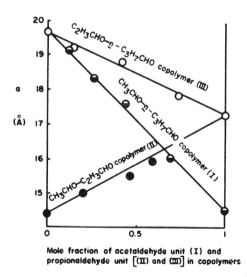

Fig. 46. Variation of *a* in the crystalline copolymers of aldehydes. [Reproduced from A. Tanaka, Y. Hozumi, K. Hatada, S. Endo, and R. Fujishige, *J. Polymer Sci.*, **B2,** 181 (1964), with permission of Wiley-Interscience.]

Analogous isomorphism phenomena have been observed, for instance, in many isotactic copolymers, between differently substituted styrenes (*89*), between different α-olefins (*87*), and in 1,4-*trans* copolymers between 1,3-pentadiene and butadiene (*86*).

G. Polymorphism in Polymers

Polymorphism is commonly encountered among polymers. A classification of the cases of polymorphism in polymers as enantiotropic or monotropic is very difficult at the moment, since the necessary thermodynamic studies have very seldom been performed.

Among the few cases of enantiotropy so far known with certainty for polymers, the clearest is that of 1,4-*trans*-polybutadiene, which has been studied in its essential features by Natta et al. (*90*). As regards monotropic polymeric systems, a thorough investigation from the thermodynamic viewpoint has been performed by several authors in the case of poly-1-butene (*91*).

Not very much is known, at present, about the crystal structures of the various crystalline modifications that can be obtained from one given polymer. It is clear, however, that we can distinguish, from the structural viewpoint, two broad categories of polymorphism:

1. Polymorphism due to a different chain conformation, which we shall call "conformational polymorphism;"

2. Polymorphism associated with identical chain conformations but with a different mode of packing, which we shall call "packing polymorphism."

We can further distinguish the conformational polymorphism according to the fact that different chain conformations can be found within the same conformational potential energy well (type 1) or in nonequivalent conformational potential energy wells (type 2).

It has been established that all three crystalline modifications of isotactic polypropylene, and also the paracrystalline modification, have the same threefold helix chain conformation (*92*). Thus, isotactic polypropylene shows packing polymorphism. Like isotactic polypropylene, packing polymorphism is shown, for instance, by polyethylene (*93*) and poly 1-substituted 1,4-*trans*-butadienes (*86*) (which can be obtained in a paracrystalline or in an orthorombic modification).

Conformational polymorphism of type 1 (different chain conformations within the same potential energy well) is furnished, for instance, by poly-1-butene for which two different helix chain conformations have been described, having, respectively, 3 m.u. in one turn or 11 m.u. in three turns. The internal rotation angles characteristic of the two conformations can be found in the same minimum of a $E(\sigma_1,\sigma_2)$ plot similar to that shown in Fig. 12 for isotactic polypropylene. The internal energy difference between the two conformers is probably lower than 0.1 kcal/m.u. Conformational polymorphism of type 1 is shown also, for example, by polyoxymethylene (60,61) and is the only possible type of conformational polymorphism which can be found for isotactic vinyl polymers.

Conformational polymorphism of type 2 (different chain conformations in nonequivalent potential energy wells) is shown by syndiotactic polypropylene, for which two crystalline modifications have been found. The one observed first contains helical chains of symmetry $s(2/1)2$ and internal rotation angles $\sigma_1 = 180°$ and $\sigma_2 = 60°$, or, for the enantiomorphic chain $\sigma_1 = -60°$ and $\sigma_2 = 180°$. These values of internal rotation angles correspond to the two equivalent minima of Fig. 13. The second modification contains zigzag planar chains, with tc symmetry, and corresponds to the $\sigma_1 = 180°$ and $\sigma_2 = 180°$ minimum of the same figure, well separated from the one discussed above.

The conformational internal energy difference between the zigzag planar and the helical conformations appears to be very low on the basis of calculations (less than 0.2 kcal/m.u.).

The polymorphism shown by 1,4-*trans*-polybutadiene can also be classified as a conformational polymorphism of type 2 (91). The chain conformation of modification 2 probably does not correspond to a regular succession of equivalent structural units. It has been supposed that in the high-temperature polymorph of polybutadiene, monomeric units having two different conformations more or less randomly succeed one another along the axis of the macromolecule.

REFERENCES

1. J. D. Dunitz and V. Prelog, communication at the *Conference on Stereochemistry, Burgenstock, 1966.*
2. International Union of Pure and Applied Chemistry, *J. Polymer Sci.*, **8**, 257 (1952).
3. M. L. Huggins, G. Natta, V. Desreux, and H. Mark, *J. Polymer Sci.*, **56**, 153 (1962); M. Farina, M. Peraldo, and G. Natta, *Angew. Chem.*, **4**, 107 (1965).
4. R. S. Cahn, C. K. Ingold, and V. Prelog, *Experientia*, **12**, 93 (1956).
5. The term "isotactic" was first introduced by G. Natta in 1954 (*Rend. Accad. Nazl. Lincei*, **4**, 61 (1955)); the term "syndiotactic" was first introduced by G. Natta and P. Corradini in 1956 (*J. Polymer Sci.*, **20**, 251 (1956)).
6. A. F. Bovey and G. V. D. Tiers, *J. Polymer Sci.*, **44**, 173 (1960).
7. G. Natta, P. Corradini, and I. W. Bassi, *J. Polymer Sci.*, **51**, 505 (1961).

8. G. Natta, P. Corradini, and I. W. Bassi, *Rend. Accad. Nazl. Lincei*, **23**, 363 (1957).
9. See, for example, T. G. Fox, B. S. Garrett, W. E. Goode, S. Gratch, J. F. Kincaid, A. Spell, and J. D. Stroupe, *J. Am. Chem. Soc.*, **80**, 1768 (1958); A. M. Liquori, G. Anzuino, V. M. Coiro, M. D'Alagni, P. De Santis, and M. Savino, *Nature*, **206**, 358 (1965).
10. G. Natta, P. Corradini, and G. Dall'Asta, *Rend. Accad. Nazl. Lincei*, **20**, 408 (1956).
11. G. Natta, M. Farina, M. Peraldo, P. Corradini, G. Bressan, and P. Ganis, *Rend. Accad. Nazl. Lincei*, **28**, 422 (1960).
12. G. Natta and P. Corradini, *Angew. Chem.*, **68**, 615 (1956).
13. G. Natta, P. Corradini, and L. Porri, *Rend. Accad. Nazl. Lincei*, **20**, 728 (1956).
14. G. Natta, L. Porri, A. Carbonaro, and G. Stoppa, *Makromol. Chem.*, **77**, 114 (1964).
15. G. Natta, L. Porri, A. Carbonaro, F. Ciampelli, and G. Allegra, *Makromol. Chem.*, **51**, 229 (1962).
16. G. Natta, L. Porri, G. Zanini, P. Corradini, and F. Ciampelli, *Rend. Accad. Nazl. Lincei*, **29**, 257 (1960).
17. G. Natta, P. Corradini, and P. Ganis, *J. Polymer Sci.*, **A3**, 11 (1965).
18. P. Corradini and P. Ganis, *Makromol. Chem.*, **62**, 97 (1963).
19. M. L. Huggins, *J. Chem. Phys.*, **13**, 37 (1945).
20. C. W. Bunn, *Proc. Roy. Soc. (London)*, **A180**, 67 (1942).
21. L. Pauling, R. B. Corey, and H. R. Branson, *Proc. Natl. Acad. Sci. U.S.*, **37**, 205 (1951).
22. G. Natta and P. Corradini, *Nuovo Cimento, Suppl.*, **15**, 9 (1960).
23. See, for example, P. Ganis and P. A. Temussi, *European Polymer J.*, **2**, 401 (1966).
24. P. Corradini, *Rend. Accad. Nazl. Lincei*, **28**, 1 (1960).
25. G. Natta and P. Corradini, *J. Polymer Sci.*, **39**, 29 (1959).
26. G. Natta, P. Corradini, and P. Ganis, *J. Polymer Sci.*, **58**, 1191 (1962).
27. C. W. Bunn and D. R. Holmes, *Discussions Faraday Soc.*, **25**, 95 (1958).
28. G. Natta and P. Corradini, *Nuovo Cimento, Suppl.*, **15**, 40 (1960).
29. G. Natta, I. Pasquon, P. Corradini, M. Peraldo, M. Pegoraro, and A. Zambelli, *Rend. Accad. Nazl. Lincei*, **28**, 539 (1960).
30. G. Natta, M. Peraldo, and G. Allegra, *Makromol. Chem.*, **75**, 215 (1964).
31. P. Corradini, *CNR e Fondazione "F. Giordani" CSC* 1, *Chimica delle Macromolecole, Varenna, 1961*, p. 193, 1963.
32. A. M. Liquori, *Rend. Accad. Nazl. Lincei, Chimica Inorganica. IV. Corso Estivo di Chimica, Varenna, 1959*, p. 311, 1961; A. M. Liquori, *J. Polymer Sci.*, **C12**, 209 (1966).
33. E. A. Mason and M. M. Kreevoy, *J. Am. Chem. Soc.*, **77**, 5808 (1955).
34. P. Corradini and G. Allegra, *Rend. Accad. Nazl. Lincei*, **30**, 182 (1961); P. Corradini, P. Ganis, and P. Oliverio, *Rend. Accad. Nazl. Lincei*, **33**, 320 (1962).
35. G. Natta, P. Corradini, and P. Ganis, *Rend. Accad. Nazl. Lincei*, **33**, 200 (1962).
36. P. Ganis, *Rend. Accad. Nazl. Lincei*, **34**, 250 (1963).
37. See Ref. *34* and G. Allegra, P. Ganis, and P. Corradini, *Makromol. Chem.*, **61**, 225 (1963).
38. P. J. Flory, J. E. Mark, and A. Abe, *J. Am. Chem. Soc.*, **88**, 639 (1966).
39. T. Shimanouchi and S. Mizushima, *J. Chem. Phys.*, **23**, 707 (1955); R. E. Hughes and J. L. Lauer, *J. Chem. Phys.*, **30**, 1165 (1959); T. Miyazawa, *J. Polymer Sci.*, **55**, 215 (1961); K. Nagai and M. Kobayashi, *J. Chem. Phys.*, **36**, 1268 (1962).
40. P. Ganis and P. A. Temussi, *Makromol. Chem.*, **89**, 1 (1965).

41. See, for instance, B. K. Vainshtein, *Diffraction of X-Rays by Chain Molecules,* Elsevier, Amsterdam, 1966.
42. G. Natta, P. Corradini, and I. W. Bassi, *Nuovo Cimento, Suppl.,* **15,** 52 (1960).
43. W. Cochran, F. H. C. Crick, and V. Vanda, *Acta Cryst.,* **5,** 581 (1952); Y. Mitsui, *Acta Cryst.,* **20,** 694 (1966).
44. G. Natta, *Makromol. Chem.,* **16,** 213 (1955).
45. G. Natta, P. Corradini, and I. W. Bassi, *Gazz. Chim. Ital.,* **89,** 784 (1959).
46. F. C. Franck, A. Keller, and A. O'Connor, *Phil. Mag.,* **4,** 200 (1954).
47. G. Natta, P. Corradini, and I. W. Bassi, *Rend. Accad. Nazl. Lincei,* **19,** 404 (1955).
48. G. Natta, P. Corradini, and I. W. Bassi, *Nuovo Cimento, Suppl.,* **15,** 68 (1960).
49. P. Corradini and P. Ganis, *Nuovo Cimento, Suppl.,* **15,** 96 (1960).
50. P. Corradini and P. Ganis, *J. Polymer Sci.,* **43,** 311 (1960).
51. G. Natta, P. Corradini, and I. W. Bassi, *Makromol. Chem.,* **33,** 247 (1959).
52. I. W. Bassi and P. Corradini, *J. Polymer Sci.,* in press.
53. G. Dall'Asta and N. Otto, *Chim. Ind. (Milan),* **42,** 1234 (1960).
54. G. Natta, I. W. Bassi, and P. Corradini, *Makromol Chem.,* **18–19,** 455 (1956).
55. G. Natta, P. Corradini, and P. Ganis, *Rend. Accad. Nazl. Lincei,* **34,** 3 (1963)
56. G. Natta, P. Corradini, and I. W. Bassi, *Nuovo Cimento, Suppl.,* **15,** 83 (1960).
57. A. Turner Jones, *Makromol. Chem.,* **71,** 1 (1964).
58. G. Perego and I. W. Bassi, *Makromol. Chem.,* **61,** 198 (1963).
59. G. Natta, G. Dall'Asta, I. W. Bassi, and G. Carella, *Macromol. Chem.,* **91,** 87 (1966).
60. G. A. Carazzolo, *J. Polymer Sci.,* **A1,** 1573 (1963).
61. G. A. Carazzolo and M. Mammi, *J. Polymer Sci.,* **A1,** 965 (1963).
62. H. Tadokoro, Y. Chatani, T. Yoshihara, S. Tahara, and S. Murahashi, *Makromol. Chem.,* **73,** 109 (1964).
63. M. Cesari, G. Perego, and W. Marconi, *Makromol. Chem.,* **94,** 194 (1966).
64. K. Imada, T. Miyakawa, Y. Chatani, H. Tadokoro, and S. Murahashi, *Makromol. Chem.* **83,** 113 (1965).
    M. Cesari, G. Perego, and A. Mazzei, *Makromol. Chem.,* **83,** 196 (1965).
65. J. Furukawa, T. Saegusa, T. Tsuruta, S. Ohta, and G. Wasai, *Makromol. Chem.,* **52,** 230 (1962).
66. N. P. Borisova and T. M. Birshtein, *Polymer Sci., USSR, English Transl.,* **4,** 907 (1963–1964).
67. A. I. Kitajgorodskij, *Acta Cryst.,* **18,** 585 (1965).
68. C. W. Bunn, *Trans. Faraday Soc.,* **35,** 482 (1939).
69. E. S. Clark and L. T. Muus, *Z. Krist.,* **117,** 119 (1962).
70. A. M. Liquori, *Acta Cryst.,* **8,** 345 (1955).
71. H. D. Noether, *International Symposium on Macromolecular Chemistry, Prague, 1965,* Preprint p. 97: *J. Polymer Sci.,* **C16** (2), 725 (1967).
72. G. Natta and P. Corradini, *Ind. Chim. Belge,* **24,** 1 (1964).
73. A. I. Kitajgorodskij, *Organic Chemical Crystallography,* Consultants Bureau, New York, 1962.
74. P. Corradini and P. Ganis, *Nuovo Cimento, Suppl.,* **15,** 104 (1960).
75. C. W. Bunn, *Proc. Roy. Soc. (London),* **A180,** 40 (1942).
76. G. Natta, P. Corradini, and I. W. Bassi, *Rend. Accad. Nazl. Lincei,* **31,** 17 (1961).
77. R. Hosemann, *Polymer,* **3,** 349 (1962).
78. L. Mandelkern, *Crystallization of Polymers,* McGraw-Hill, New York, 1964.

79. G. Natta, P. Corradini, and I. W. Bassi, *Rend. Accad. Nazl. Lincei*, **26**, 14 (1959).
80. P. Corradini, *Rend. Ist. Lombardo Sci. Lettere*, **A91**, 889 (1957).
81. G. Natta, P. Corradini, and M. Cesari, *Rend. Accad. Nazl. Lincei*, **22**, 11 (1957).
82. G. Challa, P. H. Hermans, and A. Weidinger, *Makromol. Chem.*, **56**, 169 (1962); P. H. Hermans and A. Weidinger, *Makromol. Chem.*, **44–46**, 24 (1961); A. Weidinger and P. H. Hermans, *Makromol. Chem.*, **50**, 98 (1961).
83. G. Zerbi, F. Ciampelli, and V. Tramboni, *J. Polymer Sci.*, **C7**, 141 (1964).
84. F. Danusso, G. Moraglio, and G. Natta, *Ind. Plastiques Mod. (Paris)*, **10**, No. 1, 40 (1958).
85. B. Ke, *J. Polymer Sci.*, **42**, 15 (1960).
86. G. Natta, L. Porri, A. Carbonaro, and G. Lugli, *Makromol. Chem.*, **53**, 52 (1962).
87. A. Turner Jones, *Polymer*, **7**, 23 (1966); **6**, 249 (1965).
88. A. Tanaka, Y. Hozumi, K. Hatada, S. Endo, and R. Fujishige, *J. Polymer Sci.*, **B2**, 181 (1964).
89. G. Natta, P. Corradini, D. Sianesi, and D. Morero, *J. Polymer Sci.*, **51**, 527 (1961).
90. G. Natta and P. Corradini, *Nuovo Cimento, Suppl.*, **15**, 9 (1960); G. Natta and G. Moraglio, *Rubber Plastics Age*, **44**, 42 (1963).
91. F. Danusso, G. Gianotti, and G. Polizzotti, *Makromol. Chem.*, **80**, 13 (1964).
92. A. Turner Jones, J. M. Aizlewood, and D. R. Beckett, *Makromol. Chem.*, **75**, 134 (1964).
93. J. G. Fatou, C. H. Baker, and L. Mandelkern, *Polymer*, **6**, 243 (1965).

CHAPTER 2

High-Resolution Nuclear
Magnetic Resonance of Synthetic Polymers

James C. Woodbrey

MONSANTO COMPANY
CENTRAL RESEARCH DEPARTMENT
ST. LOUIS, MISSOURI

I. INTRODUCTION

Pioneer nuclear magnetic resonance (NMR) experiments on polymers were so-called "wide-line" or "broad-line" studies of partially crystalline solids, amorphous glasses, or highly viscous rubbers. NMR absorptions in such materials are strongly influenced by nuclear magnetic dipole interactions which give rise to broad absorptions. Analyses of these absorptions have given information about certain motions of polymer chain segments and about the packing of long-chain molecules in a few partially crystalline polymers. These results have contributed to the understanding of some of the physical properties of polymers. Wide-line NMR studies of polymers were reviewed in 1958 (*1*) and 1960 (*2*), and some wide-line investigations of polymers are discussed in Chapter 5, this volume.

Nuclear magnetic dipole interactions become averaged when molecules undergo Brownian motion or other very rapid reorientation processes. This motional averaging usually leads to very narrow resonance lines and to so-called high-resolution NMR spectra in low-viscosity fluids. Narrow-line or high-resolution NMR spectra of many polymers in dilute solutions have been obtained during the last few years. A number of these spectra have given unique information about localized fragments of molecular structure (microstructures) in polymer molecules. This chapter deals with these investigations, particularly as they relate to problems concerning the structures of synthetic macromolecules. Bovey and Tiers reviewed this subject in 1963 (*3*), and it was reconsidered in 1964 (*4*). Since these reviews, structures of some polymers have been reinvestigated in greater detail by high-resolution NMR, and the structures of many other polymers have been characterized by high-resolution NMR for the first time. The present chapter concentrates on the more important aspects of recent investigations.

II. SOME PRINCIPLES OF THE NUCLEAR MAGNETIC RESONANCE PHENOMENON

Some of the principles of NMR are introduced in this section for readers who are not familiar with the NMR phenomenon. Many accounts of NMR are available for the reader who desires to delve into the principles, applications, and techniques of NMR research. Bovey has given a short introduction which describes the scope of applications of high-resolution NMR spectroscopy (*5*). Others have presented more thorough introductions (*6–8*) and reviews (*9–13*), and still others have treated the subject in great detail (*14,15*).

A. Some Properties of Atomic Nuclei

All atomic nuclei possess the fundamental properties of mass and charge. Many nuclei also have the intrinsic properties of spin angular momentum and magnetic moment. According to the principles of quantum mechanics, the maximum measurable component of angular momentum must be an integral or half integral multiple of $\hbar = h/2\pi$, where h is Planck's constant. This component of the nuclear angular momentum is designated I and is called the spin quantum number.

In a magnetic field H, the energy of a nucleus with spin I separates into the following $2I + 1$, equally spaced energy levels: $-\mu H, -(I - 1)\mu H/I$, $\cdots (I - 1)\mu H/I, \mu H$. The quantity μ is the maximum observable component of the nuclear magnetic moment. Since the magnetic moment $\boldsymbol{\mu}$ and the angular momentum vector $\mathbf{p}$ are always parallel, $\boldsymbol{\mu} = \gamma\mathbf{p}$ or $\mu = \gamma(I\hbar)$; γ is a characteristic constant for each type of nucleus and is called the magnetogyric or gyromagnetic ratio. Transitions between adjacent energy levels may be accompanied by absorption or emission of radiation. These absorptions or emissions are the basis for all NMR experiments.

The condition for transitions between adjacent energy levels,† or the condition for resonance of the nuclear magnets, is $h\nu = \mu H/I$ or $\nu = \gamma H/2\pi$. This last equality shows that the frequency ν of the absorbed or emitted radiation is proportional to the magnetic field at the nucleus and to the characteristic magnetogyric ratio. NMR frequencies ν_0 for some magnetic nuclei in a field $H_0 = 10,000$ gauss are listed in Table 1. These frequencies fall in the accessible HF and VHF radiofrequency ranges. The proton has the highest NMR sensitivity among all the atomic nuclei, and it has a very high natural abundance. These factors make proton magnetic resonance (PMR) extremely valuable for structural studies of organic molecules, and it is by far the largest field of NMR.

B. Nuclear Magnetic Resonance Experiment

In the NMR experiment, a sample of atoms or molecules with nuclei of spin I is immersed in a strong, steady magnetic field H_0. At thermal equilibrium, the spins populate their allowed energy levels according to the Boltzmann distribution. The probabilities of finding a nucleus in lower energy levels at thermal equilibrium are only slightly greater than those for the higher levels. For example, the excess number of protons in the lower of the proton's two energy levels is only a few parts per million (ppm) at thermal equilibrium in a 10,000 gauss field. Such equilibrium imbalances in populations are still smaller for other nuclei. Nevertheless,

† Only transitions between adjacent energy levels generally are induced by a uniform oscillating magnetic field. Since the energy levels are equally spaced, a collection of identical nuclei in the same magnetic field emit or absorb only one characteristic frequency.

TABLE 1

Properties of Some Nuclei Used in Nuclear Magnetic Resonance

Nucleus	NMR Frequency[a] ν_0, Mc/sec	Spin I, h	Natural abundance, %	Magnetic moment μ, nm $= eh/4\pi$ Mc	Relative sensitivity[b]
^{1}H	42.578	1/2	99.9844	2.7927	1.0000
^{2}H (D)	6.536	1	0.0156	0.8574	0.0096
^{10}B	4.575	3	18.83	−1.1774	0.0199
^{11}B	13.660	3/2	81.17	1.8006	0.165
^{13}C	10.705	1/2	1.108	0.7022	0.0159
^{14}N	3.076	1	99.635	0.4036	0.0010
^{15}N	4.315	1/2	0.365	−0.2830	0.0010
^{17}O	5.772	5/2	0.037	−1.8930	0.0291
^{19}F	40.055	1/2	100	2.6273	0.834
^{31}P	17.235	1/2	100	1.1305	0.0664

[a] For a 10,000 gauss field.
[b] For constant field and equal numbers of nuclei.

absorptions of energy are detectable when some of the excess numbers of nuclei in lower energy levels undergo transitions to higher levels.

In addition to the strong field H_0, the NMR sample also is irradiated with a weak alternating field of magnitude H_1 and radiofrequency ν_0. If the strong, applied field is swept through the resonance (transition) value $H_0 = 2\pi\nu_0/\gamma$, some of the nuclei in lower energy levels absorb energy from the applied radiofrequency field and undergo transitions to higher levels. These absorptions may be detected by sensitive measurements of changes in the Q value of a radiofrequency coil which is used to irradiate the sample.

Alternatively, the nuclear spins may be visualized in a classical mechanical sense as very tiny permanent magnets. For example, magnetic moments of nuclei with spin $I = \frac{1}{2}$ tend to align parallel to H_0 when in the lower energy level. Those in the upper level tend to align antiparallel to H_0. When H_0 is swept through the resonance value and absorptive transitions occur in some of the nuclei, the magnetic moments of these nuclei will change their direction with respect to H_0. This flipping of magnetic moments can induce a detectable radiofrequency voltage in a receiver coil surrounding the sample. The magnitude of the amplified radiofrequency signal is normally plotted on the ordinate vs. the value of the strong field H_0 on the abscissa. Such a graph is an NMR spectrum.

C. Spin–Lattice Relaxation

Numerous factors may effect the nature of NMR signals. One of these is the rate at which the assembly of nuclei approaches its equilibrium distribution of energies. The excess numbers of nuclei in lower energy levels are diminished below their equilibrium values by absorptive transitions. Eventually, the energy levels would become equally populated if absorptive transitions were continued. In order to achieve a steady state signal, there must be some mechanism by which nuclei in upper energy levels may relax to lower levels. The only way this can occur for spherical nuclei ($I = \frac{1}{2}$) is through interactions of the nuclear magnetic moments with local fluctuating magnetic fields.† This process is called spin–lattice relaxation (*18,19,21,22*).§

The inverse spin–lattice relaxation time T_1^{-1} is a measure of the rate at which the system approaches thermal equilibrium. The value of T_1 is usually 10^{-2}–10^2 sec for nuclei of spin $I = \frac{1}{2}$ in liquids free of paramagnetic impurities. In such materials, the lifetimes of nuclei in excited energy states usually are determined by spin–lattice relaxation, and the NMR natural line widths in units of frequency are of the order T_1^{-1}. Nonspherical nuclei ($I > \frac{1}{2}$) also have electric quadrupole moments. These nuclei can undergo additional spin–lattice relaxation through interactions of the quadrupole moments with local fluctuating electric fields. Thus, nuclei with spins $I > \frac{1}{2}$ usually have smaller values of T_1 and give broader resonance lines than nuclei with spin $I = \frac{1}{2}$.

D. Nuclear Magnetic Dipole Interactions

In solids and viscous liquids, where the nuclei remain in the same relative positions for a long time, NMR line widths frequently are 10^3–10^5 times broader than in fluids of low viscosity. These broad lines are not due to spin–lattice relaxation. Rather, they result from direct, through-space interactions of neighboring nuclear magnetic dipoles.

The strengths of interactions of neighboring dipoles, and their effects on line shapes, attenuate rapidly with distance between the interacting nuclei. The influence that these dipolar interactions have on line shapes also depends on the relative orientations of interacting nuclei with respect to the direction of H_0 and on the rate of change of these orientations. Quantitative studies of these effects often yield information about atomic

---

† These local fluctuating magnetic fields are most commonly produced by random motions of neighboring nuclear magnets.

§ To an individual nuclear spin, the lattice is any other degree of freedom.

packing and rates of certain kinetic processes. Such studies fall in the realms of wide-line and "spin-echo" NMR and are not of main concern here. These aspects of NMR have been described elsewhere (*16–18,20,21*).

Motional averaging in low-viscosity fluids removes nearly all the effects of line broadening due to direct magnetic dipole interactions. Thus, NMR lines of most diamagnetic liquids are very narrow. Provided that the applied field H_0 is homogeneous over the volume of the sample, PMR lines of organic liquids are often about 0.01 ppm of the applied field H_0 in width. The resolution of such narrow lines can be very high, and it will be seen that high-resolution NMR spectroscopy can yield unique information about the structures of molecules.

E. Saturation

The strength of the applied radiofrequency field H_1 may have marked effects on NMR signals. The radiofrequency field tends to equalize the populations of the energy levels via inductions of absorptive transitions when H_0 is at the resonance value. The tendency is often greater than the opposing relaxation processes which tend to restore the equilibrium distribution of energy populations. The intensity of the resonance signal then may diminish in time and eventually may disappear completely. This effect is called radiofrequency saturation.

If H_1 is very low, the effect of saturation may be negligible. The integrated intensity of the NMR signal is then proportional to the number of nuclei in the sample of the type undergoing resonance. This proportionality permits direct determinations of relative concentrations by NMR. In addition, the measured line width is frequently the natural line width in the absence of radiofrequency saturation.

At intermediate values of H_1, the degree of radiofrequency saturation becomes significant; it tends to decrease the intensity of the NMR signal more in the central maximum portion than in the wings of the signal. The integrated intensity is then no longer proportional to the number of nuclei of the type undergoing resonance. Moreover, the observed resonance line is broader than the natural line. These effects of partial saturation are often deceptive. The importance of such effects usually should be assessed via measurements with several different values of H_1.

F. Magnetic Shielding and Chemical Shifts

On the basis of the preceding discussion, one might expect all nuclei of a common species to resonate at the same frequency when placed in the same magnetic field. Actually, nuclei of a common species, but in different molecular environments, resonate at different positions, i.e., at different frequencies v_0 in the same applied magnetic field H_0 or vice versa. This is the primary reason that NMR is of great value for studies of molecular structures in the liquid state.

The applied field H_0 induces additional, small magnetic fields by causing the circulation of electrons. Most of these induced fields oppose H_0 at the nuclei so that the electrons effectively shield the nuclei against the applied field. The strength of the induced field at a nucleus, or the magnetic shielding of a nucleus, is proportional to H_0. The local field at the nucleus may be expressed as $H_{local} = (1 - \sigma)H_0$, where σ is called the screening constant. Generally speaking, the value of σ depends on the type of nucleus and on the molecular structure surrounding the nucleus.

Since H_{local} is proportional to H_0, the separations or resolutions of multiple lines due to shielding differences increase with H_0. Moreover, the polarization of the nuclear magnets increases with H_0 so that the sensitivity (signal-to-noise ratio) of the experiment also increases with H_0. The advantages of working at high applied fields, which require high applied radiofrequencies, usually are limited by the strength, volume, and homogeneity of the field produced by the magnet.†

The positions of resonance lines are measured with respect to that of some reference line. The difference between the shielding of a nucleus or group of nuclei and that of the reference nuclei is called the chemical shift. It is measured as the difference in the positions of the corresponding resonances in frequency units of cycles per second (cps). The experimental chemical shift in units of cps is proportional to the shift in units of magnetic field, and the shift in either set of dimensional units is proportional to H_0 or v_0.

The necessity of reporting experimental values of v_0 or H_0 with chemical shifts in dimensional units customarily is avoided by expressing the shifts in dimensionless units of ppm of H_0 or ppm of v_0. There are innumerable ways in which chemical shifts may be expressed in dimensionless units. Fortunately, only a few methods are used for the more common types of NMR. Proton shifts in dimensionless δ units are expressed as $\delta = 10^6 \Delta v / v_0$ ppm; Δv is the experimental shift in cps between the resonance position in question and that of the protons of the arbitrary PMR reference tetramethylsilane (TMS).§ The measured shift Δv most often is taken

† Commercial electromagnet NMR spectrometers operate at fields up to about 23,500 gauss, and a few superconducting-magnet spectrometers now operate at fields exceeding 50,000 gauss.

§ All the protons of TMS have the same effective shielding because of the symmetry of the molecule and the rapid internal rotation about the C—Si bonds.

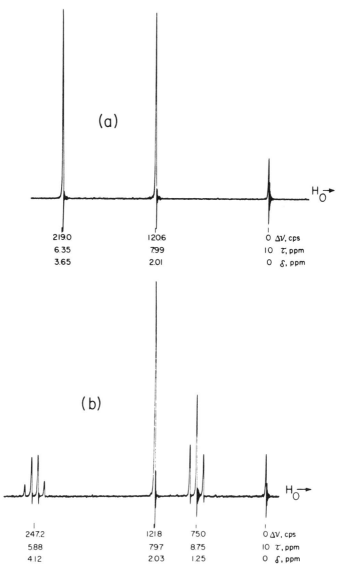

Fig. 1. High-resolution PMR spectra of about 30 vol. % (a) methyl acetate and (b) ethyl acetate in carbon tetrachloride solutions at room temperature; $\nu_0 = 60$ Mc/sec; internal reference is TMS at $\Delta\nu \equiv 0$ cps or at $\tau = 10 - \delta \equiv 10$ ppm.

as positive when the protons of TMS resonate at a higher applied field than the protons in question. Then δ decreases with increasing H_0. Another very widely used dimensionless unit for proton shifts is the τ unit. It is defined as $\tau = 10 - \delta$ ppm, and it always increases with H_0. Similar arbitrary methods are used for reporting chemical shifts of other nuclei in dimensionless units.

Both theoretical considerations (23,24) and empirical correlations (25–28) have shown that chemical shifts are very sensitive to changes in molecular structure.† Chemical shifts are usually different for the same nuclear species in different chemical functional groups. For example, Fig. 1(a) shows that an easily resolveable chemical-shift difference of 1.64 ppm exists between the three equivalent methoxyl and the three equivalent acetyl protons of methyl acetate. Note in Fig. 1(a) that the intensities of the two proton resonances of methyl acetate are equal. This equality results from the direct proportionality between the intensity of each resonance line and the number of protons in the sample of the type giving rise to each resonance. The sensitivities of chemical shifts to neighboring functional groups and molecular geometry make high-resolution NMR particularly useful for studies of microstructures in polymer chains.

G. Electron-Coupled Spin Interactions

In addition to direct, through-space interactions of nuclear magnetic dipoles, nuclear spins $\mathbf{I} = \mathbf{p}/\hbar$ can couple via partial polarizations of valence electrons in intervening chemical bonds. Electron-coupled spin–spin interactions are manifested by splittings of the lines arising from the coupled nuclei into doublets, triplets, or other more complicated multiplets. Spin coupling is observed only between magnetically nonequivalent nuclei.§ The spacings of components in spin–spin multiplets are measures of the

† Proton chemical shifts fall in a range of about 10 ppm of the applied field H_0. Variations in the shieldings of other nuclei and chemical-shift differences between nuclei are generally very much larger. This last fact enables one to observe resonances of one species of magnetic nuclei (e.g., protons) without direct complications due to resonances of other species of magnetic nuclei (e.g., nitrogen, fluorine, phosphorus).

§ A chemical-shift difference between nuclei is a sufficient but not a necessary condition for magnetic nonequivalence. Occasionally, spin coupling is observed between nuclei with the same chemical shift. One example is $CF_2{=}CH_2$, where both protons have the same chemical shift and both fluorine nuclei have the same chemical shift. In this case, the nonequivalent *cis* and *trans* proton–fluorine spin–spin couplings make the two protons magnetically nonequivalent so that the proton–proton couplings are observed in the NMR spectrum. The fluorine–fluorine couplings are observed for the same reason.

strength of the coupling which is designated for fluids by the nuclear spin–spin coupling constant J in units of cps.

The energy of interaction of two electron-coupled magnetic nuclei A and B, $J_{AB}(\mathbf{I}_A \cdot \mathbf{I}_B)$, attenuates rapidly with the number of chemical bonds through which coupling occurs. For example, the coupling constant for protons separated by three bonds in acyclic saturated hydrocarbons is about 7 cps. The value of J for similar coupling through four or five bonds is zero or just a fraction of a cps.

Unlike the experimental chemical shift in dimensional units, the spin–spin coupling constant is independent of the applied field H_0 and the applied radiofrequency ν_0. In addition, chemical-shift differences most often are more dependent on temperature, type of solvent, and concentration than are spin–spin coupling constants. Thus, spectral multiplicities arising from chemical-shift differences can be differentiated from those arising from spin–spin couplings.

The nature of spin–spin coupling depends on numerous factors other than the number of bonds through which coupling occurs. The magnitudes and relative signs of coupling constants generally depend on the type of nuclei coupled and on the kind and geometry of chemical bonds surrounding the coupled nuclei. Rather extensive theoretical (29–31) and empirical (25,28,32,33) correlations among these variables have been developed. Thus, determinations of coupling constants by analyses of experimental spectra may give additional information about isolated fragments of molecular structure.

H. Analyses of High-Resolution Nuclear Magnetic Resonance Spectra

Analyses of weakly coupled spin systems are frequently very simple. If n_A equivalent nuclei of type A are weakly coupled to n_X equivalent nuclei of type X (i.e., if $|J_{AX}|/|\Delta\nu_A - \Delta\nu_X| \ll 1$), the A resonance has $2n_X I_X + 1$ components, and the X resonance has $2n_A I_A + 1$ components, and the spacings between components in each multiplet are equal to $J_{AX} = J_{XA}$, and each multiplet is symmetrical. Relative intensities of components in the A multiplet are given by the coefficients of the binomial expansion of order n_X if $I_X = \frac{1}{2}$, and relative intensities of components in the X multiplet are given by the coefficients of the binomial expansion of order n_A if $I_A = \frac{1}{2}$. The total intensity of the A components is proportional to n_A, and the total intensity of the X components has the same proportionality to n_X if A and X belong to the same nuclear species.

The ethyl protons of ethyl acetate are an example of an approximate weakly coupled spin system when $\nu_0 \geqslant ca.$ 60 Mc/sec. As shown in Fig. 1(b), the three equivalent methyl protons of the ethyl group (A_3) are weakly coupled to the two equivalent methylene protons (X_2). The X_2 protons split the A_3 proton resonance into a nearly symmetrical triplet with component intensity ratios of approximately 1:2:1 and equal spacings of $J_{AX} = 7.3$ cps. Similarly, the A_3 protons split the X_2 proton resonance into a nearly symmetrical quartet with component intensity ratios of approximately 1:3:3:1 and equal spacings of J_{AX}. The chemical-shift difference between the center of the quartet and the center of the triplet is 172.2 cps so that $|J_{AX}|/|\Delta \nu_A - \Delta \nu_X| = 7.3/172.2 = 0.0424 \ll 1$. The total intensity of the triplet is $\frac{3}{2}$ that of the quartet and equal to the intensity of the singlet methyl proton resonance of the acetyl group. Spin couplings between the ethyl protons and the acetyl protons are attenuated essentially to zero by the intervening five or six chemical bonds. Weak couplings among three or more nonequivalent groups of nuclei may be analyzed in a similar manner. It is seen, therefore, that not only are coupling constants easily extracted from weakly coupled spin systems, but characteristic multiplet patterns actually aid in assigning chemical shifts to differently shielded groups of nuclei.

When spin coupling is stronger, i.e., when the chemical-shift difference in dimensional units is comparable to or smaller than the coupling constant, the simple rules described above for weak coupling are not valid. The NMR spectrum of a simple two-spin or AB type of system with $I_A = I_B = \frac{1}{2}$ is usually recognizable as a symmetrical quartet. The four components of such a quartet have the following resonance positions and relative intensities:

$$(J_{AB}/2) + C \quad \text{and} \quad 1 - (J_{AB}/2C)$$
$$(-J_{AB}/2) + C \quad \text{and} \quad 1 + (J_{AB}/2C)$$
$$(J_{AB}/2) - C \quad \text{and} \quad 1 + (J_{AB}/2C)$$
$$(-J_{AB}/2) - C \quad \text{and} \quad 1 - (J_{AB}/2C)$$

respectively; where $C \equiv (\frac{1}{2})[(\Delta \nu_A - \Delta \nu_B)^2 + J_{AB}^2]^{1/2}$. When the coupling is very strong, i.e., when $|J_{AB}| \gg |\Delta \nu_A - \Delta \nu_B|$, the AB quartet may be deceptively simple. Under conditions of very strong coupling, the intensities of the highest- and lowest-field components are frequently below the detectable limit, and the two central components appear as a closely spaced and possibly unresolveable doublet. The multiplets of more complex, strongly coupled spin systems are very often too complex to interpret by simple inspection. Complete analyses of spectra of the more complex spin systems are beyond the scope of this section. Such analyses have been reviewed elsewhere (34–36).

High-resolution NMR spectra frequently can be simplified by certain experimental methods. Some of the more convenient methods are the so-called spin-decoupling or multiple-resonance experiments. For a simple example of such experiments, consider the approximate A_3X_2 type spin system formed by the ethyl protons of ethyl acetate. Suppose one observes the A_3 methyl proton resonance with the usual radiofrequency field H_1 while irradiating the sample with a second, much stronger alternating field H_2 at the resonant frequency of the X_2 methylene protons. One finds that the A_3 methyl proton triplet collapses to a singlet. The field H_2 quantizes the magnetic moments of the X_2 methylene protons perpendicular to H_0 rather than parallel to it as usual, and the coupling between the A_3 and X_2 protons is effectively removed. Similarly, irradiation with the stronger radiofrequency field H_2 at the resonant frequency of the A_3 methyl protons, while observing the X_2 methylene protons with H_1, results in the collapse of the X_2 quartet to a singlet. There are several modifications of such experiments. In general, they aid determinations of chemical shifts of spin–spin coupled nuclei and in identifications of different spin–spin couplings among a number of mutually interacting nuclear spins. This aspect of high-resolution NMR was reviewed in 1963 by Baldeschweiler and Randall (37).

A second useful method for simplifying spectra is that of isotopic substitution. Such substitution has only a very small effect on electronic structure of molecules so that the chemical shifts of surrounding nuclei remain essentially unchanged. Substitution by an isotope of zero spin erases all complications due to spin coupling and resonance of the substituted magnetic nuclei. Since deuteron–proton coupling is very much weaker than proton–proton coupling, substitution of hydrogen by deuterium is occasionally a convenient way to simplify complex PMR spectra.

Another way to simplify spectra is to use higher values of H_0 and ν_0, which, as mentioned earlier, enhances the observed chemical-shift differences. Such enhancements decrease the ratios of the coupling constants to the chemical-shift differences and make the spin couplings conform more closely to the simple rules of weak coupling. Thus, the NMR spectrum can be interpreted more easily.

I. Exchange Averaging

Certain types of kinetic processes, such as internal rotations about chemical bonds and atomic exchange reactions, have important effects on high-resolution NMR spectra. For an example of such effects, consider nuclei in two different environments or "sites" A and B which have a chemical-shift difference of $\delta\nu_{AB}$ cps. In the absence of kinetic exchange of nuclei between the sites, or in the presence of very slow exchange (i.e., when $\tau_{AB}\delta\nu_{AB} \gg 1$, where τ_{AB} is the mean lifetime of nuclei in the sites in units of seconds), two narrow resonances separated by $\delta\nu_{AB}$ cps are observed to have relative intensities p_A and $p_B = (1 - p_A)$. The quantities p_A and p_B are the relative populations of nuclei in the two respective sites. As the rate of exchange increases, the two lines broaden and move closer together. The resonances coalesce to a single broad line when $\tau_{AB}\delta\nu_{AB} \sim 1$. Still faster exchange causes narrowing of the coalesced line, and complete exchange averaging yields a single narrow resonance at $p_A\nu_A + p_B\nu_B$ when $\tau_{AB}\delta\nu_{AB} \ll 1$. Similar effects of exchange averaging on spin–spin multiplets can occur also. Quantitative studies of exchange averagings have yielded unique information about rates and mechanisms of certain kinetic processes (38–40).

Complete exchange averaging among an assembly of n differently shielded sites leads to a single resonance at

$$\sum_{i=1}^{n} p_i\nu_i$$

Thus, several nuclei in a chemical functional group, such as the protons of a methyl group, may have the same effective, exchange-averaged chemical shift because of symmetry and very rapid internal rotation. Chemical shifts and coupling constants for polymers in solution usually are observed under conditions of complete exchange averaging among various chain conformations. Since the relative populations of chain conformations usually are affected by the stereochemical structure of the chain and the type of solvent used, the observed chemical shifts and coupling constants may be expected to depend on such factors also.

J. General Considerations

High-resolution NMR studies of polymers in solution present certain problems not encountered with solutions of small molecules. Nonrigid macromolecules permeate and encompass very large volumes of solution compared to their molecular volumes. Consequently, intermolecular interactions severely constrain the over-all macromolecular motions, and the averaging of dipole interactions results mainly from motions of segments of the macromolecular chains. Intramolecular interactions restrict these segmental motions more than intermolecular interactions restrict Brownian motions of small molecules in solution. Dipole interactions in dissolved polymers, therefore, are not completely averaged, and the widths

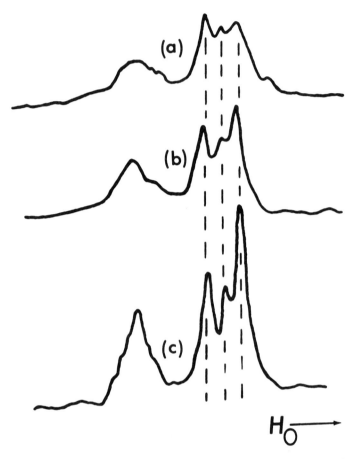

Fig. 2. Partial PMR spectra of a stereoblock poly(methyl methacrylate); about 7 vol.% polymer in chloroform solution; $\nu_0 = 40$ Mc/sec: (a) 35°, (b) 82°, (c) 90°C. [Reproduced from Y. Kato and A. Nishioka, *J. Polymer Sci.*, **B3**, 739 (1965), by permission of Wiley-Interscience.]

of lines due to dissolved polymers usually are larger than those due to small molecules in solution. Motional narrowing can be increased somewhat by reducing the concentration of polymer in solution, but this approach is limited by the sensitivity of the experiment.† Increasing the temperature enhances segmental motions and often leads to much narrower

† Concentrations normally used are in the range 5–20 vol.% polymer.

resonance lines.† An example of this effect of temperature on line widths of polymer NMR spectra is illustrated in Fig. 2. There it is shown that temperature has a nonequivalent effect on the motional narrowing of some of the PMR resonances of poly(methyl methacrylate). Because of solvent–polymer interactions, the shielding of nuclei in a polymer and the motional

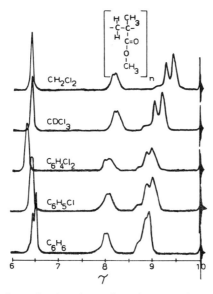

Fig. 3. PMR spectra of a predominantly syndiotactic commerical sample of poly(methyl methacrylate) in various solvents at 37°C; $v_0 = 100$ Mc/sec; internal reference is TMS at $\tau \equiv 10$. [Reproduced from K. C. Ramey and J. Messick, *J. Polymer Sci.*, A4(2), 155 (1966), by permission of Wiley-Interscience.]

narrowing of the polymer NMR spectrum may depend markedly on the type of solvent used. Examples of these effects are shown in Fig. 3, where it is shown that the solvent yielding the best resolution of the high-field (high-τ) group of lines is different from the solvent yielding the best resolution of the low-field (low-τ) group of lines.

Segmental motions in many of the more rigid macromolecules in solution are ineffective in averaging dipole–dipole interactions. Thus, many biopolymers and biolike polymers, which retain some secondary or tertiary

† Because of the high volatility of TMS, the proton resonance of dissolved hexamethyl-disiloxane (HMDS) frequently is used as a secondary reference for PMR studies at elevated temperatures; $\tau_{HMDS} = 10 - \delta_{HMDS} = 9.95$ ppm at room temperature.

structure in solution, give rather broad resonance lines. In order to obtain high-resolution spectra of such polymers, it is usually necessary to render the chains more flexible by at least partial conversion of the chains to nearly random coils, e.g., denaturation of helical polypeptides.

III. SOME GENERAL STRUCTURAL FEATURES, NOMENCLATURE, AND STATISTICAL RELATIONSHIPS

A. Structural Isomerism

Many vinyl and related types of monomers undergo addition reactions to form high molecular weight chainlike polymer molecules. These polymerizations usually occur with high regularity via so-called head-to-tail addition reactions. Head-to-tail additions of monomers such as CH_2=CRR' (where $R \neq R'$, R' may be hydrogen) yield structurally regular sequences of the type —CH_2—CRR'—CH_2—CRR'—.† Polymer chains consisting of such sequences are subject to a number of possible structural irregularities. In some cases, the lengths of structurally regular sequences, which result from successive head-to-tail additions, are limited by the occurrence of head-to-head and tail-to-tail additions yielding structures such as —CH_2—CRR'—CRR'—CH_2— and —CRR'—CH_2—CH_2—CRR'—, respectively. Head-to-head and tail-to-tail type additions are sometimes called "backwards" additions. Occasionally, intra- and intermolecular side reactions lead to additional structural irregularities such as branching and cross-linking of the polymer chains.

B. Steric Isomerism

Another important aspect of polymer structure is steric isomerism or tacticity. A structurally regular polymer molecule is stereoregular or tactic if the steric configurations around the main-chain sites of steric isomerism form an ordered sequence throughout the molecule. A structurally regular polymer molecule such as $\{CH_2$—$CRR'\}_n$ is isotactic if the configurations around all main-chain sites of steric isomerism are the same (i.e., if the configurations around all the main-chain pseudoasymmetric carbon atoms of the —CRR'— groups are the same).§ The molecule is syndiotactic if the

† Quite arbitrarily, the —CRR'— group is called the head and the —CH_2— group is called the tail.

§ A more complete discussion of nomenclature is given in Chapter 1, this volume. This topic has also been reviewed recently by a committee of the International Union of Pure and Applied Chemistry (*41*).

configurations around the main-chain sites of steric isomerism alternate regularly throughout the chain. In an atactic polymer molecule, the configurations around main-chain sites of steric isomerism are distributed with complete randomness. Polymers with low degrees of steric order in the main chains customarily are called atactic if their macroscopic properties are practically the same as the strictly atactic polymer. The stereoblock polymer molecule is structurally regular and consists of at least two kinds of blocks, tactic or atactic. This specification often is limited to cases where the lengths of at least one of the kinds of tactic blocks are long enough to produce some macroscopic properties characteristic of the tactic polymers; e.g., characteristic chain helicity or crystallinity.

When characterizing the steric isomerism of polymers, it is convenient to refer to structures of localized segments of the chains. A sequence of two successive monomer units in a structurally regular polymer chain such as $\{CH_2-CRR'\}_n$ is called a tactic placement (42) or tactic dyad (43). An isotactic placement or isotactic dyad in the planar zigzag or all *trans* conformation is illustrated by structure (1). Similarly, a syndiotactic

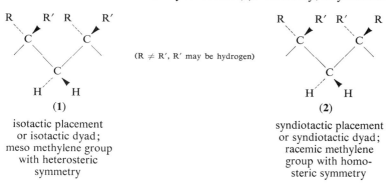

(R ≠ R', R' may be hydrogen)

(1)
isotactic placement
or isotactic dyad;
meso methylene group
with heterosteric
symmetry

(2)
syndiotactic placement
or syndiotactic dyad;
racemic methylene
group with homo-
steric symmetry

placement or syndiotactic dyad is illustrated by structure (2). The stereochemical configurations around the two main-chain pseudoasymmetric carbon atoms are the same in the isotactic placement or dyad and opposite in the syndiotactic placement or dyad. It is usually desirable to refer to the central methylene group of an isotactic placement as a meso methylene group or an *m* unit (43,44). Similarly, the central methylene group of a syndiotactic placement is a racemic methylene group or an *r* unit.

A sequence of three successive monomer units in a structurally regular polymer chain such as $\{CH_2-CRR'\}_n$ is called a tactic triad (43). All three main-chain sites of steric isomerism have the same configuration in an isotactic triad [e.g., structure (3)]. The central unit in an isotactic triad is called an *i* unit which is equivalent to an *mm* sequence. The main-chain sites of steric isomerism alternate in a syndiotactic triad [e.g., structure (**4**)], and the central unit is called an *s* unit which is equivalent to an *rr* sequence. In a heterotactic triad [e.g., structure (**5**)], two adjacent main-chain sites of steric isomerism have the same configuration and the third site has the opposite configuration. The central unit of a heterotactic triad is called an *h* unit which is equivalent to an *mr* or an *rm* sequence.

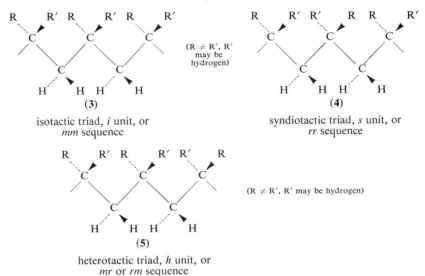

(3)   (4)

isotactic triad, *i* unit, or   syndiotactic triad, *s* unit, or
mm sequence   *rr* sequence

(5)

heterotactic triad, *h* unit, or
mr or *rm* sequence

Six tactic tetrad sequences of monomer units in a polymer of the type $+CH_2-CRR'+_n$ may be observationally distinguishable. They are *mmm*, *mmr* ≡ *rmm*, *rmr*, *mrr* ≡ *rrm*, *mrm*, and *rrr*. Similarly, 10 different tactic pentads may be observationally distinguishable; they are *iii* ≡ *mmmm*, *iih* ≡ *mmmr* ≡ *hii* ≡ *rmmm*, *his* ≡ *rmmr*, *ihh* ≡ *mmrm* ≡ *hhi* ≡ *mrmm*, *hhh* ≡ *rmrm* ≡ *mrmr*, *ihs* ≡ *mmrr* ≡ *shi* ≡ *rrmm*, *hhs* ≡ *rmrr* ≡ *shh* ≡ *rrmr*, *hsh* ≡ *mrrm*, *ssh* ≡ *rrrm* ≡ *hss* ≡ *mrrr*, and *sss* ≡ *rrrr*.

Tactic polymers of the type $+CH_2-CRR'+_n$ are monotactic in the sense that the base unit or structural repeat unit contains only one main-chain site of steric isomerism. When more than one type of site is present, several other types of tacticity are possible, as for example, in the chain of *erythro* diisotactic poly(1-R)(2-R') ethamer shown in structure (**6**) and the chain of *threo* diisotactic poly(1-R)(2-R') ethamer shown in structure (**7**). *Erythro* disyndiotactic and *threo* disyndiotactic polymers have definitions analogous to those of the corresponding diisotactic polymers.

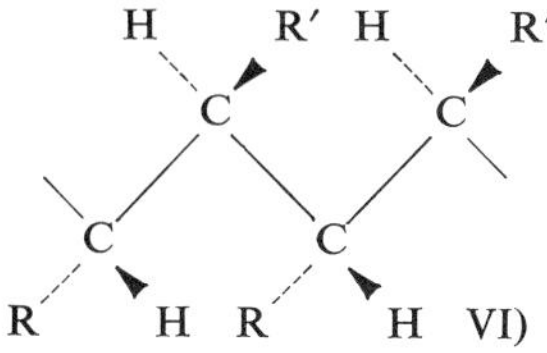

(6)

segment of *erythro* diisotactic poly(1-R)(2-R′)
ethamer

$H \neq R \neq R' \neq H$

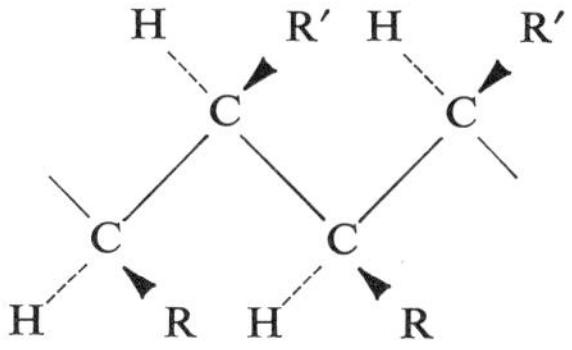

(7)

segment of *threo* diisotactic
poly(1-R)(2-R′) ethamer

Monomers such as CH_2=CR—CH=CH_2 can undergo 1,2 polymerization or 3,4 polymerization yielding structurally regular sequences illustrated
by structures (8) and (9), respectively. These sequences have main-chain
steric isomerism of the type described in the foregoing. Another type of
steric isomerism encountered in polymers is geometrical or *cis–trans*
isomerism. Numerous CH_2=CR—CH=CH_2 and related types of monomers undergo 1,4 polymerization yielding *cis* (10) or *trans* (11) isomerism
in the main chain. Structurally regular polymers such as (10) and (11) are
called *cis* tactic and *trans* tactic, respectively. Still other polymers have

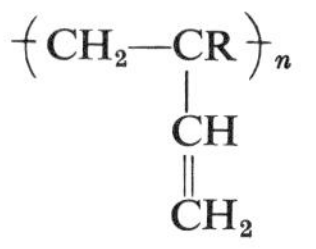

(8)

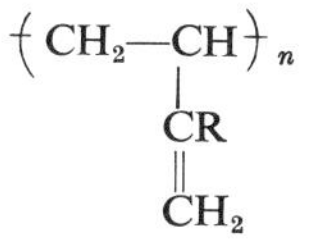

(9)

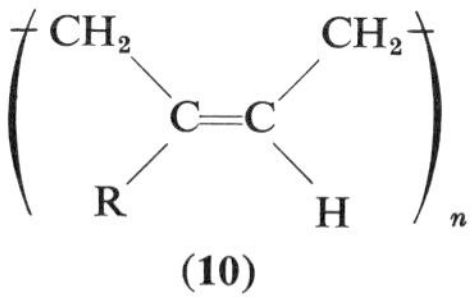

(10)

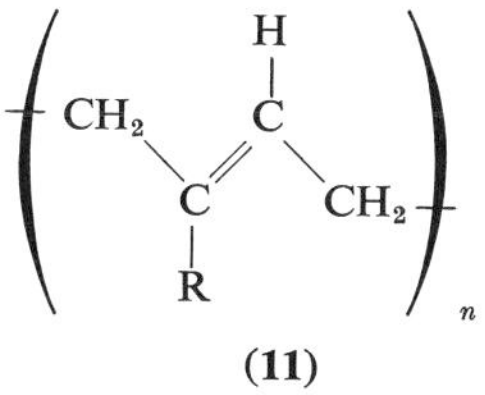

(11)

main-chain steric isomerism resulting from both pseudoasymmetric
atoms and geometrical isomerism. Examples of such polymers have
been described in Chapter 1 and in Ref. (41) and the references cited
therein.

Relationships between magnetic shielding of nuclei and certain aspects
molecular symmetry are very important in characterizing tacticities of
polymers by NMR. Barring fortuitous situations, otherwise similar nuclei
that occupy geometrically nonequivalent positions in a molecule generally

also have nonequivalent magnetic shieldings.† Thus, observation of a shielding difference between protons of a methylene group in a polymer such as $-(\text{CH}_2-\text{CRR}')-_n$ gives unique information about the local molecular symmetry and tacticity.§

The symmetry of a methylene group in which the protons are differentiated by symmetry arguments has been termed heterosteric, and that of a methylene group in which the protons are equivalent (except for accidental equivalence) has been termed homosteric. The same classifications apply to —CM_2— groups in general (45). These symmetry classifications are independent of molecular conformation in the sense that the exchange-averaged shieldings of the protons of a homosteric methylene group always are equivalent for any real distribution of molecular conformers. The shieldings of the protons of a heterosteric methylene group generally are nonequivalent. Exceptions to this latter rule may result from accidental distributions of molecular conformers and solvent effects¶ which produce virtually equivalent exchange-averaged magnetic shielding for the protons of a heterosteric methylene group. Thus, observation of magnetic equivalence of methylene protons in a polymer such as $-(\text{CH}_2-\text{CRR}')-_n$ is a strong indication, but not proof, that the methylene group has homosteric symmetry and is racemic (in the center of a syndiotactic placement). Observation of a shielding difference between protons of a methylene group in such a polymer is absolute proof that the methylene group has

† Nonequivalent magnetic shielding usually results from geometrical nonequivalence mainly because of the nonequivalent shielding contributions from surrounding, magnetically anisotropic chemical bonds comprising the molecule. These contributions to the total shielding of a nucleus depend on the anistropies of the bonds in question and on the positions and orientations of these bonds with respect to the position of the nucleus in question. The magnitude of such a shielding contribution attenuates very rapidly with increasing distance between the anisotropic bond and the nucleus (23,24).

§ A shielding difference between protons of a methylene group manifests the geminal spin–spin coupling and, in the absence of vicinal and other spin couplings, gives rise to two doublets or a symmetrical quartet of PMR resonances characteristic of an *AB*-type spin system. Magnetically equivalent methylene protons give rise to a single resonance line in the absence of vicinal or other spin–spin couplings.

¶ Solvation may diminish or amplify the shielding difference between the protons of a heterosteric methylene group. Direct shielding effects from the solvent may contribute nonequivalently to the total shieldings of the two methylene protons, and the solvent may also produce indirect shielding effects by perturbing the populations of conformations of the molecule. Similar perturbations of the populations of conformations about a homosteric methylene group cannot produce a shielding difference between the two methylene protons. Also, symmetry arguments require that direct shielding effects from the solvent contribute equally to the total shieldings of protons in a homosteric methylene group.

heterosteric symmetry. Such a methylene group is either meso (in the center of an isotactic placement) or racemic and in the center of tactic sequences such as *mrr*, *mrrrr*, etc.

The through-chain distances between the protons of a heterosteric methylene group and the bonds giving rise to shielding differences are much smaller for meso methylene groups than for racemic methylene groups in the center of sequences such as *mrr*, *mrrrr*, etc. Since the corresponding through-space distances usually increase with the through-chain distances, and since shielding contributions from anisotropic bonds attentuate rapidly with increasing through-space distances, the magnetic nonequivalence of protons in a meso methylene group is usually larger than that of protons of a heterosteric racemic methylene group.

Of the six observationally distinguishable tactic tetrads of monomer units in a polymer such as $+CH_2—CRR'+_n$, the four of types *mmm*, *mmr* $\equiv$ *rmm*, *rmr*, and *mrr* $\equiv$ *rrm* each have central methylene groups with heterosteric symmetry. Each of these groups can, in principle, give rise to two different proton chemical shifts. As explained in the preceding paragraph, such chemical-shift differences generally should be larger for the first three tactic tetrads mentioned than for the last one. The *mrm* and *rrr* tactic tetrads have central methylene groups with homosteric symmetry, and the protons of each of these groups can give rise to only one proton chemical shift.

C. Some General and Specific Statistical Relationships

NMR data on the structures of segments of macromolecules are often unique, and occasionally they enable one to calculate important characteristics of polymerization chemistry and over-all macromolecular structure. This section is confined to characterizations of steric isomerism in homopolymers and stereochemistry of homopolymerizations. The concepts and relationships employed, however, are essentially identical to those used for characterizing structural isomerism in copolymers and chemistry of copolymerizations.

The relative numbers of tactic placements (*m* and *r* units) in numerous vinyl and related types of homopolymers can be determined directly from high-resolution NMR spectra. Frequently, the relative numbers of tactic triads and, occasionally, some of the tactic tetrad contents can be determined also. Further development of very high field NMR experiments probably will permit the resolution of much smaller shielding differences than is now possible. Then, direct measurements of relative numbers of tactic pentads probably will be possible in at least a few polymers. Very often it is desirable to calculate some of the tactic placement, triad, or tetrad contents in a polymer from experimental values of the relative numbers of other tactic sequences of similar or longer length. Such calculations may be made through use of the following relationships which are valid for any distribution of tactic placements.†

$$(m) = (i) + (h)/2 \tag{1}$$

$$(r) = 1 - (m) = (s) + (h)/2 \tag{2}$$

$$(i) \equiv (mm) = 1 - (h) - (s) = (mmm) + (mmr)/2 \tag{3}$$

$$(h) \equiv (mr) = 2(mrm) + (rrm)$$
$$= 2(rmr) + (mmr) \tag{4}$$

$$(s) \equiv (rr) = (rrr) + (rrm)/2 \tag{5}$$

$$(mmm) + (mmr) + (rmr) + (rrr) + (rrm) + (mrm) = 1 \tag{6}$$

Closed isotactic sequences of length n have n successive m units flanked by r units; i.e., $\ldots rm_n r \ldots$. A closed syndiotactic sequence of length n has n successive r units flanked by m units; i.e., $\ldots mr_n m \ldots$. Neglecting chain ends in a high molecular weight polymer, each closed isotactic and syndiotactic sequence terminates with an h unit. The number-average closed isotactic and syndiotactic sequence lengths for any distribution of tactic placements are given, respectively, by

$$\langle m \rangle = 2(m)/(h) \tag{7}$$

$$\langle r \rangle = 2(r)/(h) \tag{8}$$

The tacticity of a polymer is described best in terms of the distribution of closed tactic sequences comprising the polymer chains. Occasionally, knowledge of tactic triad and tetrad contents in a polymer enables one to establish the specific, most probable statistical rules obeyed by the stereochemistry of the polymerization process. Such information contributes greatly to the understanding of the polymerization mechanism and enables one to calculate the entire statistical distribution of closed tactic sequences in the polymer. Such distributions define most directly the effects of tacticity on physicochemical properties of polymers (42,46–51).

Many papers have described the statistical features of various types of copolymerization and stereoisomeric homopolymerization processes (3,

† Brackets around sequence designations indicate the relative numbers of those sequences in the polymer among all sequences of the same length. Parentheses around sequence designations indicate the same relative numbers of observationally distinguishable sequences (45b); e.g., (mr) = (rm) = [mr] + [rm], and (mrm) = [mrm].

42,43,45b–47,52–77).† The tactic placements or the configurations of main-chain sites of steric isomerism in a structurally regular polymer such as $\{CH_2—CRR'\}_n$ may be distributed according to the rules of Bernoullian, Markoffian, or non-Markoffian statistical processes. In a Bernoullian statistical process (i.e., a 0th order Markoffian process) the result of an event is characterized by a single probability which is independent of the results of all previous events (*42,60,63*). The probability of occurrence of a particular sequence U^n of n tactic placements in a Bernoullian distribution of tactic placements is independent of the nature of any other preceding sequence W^m of m tactic placements.§ In such cases,

$$(r) = (rr)/(r) = (rrr)/(rr) = (mrr)/(rm)$$
$$= (mr)/2(m) = (mmr)/2(mm) = 2(rmr)/(rm) = \cdots \tag{9}$$

or

$$\rho = \eta_r = \eta_{mr} = \eta_{rr} = 1 \tag{10}$$

where

$$\rho \equiv 2(m)(r)/(mr) \qquad \eta_r \equiv (rr)/(r)^2 \tag{11a,b}$$
$$\eta_{mr} \equiv (mrr)/(r)(mr) \qquad \eta_{rr} \equiv (rrr)/(r)(rr) \tag{12a,b}$$

and $\eta_m \equiv (mm)/(m)^2$ and $\eta_{mm} \equiv (mmm)/(m)(mm)$ are called specific persistence ratios, and $0 < (r) \leqslant 1$ (*63,65,77*). The probability of occurrence of a particular sequence U^n of n main-chain steric configurations in an enantiomorphically paired Bernoullian distribution of main-chain steric configurations is independent of the nature of any other preceding sequence W^m of m main-chain steric configurations and, in effect, is dependent on the configuration of the process catalyst site only (*70,71*). These types of homopolymerizations are characterized by $0 \leqslant (r) \leqslant 0.5$, and

$$(r) = 2(rr) = (mr) = \tfrac{2}{3}\{1 - (mm)\} \tag{13}$$

Bernoullian processes are generally biased random processes. An unbiased random process is an extremely unique limiting case for either of the two Bernoullian processes just described. The unbiased random

† Several types of nomenclature and many types of symbolic designations have been used. None of them, including the types used here, appear to be generally advantageous.

§ The same type of polymerization is symmetric and first-order or symmetric and simple Markoffian if one takes the absolute configurations of main-chain sites of steric isomerism as the statistical chain units, rather than adjacent relative configurations or tactic placements (*70,71*). The probability of occurrence of a particular sequence U^n of n main-chain steric configurations in a simple Markoffian distribution of main-chain steric configurations is dependent only on the steric configuration of the preceding (penultimate) main-chain site of steric isomerism.

homopolymerization obeys Eq. (10) or Eq. (13) and yields a strictly atactic polymer in which $(r) = (m) = 2(mm) = 2(rr) = (mr) = 0.5$. Equations (10) and (13), and knowledge of tactic triad contents in a polymer, generally enable one to distinguish a biased Bernoullian polymerization controlled by the configuration of the catalyst from one controlled by the configuration of the terminal main-chain site of steric isomerism (70,71). Agreement between tactic triad contents and Eq. (10) is a necessary, but not a sufficient, condition for the applicability of Bernoullian statistics to distributions of tactic placements. Disagreement between tactic triad and/or tetrad contents and Eq. (10) proves that the distribution of tactic placements is non-Bernoullian. For example, a chain such as

$$\ldots mmrrmmmrrmmrr \ldots$$

is a very special non-Bernoullian distribution where the tactic triad contents conform to Eq. (10), $\rho = \eta_r = 1$, but the tactic tetrad contents do not, $0 = \eta_{rr} \neq 1 \neq \eta_{mr} = 2$. Values of $\rho > 1$ show that closed tactic sequences are longer than in the case of a Bernoullian distribution of tactic placements with the same value of (m) (63,65,77). The reverse is true for $\rho < 1$. Polymers with $\rho > 1$ are occasionally called stereoblock polymers, and the positive deviations of ρ from unity are then used as measures of stereoblock character.

The probability of occurrence of a particular sequence U^n of n tactic placements in a Markoffian distribution of tactic placements of order N is dependent only on the nature of the preceding sequence V^N of N tactic placements (63). In a first-order or simple Markoffian distribution of tactic placements ($N = 1$), the distribution is determined by two independent conditional probabilities, e.g., (r/r) and (r/m), which are the probabilities that any particular placement is syndiotactic, given that the preceding (penultimate) placement was syndiotactic or isotactic, respectively. Generally, for such distributions,

$$(r) \neq (r/r) = (rr)/(r) = (rrr)/(rr) = (mrr)/(mr)$$
$$\neq (r/m) = (rm)/2(m) = (mmr)/2(mm) = 2(rmr)/(rm) \quad (14)$$

or

$$1 \neq \rho \neq \eta_r = \eta_{rr} = \eta_{mr} \neq 1 \quad (63,65,77) \quad (15)$$

Agreement between tactic tetrad contents and Eq. (15) is a necessary, but not sufficient, condition for the applicability of simple Markoffian statistics to distributions of tactic placements. Cases of insufficiency demand rather special distributions which, conceivably, might result from polymerization mechanisms that involve specific interactions among the monomer, catalyst sites, and/or polymer chains. Disagreement between tactic tetrad contents and Eq. (15) proves that the distribution of tactic placements is not simple Markoffian.

Distributions of tactic placements which are Markoffian of order higher than 1 or are non-Markoffian generally obey neither Eq. (10) nor Eq. (15). The characteristics of some of these distributions, and some plausible mechanisms for generating them, have been discussed elsewhere (60,62–65, 72). Certain aspects of these distributions will be mentioned in later sections.

IV. STUDIES OF VINYL AND RELATED TYPES OF HOMOPOLYMERS

Structural regularities of high molecular weight vinyl and related types of homopolymers are frequently so high that some of the properties of a given type of polymer depend on tacticity alone. Since the effects of tacticity on some polymer properties are frequently quite marked, a great deal of effort has been expended on elucidations of tactic structures. Tacticities of some polymers have been assessed indirectly through measurements of properties which are at least partially characteristic of the purely tactic species (78).† Although such indirect methods occasionally have rather broad applicability and yield important information, the results usually cannot be interpreted in terms of tacticity alone. In contrast, high-resolution NMR often yields direct measurements of polymer tacticities and, in some cases, of structural irregularities resulting from such processes as backwards additions also. Occasionally, NMR studies of vinyl and related types of homopolymers also can yield important information about conformations of polymer chains in solution and about mechanisms of addition polymerizations.

A. Stereochemical Structures or Tacticities

1. Poly(methyl methacrylate)

The properties of high molecular weight poly(methyl methacrylates) (PPMAs) vary markedly with synthesis conditions due to very large variations in tacticity. Although some of these variations were revealed by experiments other than NMR (46,79,80), a much clearer account has resulted from direct PMR determinations of the relative amounts of short

---

† Examples of properties which may be sufficiently characteristic are chain conformation or helicity, crystallinity, various dilute-solution properties, glass-transition temperature, optical rotation, and rate of chemical hydrolysis.

tactic sequences in the polymers. Such determinations were first described by Bovey and Tiers (*43*). Subsequently, many other investigators have used PMR to examine steric isomerism in PMMAs made under various conditions (*3,4,44,45b,59,65,76,77,81–108,274,313*).

Bovey and Tiers' (*43*) original PMR spectra of PMMAs having different tacticities are shown in Fig. 4. On the basis of chemical-shift data for

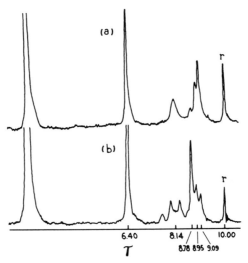

Fig. 4. PMR spectra of (a) predominantly syndiotactic poly(methyl methacrylate) prepared with free-radical initiator at 100°C and (b) predominantly isotactic poly(methyl methacrylate) prepared with *n*-butyllithium in toluene at −62°C; about 15 vol.% polymers in chloroform solutions at 90°C; $\nu_0 = 40$ Mc/sec; internal reference (*r*) is TMS at $\tau \equiv 10$. [Reproduced from F. A. Bovey and G. V. D. Tiers, *J. Polymer Sci.*, **44**, 173 (1960), by permission of Wiley-Interscience.]

small molecules (*25–28*), the resonances at about 6.4τ in Fig. 4 are assigned to methoxyl protons of PMMA, and those at 8.78, 8.95, and 9.09τ are due to the α-methyl protons. The relatively broad singlet at about 8.14τ in Fig. 4(a) and the quartet centered at about 8.1τ in Fig. 4(b) are due to the methylene proton resonances. The resonances at lowest and highest fields (extreme left and right) are due to the chloroform solvent and the TMS reference, respectively.

Steric isomerism in PMMA has only a small effect on the shielding of the methoxyl protons. Thus, the methoxyl proton resonance appears as a single line in Fig. 4.† The effects of steric isomerism on the shielding of the α-methyl protons is very much greater. The lines at 8.78, 8.95, and 9.09τ are assigned to protons of α-methyl groups in the centers of isotactic, heterotactic, and syndiotactic triads of monomer units, respectively. These assignments agree with the conclusion that PMMAs prepared with n-butyllithium in hydrocarbon solvents have a predominance of isotactic placements (46,79,80). This conclusion and the assignments for the α-methyl proton resonances are proven absolutely by the nature of the methylene proton resonances.

The relatively broad singlet at about 8.14τ in Fig. 4(a) could arise mainly from protons of homosteric, racemic methylene groups or mainly from fortuitously equivalent protons of heterosteric, meso methylene groups. The latter alternative requires that the polymer characterized by Fig. 4(b) have a predominance of syndiotactic placements of monomer units and that the protons of homosteric, racemic methylene groups which then predominate be magnetically nonequivalent. This latter requirement is impossible. Thus, the singlet at 8.14τ in Fig. 4(a) is due to protons of racemic methylene groups, and the quartet centered at 8.1τ in Fig. 4(b) arises mainly from geminal spin–spin coupling ($|J| \approx 15$ cps) between the magnetically nonequivalent (ca. 0.6 ppm) protons of each heterosteric, meso methylene group.§

The tactic triad contents in PMMAs may be determined by use of the assignments described above and the intensities of the α-methyl proton resonances (43). The relative numbers of tactic placements can then be calculated from Eq. (1) and (2). Under conditions of sufficiently high resolution, values of (m) and (r) also can be determined from the intensities of the various methylene proton resonances. Although these two methods for obtaining (m) and (r) generally are in good agreement, the determinations based on experimental triad contents usually are more accurate; because, as will be seen later, the methylene proton resonances are somewhat more complicated than described in the foregoing.

Tactic placement and triad contents of the PMMA characterized by

† Under conditions of higher resolution in certain solvents, the methoxyl protons of PMMA do experience small, resolvable shielding differences resulting from variations in steric isomerism (101); e.g., see Fig. 3.

§ Protons of heterosteric, racemic methylene groups in the center of mrr sequences can, in principle, be magnetically nonequivalent and give rise to such a quartet also. However, the contribution that such methylene groups make to the quartet in Fig. 4(b) must be small compared to those from m units; for the α-methyl proton resonances in Fig. 4(b) show that (i) > (h) > (r).

Fig. 4(a) are specified by $(r) = 0.725$ and $(s) = 0.53$ (*43*). These results, which are subject to an experimental error of about 5%, yield $\rho = \eta_r = \eta_m = 1$. Thus, the free-radical polymerization gave a predominantly syndiotactic polymer, i.e., $(r) > 0.5$, and the tactic triad contents are consistent with a Bernoullian distribution of tactic placements. The results of Fox and co-workers (*79*), Bovey and Tiers (*43*), and subsequent studies (*83,87,91, 94,102,103,107*) have shown that homogeneous, free-radical polymerizations of methyl methacrylate always yield predominantly syndiotactic polymers. The tactic triad contents of such polymers never show large deviations from Bernoullian distributions of tactic placements.

The syndiotactic placement contents of PMMAs made with free-radical initiators increase with decreasing polymerization temperature; e.g., $(r) \approx 0.73$ at $100°C$ and $(r) \approx 0.9$ at $-78°C$. The polymers made below about $0°C$ are partially crystallizable, whereas those made above $0°C$ are not (*79*). The temperature dependence of (r) for PMMAs prepared with free-radical initiators yields $\Delta H_m^{\ddagger} - \Delta H_r^{\ddagger} \approx 1$ kcal/mole and $\Delta S_m^{\ddagger} - \Delta S_r^{\ddagger} \approx 1$ e.u./mole for the differences between the enthalpies and entropies of activation for formations of isotactic and syndiotactic placements, respectively (*83, 87,102*). Walling and Tanner have studied the dependence of tacticity of PMMAs prepared with a free-radical initiator on polymerization pressure at $51°C$ (*91*). The difference between the volumes of activation for formations of syndiotactic and isotactic placements, $\Delta V_r^{\ddagger} - \Delta V_m^{\ddagger}$, is positive and very small in the range $1-4750$ kg/cm² but increases to 5.5 cm³/mole in the range $4750-7950$ kg/cm².

Variations in tacticity of PMMAs prepared with ionic catalysts can be much larger than that of polymers made with free-radical catalysts. The relative amounts and the distributions of tactic placements in PMMAs prepared with anionic catalysts vary markedly with polymerization conditions. These variations are of particular chemical interest and have been the subject of many investigations (*43,46,59,62,65,77,79,80,85,86,88,90, 92-96,102,104,106,108,274*).

It has been known for several years that tactic triad contents of many PMMAs prepared with anionic catalysts were inconsistent with Bernoullian distributions of tactic placements (*43*). For example, $(m) = 0.73$ and $(i) = (mm) = 0.63$ for the polymer characterized by Fig. 4(b). Thus, $\eta_r = 2.3 > \rho = 2.1 > \eta_m = 1.2$ so that Eq. (10) is not obeyed. Since these results also are inconsistent with Eq. (13), the polymer characterized by Fig. 4(b) is either a stereoblock polymer or a mixture of predominantly isotactic and predominantly syndiotactic PMMA molecules. In any case, the anionic polymerization which yielded this sample was non-Bernoullian in nature. Similar conclusions apply to the polymer characterized by Fig. 2 and to many other PMMAs made with anionic catalysts.

Several attempts have been made to interpret steric structures of PMMAs in terms of tactic triad contents and simple Markoffian distributions of tactic placements (*59,88,90,94,95*). For a given polymer, these interpretations use the two independent tactic triad contents obtained from PMR measurements for calculating the two independent conditional probabilities which characterize a simple Markoffian distribution. Such probabilities are, of course, closely related to the nature of a Markoffian polymerization mechanism, and they enable one to calculate the complete statistical distribution of all tactic sequences in a Markoffian polymer chain. The tactic triad contents alone, however, can only prove the existence of non-Bernoullian distributions. Information about the relative amounts of tactic tetrads or longer tactic sequences is required to "test" for the possible existence of a simple Markoffian distribution of tactic placements.

Some PMMAs that have been analyzed in terms of simple Markoffian distributions of tactic placements (which requires two independent probabilities) have tactic triad contents that can be calculated from a single probability according to Eq. (13). Experimental PMR results for some PMMAs of this type are compared with Eqs. (13) and (9) in Table 2. Such results alone confirm, but do not prove, the existence of mechanisms where, in effect, configurations of the catalyst sites control the stereochemistry of addition. Tactic triad contents of PMMAs made with the same or similar catalysts as listed in Table 2, but under different conditions of concentration, temperature, or type of solvent, generally do not conform to Eq. (13). Thus, the agreement of most of the results in Table 2 with Eq. (13) is probably fortuitous, and most of the polymers listed in Table 2 probably have steric structures which are quite different from enantiomorphically paired Bernoullian distributions of main-chain steric configurations.

Coleman and Fox have suggested that PMMAs made with some anionic catalysts may have non-Markoffian distributions of tactic placements resulting from changes in the state of the catalyst site during the growth of a polymer chain (*62,65*). In some instances, the tactic triad contents generated by the proposed multistate mechanisms should be markedly dependent on the monomer concentration during polymerization. One should, in principle, be able to confirm, but not prove, the existence of special non-Markoffian distributions by observing the predicted strong dependence of tactic triad contents on monomer concentration. Coleman and Fox have discussed the ramifications of many of the pertinent PMR

TABLE 2

PMR Results for Some Poly(methyl methacrylates) with non-Bernoullian Distributions of Tactic Placements

Sample	Catalyst	Solvent	Temp., °C	Catalyst concn., mmole/liter	Monomer concn., mole/liter	Conversion, %	(r)	(mr)	γ^a	ρ^b	Ref.
7	n-BuLi	Toluene	25				0.22	0.20	1.10	1.72	43
10a	C₆H₅MgBr	Toluene	0				0.29	0.26	1.10	1.58	43
SK125	n-BuLi	Toluene	−30	3.85	0.500	34	0.325	0.31	1.05	1.42	86
SK121	n-BuLi	Toluene	−30	3.85	0.500	73	0.19	0.18	1.06	1.71	86
JALP	n-BuLi	Toluene	−70				0.20	0.20	1.00	1.60	59
MA601	n-BuLi	Toluene	0	60	1.0	97.6	0.193	0.173	1.11	1.80	90
MA604	n-BuLi	Toluene	−70	60	1.0	88.2	0.227	0.205	1.11	1.71	90
MP24	Amyl Na	Ethyl ether	−70	28	1.0	24.6	0.29	0.30	0.97	1.37	90
R703	Amyl Na	Pet. ether	−30	28	1.0	60.8	0.30	0.30	1.00	1.40	90
MA624	Octyl K	Toluene	−70	60	1.0	90.3	0.43	0.402	1.07	1.23	90
MA621	Octyl K	Toluene	0	60	1.0	88.7	0.44	0.421	1.05	1.17	90
WB	DPHL^c	Toluene	−30	3.2	0.125	100	0.08	0.08	1.00	1.84	96
TMK	SrZnEt₄₍ₛ₎	Toluene	−70	2 mole % of monomer	20 vol. % of solvent	47.3	0.225	0.23	0.98	1.52	102

^{a} $\gamma \equiv (r)/(mr)$. $\gamma = 1$ for enantiomorphically paired Bernoullian distributions of main-chain steric configurations; see Eq. (13); the values of (r) and (mr) are subject to an experimental error of about 5% which corresponds to an error in γ of about ±0.1.

^{b} $\rho \equiv 2(m)(r)/(mr)$. $\rho = 1$ for Bernoullian distributions of tactic placements; see Eq. (9).

^{c} DPHL is 1,1-diphenylhexyl lithium; this polymerization mixture also contained 0.6 mmole MeOH/liter.

results for PMMAs (*65*). Although these results did not confirm quantitatively the non-Markoffian mechanisms, some of the PMR results and molecular weight distributions of PMMAs made with anionic catalysts do agree with certain aspects of the proposed mechanisms.

Under conditions of high spectral resolution in certain solvents at elevated temperatures, PMR spectra of most PMMAs reveal more than

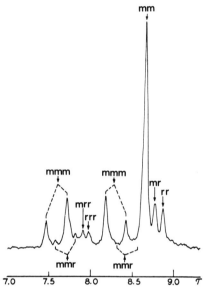

Fig. 5. Partial PMR spectrum of predominantly isotactic poly(methyl methacrylate) prepared with phenylmagnesium bromide initiator in toluene at −78°C; about 15 vol.% polymer in chlorobenzene solution at 150°C; v_0 = 60 Mc/sec. [Reproduced from F. A. Bovey, to be published in *J. Pure Appl. Chem.*, by permission of Butterworth (London).]

the three different chemical shifts expected for central methylene protons of isolated syndiotactic and isotactic placements. The spectra in Figs. 5 and 6 show resonances corresponding to at least seven differently shielded methylene protons. These shielding variations have been attributed to structural differences around the central methylene protons of the different tactic tetrads of monomer units (*5,44,45b,77,104,105b–d,106*). The two relatively intense doublets originating from about 7.6 and 8.3τ in Fig. 5 arise mainly from the nonequivalent, geminally spin-coupled protons of central methylene groups in *mmm* sequences. In most highly syndiotactic

PMMAs, the relative intensities of the lines at about 7.9 and 8.0τ increase in the order just mentioned. These lines are assigned to central methylene protons in *mrr* and *rrr* tactic tetrads, respectively (*44,45b,77,104,106*). These three assignments appear to be firmly established. Lím and co-workers have concluded (*104*) that a shielding difference of about 0.1 ppm

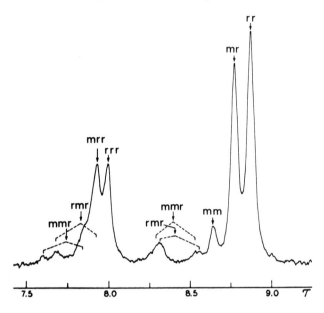

Fig. 6. Partial PMR spectrum of predominantly syndiotactic poly(methyl methacrylate) prepared with free-radical initiator at 135°C; about 15 vol. % polymer in chlorobenzene solution at 150°C; $v_0 = 60$ Mc/sec. [Reproduced from F. A. Bovey, to be published in *J. Pure Appl. Chem.*, by permission of Butterworth (London).]

exists between the central methylene protons of an *mrr* sequence in PMMA; see Fig. 7. For most practical purposes, this interpretation is the same as those (*45b,77,106*) which assign the same types of protons to be fortuitously equivalent. As shown in Fig. 7, a shielding difference of 0.1 ppm and the geminal spin coupling ($|J| \approx 15$ cps) would cause virtually all the resonance absorption to occur within 0.6 cps of the average shielding when $v_0 \leq 60$ cps.

Assignments for central methylene proton resonances of *mmr* and *rmr* sequences in PMMA do not appear to be firmly established at this time. According to the assignments of Lím and co-workers (*104*), the central methylene protons of *mmm* and *rmr* sequences have the same shieldings which are about 0.1 ppm less than those of central methylene protons in *mmr* sequences; see Fig. 7. Using these assignments, and numerical analyses of experimental methylene proton resonances of PMMAs prepared with alkali metal catalysts, they obtained tactic tetrad contents which were consistent with simple Markoffian distributions of tactic placements over wide ranges of tactic placement content and stereoblock

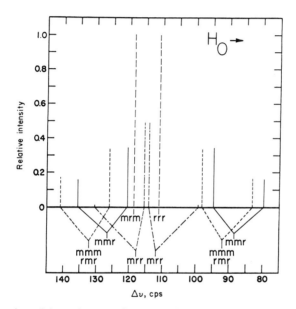

Fig. 7. Illustration of the assignments by Lím and co-workers (*104*) for the resonances of central methylene protons in tactic tetrads of monomer units of poly(methyl methacrylate); about 15 vol.% polymer in a mixture of perchloroethylene and *o*-dichlorobenzene solution at 140°C; $\nu_0 = 60$ Mc/sec; internal reference is HMDS.

character. According to the assignments of Bovey and co-workers (*45b*, *106*), however, the shieldings of protons in central meso methylene groups of tactic tetrads increase in the order *mmm* < *mmr* < *rmr*; e.g., see Figs. 5 and 6. Definitive assignments for the central methylene protons of all the tactic tetrads of monomer units in PMMAs probably will require higher resolution spectra obtained under conditions of higher signal-to-noise ratios. Such results should be achievable from spectra obtained at higher magnetic fields. Also, resolution probably can be improved somewhat by decreasing the concentration of polymers in the PMR sample solutions.

Signal-to-noise levels can be improved through use of electronic computers of average transients. Such procedures, combined with numerical analyses of the spectra in digital form with electronic computers, should yield accurate values for the tactic tetrad contents in PMMAs.

Reinmöller and Fox (77) and Coleman et al. (108) have determined (rrr), (mrr), tactic triad contents, and, in some cases, (mmm) for PMMAs made with various homogeneous anionic catalysts. After correcting for effects of overlapping lines by use of a curve resolving technique, they claimed that random errors were reduced to about ± 0.015 for (rrr) and (mrr) and to about ± 0.01 for the triad contents. The values of (rrr) and (mrr) in two PMMAs were inconsistent with simple Markoffian distributions of tactic placements; e.g., $\eta_{rr}/\eta_r = 1.14 \pm 0.06 \neq \eta_{mr}/\eta_r = 0.78 \pm 0.11$ for a PMMA prepared with 9-fluorenyllithium in 95% toluene and 5% tetrahydrofuran at $-60°C$ (108).† Values of (rrr) and (mrr) for PMMAs prepared with some other anionic catalysts were consistent with simple Markoffian distributions of tactic placements, whereas the same tetrad contents and the tactic triad contents of PMMAs made with still other anionic catalysts were consistent with Bernoullian distributions of tactic placements.

Apparently, Reinmöller and Fox assumed (77) that the high-field line of the low-field doublet due to central methylene protons of rmr sequences in PMMA does not interfere with the line due to corresponding protons in mrr sequences. Such an assumption is supported by the assignments of Lím and co-workers (Fig. 7) but not by those described by Bovey (Fig. 6). If the assignments described by Bovey are correct, then values of (mrr) obtained by Reinmöller and Fox should be too high by about 0.17 (rmr). However, such an error in their (mrr) results probably would not affect their major conclusions even when (rmr) is large in value. For, their (rrr) results, which provide sufficient basis for their conclusions, probably are sufficiently accurate.

Reinmöller and Fox also determined (rrr), (mrr), and tactic triad contents of PMMAs made with homogeneous free-radical initiators (107). Triad contents were inconsistent with Bernoullian distributions of tactic placements for polymerization temperatures below about 70°C. The deviations from Bernoullian statistics increased with decreasing polymerization temperature; e.g., $\rho = 1.07 \pm 0.03$ at 30°C and $\rho = 1.25 \pm 0.07$

† From spectra such as that in Fig. 5, Bovey has shown that PMMA prepared with phenylmagnesium bromide in toluene at $-78°C$ has a nonsimple Markoffian distribution of tactic placements (106); i.e., $(mmm) = 0.78$, $(mm) = 0.75$, and $(mr) = 0.12$ so that $\eta_{mm}/\eta_m = 1.12$.

at $-55°C$. The tactic tetrad contents were consistent with simple Markoffian distributions of tactic placements over the range of polymerization temperature -55 to $135°C$. The penultimate effects in homogeneous free-radical polymerizations of methyl methacrylate are revealed quite vividly by the following differences in enthalpies and entropies of activations: $\Delta H_{mm}{}^{\ddagger} - \Delta H_{mr}{}^{\ddagger} = -230 \pm 90$ cal/mole, $\Delta H_{rm}{}^{\ddagger} - \Delta H_{rr}{}^{\ddagger} = 1120 \pm 70$ cal/mole, $\Delta S_{mm}{}^{\ddagger} - \Delta S_{mr}{}^{\ddagger} = -2.9 \pm 0.4$ e.u./mole, and $\Delta S_{rm}{}^{\ddagger} - \Delta S_{rr}{}^{\ddagger} = 0.8 \pm 0.2$ e.u./mole, where, for example, $\Delta H_{rm}{}^{\ddagger} - \Delta H_{rr}{}^{\ddagger}$ represents the enthalpy of activation favoring formation of a syndiotactic placement over that of forming an isotactic placement when the penultimate placement is syndiotactic (*107*).

2. Other Polymethacrylics

Tacticities of poly(methacrylic anhydride) (PMAA) (*109–112*), poly-(methacrylic acid) (*102*), various polymethacrylate esters (*102,113,114*), and polymethacrylonitrile (*115,116*) have been examined by PMR after conversions of the polymers to the corresponding PMMAs. Free-radical polymerizations of methacrylic anhydride, like those of many other 1,6-heptadienes, are believed to proceed via regularly alternating intermolecular addition to the bifunctional monomer and an intramolecular cycloaddition reaction (*110,117–123*). Reinmöller and Fox recently have determined (*rrr*), (*mrr*), and tactic triad contents in PMMAs derived from PMAAs made at various temperatures with free-radical initiators (*112*). Their results are consistent with Bernoullian distributions of tactic placements in the polymers made in the range 5–135°C and with simple Markoffian distributions of tactic placements in the polymers made at -30 and $-55°C$. On the basis of statistical considerations for alternating Bernoullian and/or simple Markoffian mechanisms, Reinmöller and Fox concluded that the intramolecular cyclization step generates Bernoullian distributions of tactic placements over the range of polymerization temperature -55 to $135°C$. Their results are consistent with this reaction alternating with the intermolecular addition which, like free-radical polymerizations of methyl methacrylate, generates simple Markoffian distributions at low temperatures and Bernoullian distributions at elevated temperatures. These conclusions are consistent with results (*102*) which show that the steric structures of poly(acrylic acid) and various polymethacrylate esters made via free-radical initiation have a relatively small dependence on the nature of the substituent on the carboxyl group.

The tactic structures of poly(benzyl methacrylate), poly(β-phenyethyl methacrylate) and poly(γ-phenylpropyl methacrylate) (*124*), poly(allyl methacrylate) (*125a*), and poly(phenyl methacrylate) and poly(penta-fluorophenyl methacrylate) (*125b*) have been examined directly by PMR spectroscopy. In the first five cases, the shieldings of α-methyl protons in the centers of tactic triads increase in the same order as in PMMA, i.e., isotactic < heterotactic < syndiotactic. The assignments were made on the basis of magnetic nonequivalence between protons of heterosteric methylene groups of predominantly isotactic polymers and magnetic equivalence of protons in homosteric methylene groups of predominantly syndiotactic polymers.

Tactic placement contents of polymethacrylonitriles made via γ-irradiation and via $(C_2H_5)_2Mg$ catalysis recently have been estimated directly from the methylene proton resonances (*126*). The usual AB-type spin–spin quartet was observed for heterosteric methylene groups of the predominantly isotactic polymer made with $(C_2H_5)_2Mg$ catalyst. The single line characteristic of homosteric methylene groups falls near the center of the quartet and predominates in the polymers made via γ-irradiation. Shielding differences among α-methyl groups in the centers of tactic triads were not observed.

3. *Polyacrylics*

PMR studies of polyacrylonitriles (PANs) have yielded estimates of the tactic placement contents. On the basis of PMR spectra of poly(methyl acrylates) derived from PANs, it was suggested that most PANs contained more syndiotactic placements than isotactic placements (*127*). Subsequently, it was shown that PAN undergoes racemization upon hydrolysis to poly(acrylic acid) and that tacticity measurements on the poly(methyl acrylate), obtained from esterification of the polyacid, yield unreliable assessments of the tacticity of the original PAN (*137*). Spectra of PAN in NaCNS–D_2O solutions also were interpreted in terms of a predominance of syndiotactic placements, but the resolution of these spectra was too low to form a definite conclusion (*138*).

Matzusaki and co-workers (*139,140*) and Bargon et al. (*141*) have shown that PANs give narrow proton resonances when dissolved in some solvents. In a few solvents, the proton resonances of central methylene groups in isotactic and syndiotactic placements can be resolved (*140,141*). For example, each of the two overlapping triplets centered at 7.83 and 7.88τ in Fig. 8 is characteristic of equivalent protons of a methylene group which are vicinally spin coupled to two methine protons. A triplet is observed for each of the two types of tactic placements. The lower-field triplet centered at 7.83τ has a slightly smaller splitting (vicinal spin-coupling

constant) than the higher-field triplet centered at 7.88τ. This difference in
the vicinal coupling shows that the average chain conformation is different
for the two types of tactic placements. This interpretation of the methylene
proton resonances in Fig. 8 requires that the protons of each meso
methylene group be fortuitously equivalent or very nearly equivalent. The
equivalence, or near equivalence, of such protons has been confirmed by

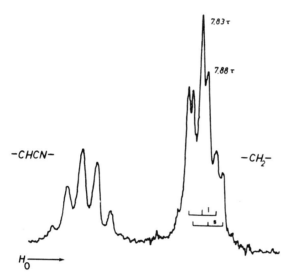

Fig. 8. PMR spectrum of polyacrylonitrile made with free-radical initiator; dilute
solution of polymer in 50 vol. CD_3NO_2/50 vol. ethylene glycol carbonate at $150°C$;
$\nu_0 = 56.4$ Mc/sec. [Reproduced from J. Bargon, K. -H. Hellewege, and U. Johnsen,
Kolloid-Z., **212**, 51 (1966), by permission of Dr. Dietrich Steinkopff.]

the observation of two singlet methylene proton resonances for poly(α-d_1-
acrylonitrile) (*140*). In contrast, PMR spectra of 2,4-dicyanopentanes in
several different solvents show that the methylene protons of the meso
compound have substantial magnetic nonequivalence (*140,142*). This
difference in magnetic shielding between the polymer and model compound
is due primarily to a difference between the average molecular conformations. As will be seen later, similar differences exist between the spectra
of several other polymers and their model compounds. The average
shielding of the methylene protons in meso-2,4-dicyanopentane in several
different solvents is slightly lower than that of methylene protons in the
racemic compound (*140,142*). Thus, the lower-field triplet in spectra such

as that in Fig. 8 has been assigned to meso methylene protons, and the higher-field triplet has been assigned to racemic methylene protons (*140, 141*).

The five-line multiplet in Fig. 8 is due to the methine protons of PAN, each of which is vicinally spin coupled to four methylene protons. Bargon and co-workers attempted to determine, via spin-decoupling experiments, the shielding differences which might exist among methine protons in the centers of the three different tactic triads (*141*). Although complete decoupling and good resolution were not achieved, indications of three different methine proton shifts at 6.84, 6.88, and 6.95τ were obtained. On the basis of methine proton shifts in spectra of racemic- and meso-2,4-dicyanopentanes (*140,142*), Bargon and co-workers have suggested the following assignments: *s* units at 6.84τ, *h* units at 6.88τ, and *i* units at 6.95τ (*141*).

From the relative intensities of the two overlapping triplets in spectra such as Fig. 8, Bargon and co-workers estimated that PANs prepared with anionic or free-radical initiators have a small predominance of isotactic placements; i.e., $(m) \approx 1.5$ $(r) \approx 0.6$. Their spectra of PANs made via anionic catalysis showed extra resonance lines at about 7.4τ. These resonances indicate that structural rearrangement, which is not yet defined, occurred during polymerization. Matsuzaki and co-workers have estimated from PMR spectra of poly(α-d_1-acrylonitriles) that polymers made with anionic or free-radical initiators have approximately the same numbers of isotactic and syndiotactic placements (*140*).

In addition to information about polymer tacticities, several of the PMR studies of polyacrylate esters (*106,127–136,317,318*) have yielded information about conformations of the polymer chains in solution or about the directions of the additions in the polymerizations. Since these last two types of information are rather unique, PMR studies of polyacrylate esters will be discussed in later sections.

4. Poly(α-methylstyrene)

The first PMR study of poly(α-methylstyrenes) (PαMSs) was reported by Brownstein et al. (*143*). Their spectra exhibited one or two resonances for the aromatic ring protons, a broad, single resonance for the methylene protons, and three methyl proton resonances. Using molecular models and considering shielding effects due to induced electron currents in the aromatic rings, Brownstein et al. tentatively assigned the three methyl proton resonances to central methyl groups of isotactic, heterotactic, and syndiotactic triads in order of increasing magnetic field. Sakurada et al. (*144*) and Braun et al. (*145*) have reported PMR spectra of PαMSs obtained at somewhat higher resolution. In some cases, their spectra revealed a shoulder on the methylene proton resonance. Otherwise, their spectra were the same as those reported by Brownstein et al. Braun et al. arrived at the same assignments for the methyl proton resonances as those suggested by Brownstein et al. On the basis of tacticities of other polymers made with cationic initiators in nonpolar solvents and an X-ray fiber diagram of a partially crystalline PαMS, Sakurada et al. suggested that the methyl proton resonances of PαMSs result from central methyl

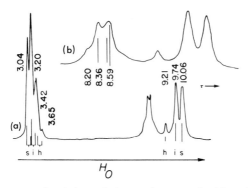

Fig. 9. PMR spectrum of poly(α-methylstyrene) prepared with sodium–naphthalene initiator in tetrahydrofuran at $-78°C$; 3–10 vol.% polymer in CS_2 solution at 30°C; $\nu_0 = 100$ Mc/sec; (a) complete spectrum and (b) high-field portion of the spectrum obtained under conditions of slow sweep. [Reproduced from K. C. Ramey and G. L. Statton, *Makromol. Chem.*, **85**, 287 (1965), by permission of Hüthig und Wepf Verlag, Basel.]

groups of isotactic, heterotactic, and syndiotactic triads in order of decreasing magnetic field.

Ramey and Statton subsequently have reported the PMR spectra of PαMSs shown in Figs. 9 and 10 (*146*). The spectrum of the polymer prepared with an anionic catalyst (Fig. 9) shows resolution of more resonances than found in the earlier PMR studies of PαMSs. The methylene protons of this polymer appear to exhibit an AB-type quartet arising from geminal spin coupling ($|J_{AB}| = 16$ cps) between magnetically nonequivalent ($\tau_A = 8.30$ and $\tau_B = 8.45$ ppm) meso methylene protons. The quartet seems to be overlapped with a relatively small singlet at about 8.60τ which is characteristic of protons of homosteric, racemic methylene groups. This interpretation and the relative intensities of the methylene proton resonances require that the PαMS made with anionic initiator have a predominance of isotactic placements; i.e., $(m) > (r)$.

The assignment for the protons of racemic methylene groups is confirmed by the spectrum in Fig. 10 of the PαMS made with a cationic initiator. The single resonance at 8.60τ in this spectrum must arise from protons of homosteric, racemic methylene groups unless meso methylene protons of PαMSs are fortuitously equivalent. In view of the multiple methylene proton resonances in Fig. 9, this latter possibility appears to be extremely

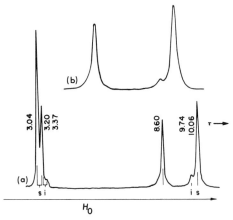

Fig. 10. PMR spectrum of poly(α-methylstyrene) prepared with BF_3 initiator in toluene at $-78°C$; 3–10 vol. % polymer in CS_2 solution at $30°C$; $\nu_0 = 100$ Mc/sec; (a) complete spectrum and (b) high-field portion of the spectrum obtained under conditions of slow sweep. [Reproduced from K. C. Ramey and G. L. Statton, *Makromol. Chem.*, **85**, 287 (1965), by permission of Hüthig und Wepf Verlag, Basel.]

unlikely. Thus, it is nearly certain that the lines at 10.06τ in Figs. 9 and 10 arise from central methyl protons of syndiotactic triads and that the polymer made with cationic initiator is highly syndiotactic.

As pointed out by Ramey and Statton (*146*), the interpretation that the polymer made with an anionic catalyst has $(m) > (r)$, the relative intensities of its methyl proton resonances in Fig. 9,† and Eqs. (1) and (2) require that the lines at 9.21 and 9.74τ in Fig. 9 arise from central methyl protons of heterotactic and isotactic triads, respectively, and that the polymer have substantial stereoblock character ($\rho = 3.7$). Such interpretations of the PMR spectra of PαMSs are unusual in one respect. They present a unique case where shieldings of central protons in heterotactic

† These relative intensities, as calculated from data given by Ramey and Statton (*146*) by use of Eqs. (1) and (2), are $I(\tau = 9.21) = 0.14$, $I(\tau = 9.74) = 0.47$, and $I(\tau = 10.06) = 0.40$.

triads are not intermediate to those of corresponding protons in isotactic and syndiotactic triads. Although such cases are conceivable, an alternate explanation for the spectrum in Fig. 9 appears to be quite probable.

Suppose that the correct assignments for the methyl proton resonances of PαMSs are those used by Brownstein et al. (*143*) and Braun et al. (*145*) (i.e., *i*, *h*, and *s* in order of increasing magnetic field). Then, the relative intensities of the methyl proton resonances in Fig. 9, which were given in the above note, and those obtained (*143–145*) for other PαMSs agree with Bernoullian distributions of tactic placements. For such a distribution of tactic placements in the polymer characterized by Fig. 9, the following tactic tetrad contents may be calculated from the relative intensities of the methyl proton resonances by use of Eq. (1)–(6) and Eq. (9): $(mmm) = 0.050_1$, $(mmr) = 0.17_2$, $(rmr) = 0.14_7$, $(mrr) = 0.29_4$, $(mrm) = 0.086_2$, and $(rrr) = 0.25_0$. Such a distribution of tactic tetrads in PαMS could yield the spectrum in Fig. 9 if, as in several other polymers, shielding variations exist among central racemic methylene protons in tactic tetrads of PαMSs. Thus, definitive assignments of all three methyl proton resonances of PαMSs will require higher resolution spectra of the methylene protons in samples such as that characterized by Fig. 9 or will require other independent evidence.

5. *Poly(vinyl chloride)*

Numerous investigators have studied the tacticities of poly(vinyl chlorides) (PVCs) by use of PMR spectroscopy (*147–162*). In the first report of such studies, Johnsen concluded that the methylene proton resonances of PVCs consist of two overlapping triplets which correspond to racemic and meso methylene groups (*147*). This interpretation requires that protons of each meso group be fortuitously equivalent and that the spectral multiplicities due to methylene protons (e.g., the high-field multiplets in Fig. 11) arise only from a shielding difference between racemic and meso methylene protons and vicinal spin coupling between methylene and methine protons.

Tincher recognized that meso methylene groups are heterosteric and that protons of such groups generally are magnetically nonequivalent (*150*). He suggested that the protons (AB) of each meso methylene group in PVC are nonequivalent ($\Delta\tau_{AB} = 0.28$ ppm) and give rise to an AB multiplet of an ABC_2 spin system which results from geminal coupling ($J_{AB} = 14$ cps) plus vicinal methylene-methine proton couplings ($J_{AC_1} = J_{AC_2} = J_{BC_1} = J_{BC_2} = 6$ cps).† According to Tincher's analysis, the high-field

† These particular geminal and vicinal coupling constants should be opposite in sign. The geminal constant most probably is negative (*30,33,162,163,168*).

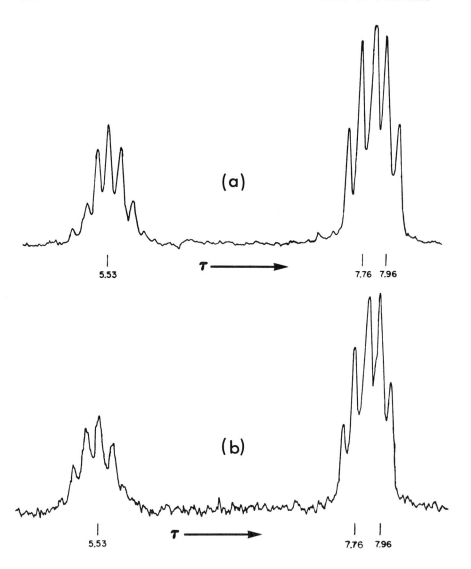

Fig. 11. PMR spectra of poly(vinyl chlorides) prepared at (a) 55°C and (b) −30°C;
(a) about 10 vol.% polymer and (b) about 5 vol.% polymer in *o*-dichlorobenzene–
tetrachloroethylene solutions at 150°C; $\nu_0 = 60$ Mc/sec. [Reproduced from S. Satoh,
J. Polymer Sci., A2, 5221 (1964), by permission of Wiley-Interscience.]

portion of the AB multiplet overlaps with a triplet due to racemic methylene protons which are vicinally spin coupled to methine protons. The specific analysis made by Tincher (150) did not appear to match the experimental relative intensities of the isolated, lower-field meso methylene proton resonances which are normally observed under conditions of low signal-to-noise ratio. This apparent discrepancy was confirmed by spectra of PVCs obtained under conditions of high signal-to-noise ratio with the aid of a computer of average transients (151).

Tincher's suggestion (150) that the protons of a meso methylene group in PVC are magnetically nonequivalent gained some support from the observations of Doskočilová (164) and others ($153,162,165–168$) which show that the methylene protons of meso-2,4-dichloropentane have a substantial difference in magnetic shieldings (about 0.25–0.37 ppm). However, normal spectra of poly(α-d_1-vinyl chloride) ($148,152$) and double-resonance spectra of PVCs ($152,153,156a$), both of which lack the complications due to the vicinal proton-proton couplings, have given strong indications that the protons of meso methylene groups in PVC have essentially the same magnetic shielding. Both types of spectra yielded two methylene proton resonances such as those shown in Fig. 12(b). Presumably, the low-field line in such doublets results mainly from fortuitously equivalent meso methylene protons and the high-field line from racemic methylene protons.

The vicinally spin-decoupled spectra of PVCs ($152,153,156a$) revealed three methine proton resonances such as those shown in Fig. 12(a). On the basis of shielding differences among central methine protons of the three stereoisomeric 2,4,6-trichloroheptanes ($161,162,167,168$), or the X-ray diffraction and infrared spectra of PVCs [e.g., see Refs. ($148,157,161$) and the references cited therein], the lines at 5.43, 5.53, and 5.69τ in spectra such as Fig. 12(a) may be assigned to central methine protons of syndio-, hetero-, and isotactic triads, respectively. The relative intensities of such lines yield quantitative measurements of the tactic triad contents of PVCs.†
Satoh (153) and Bargon et al. ($156a$) have shown that the tactic triad contents of PVCs are in good agreement with Bernoullian distributions of tactic placements.

The average shieldings of meso methylene protons in the stereoisomeric 2,4-dichloropentanes and 2,4,6-trichloroheptanes are less than those of the racemic methylene protons ($153,161,162,165–168$). In addition, Satoh has shown [by use of Eqs. (1) and (2)] that the relative intensities of the lines at 7.76 and 7.96τ in spectra such as Fig. 12(b) yield values of (m) and (r), respectively, which are in good agreement with the tactic triad contents

---

† Johnsen and Kolbe recently have shown that 100-Mc/sec, spin-decoupled methine proton resonances of PVC can be resolved into six lines characteristic of tactic pentads ($156b$).

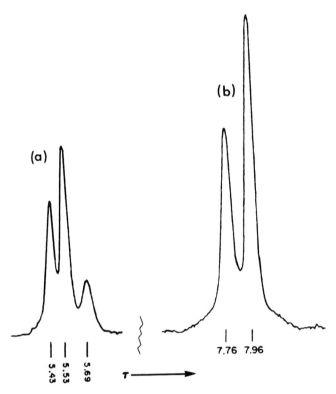

Fig. 12. Spin-decoupled PMR spectrum of poly(vinyl chloride) prepared at 55°C; about 10 vol.% polymer in *o*-dichlorobenzene–tetrachloroethylene solution at 150°C; $\nu_0 = 60$ Mc/sec; (a) methine proton resonances decoupled from methylene protons and (b) methylene proton resonances decoupled from methine protons. [Reproduced from S. Satoh, *J. Polymer Sci.*, A2, 5221 (1964), by permission of Wiley-Interscience.

obtained from spectra such as Fig. 12(a) (*153*). Thus, the two lines at 7.76 and 7.96τ in spectra such as Fig. 12(b) must, indeed, arise mainly from racemic and meso methylene protons, respectively. On the basis of the foregoing discussion, the protons of a meso methylene group must be regarded as fortuitously equivalent in PVC although substantially non-equivalent (0.25–0.37 ppm) in the 2,4-dichloropentane model compound. As mentioned in the earlier discussions of polyacrylics, analogous observations have been made for PAN and meso-2,4-dicyanopentane. A similar situation exists for isotactic polystyrene and meso-2,4-diphenylpentane (*132,169*). A shielding difference of only about 0.1 ppm exists between the methylene protons of isotactic or meso,meso-2,4,6-trichloroheptane

(*161,162,168*). Presumably, this shielding difference would decrease rapidly as the isotactic chain is lengthened.

It appears that any shielding difference between protons of a heterosteric methylene group in PVC must be relatively small and not substantially larger at $\nu_0 = 60$ Mc/sec than the usual geminal spin-coupling constant $|J_{gem}| \approx 14$ cps. In this situation, geminal coupling between magnetically nonequivalent protons of a heterosteric methylene group, as observed in vicinally spin-decoupled PMR spectra of PVCs or normal PMR spectra of

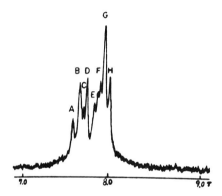

Fig. 13. PMR spectrum of poly(α-*cis*-β-d_2-vinyl chloride) prepared with free-radical initiator in carbon tetrachloride solution at 70°C; about 10 vol.% polymer in chloroform solution at room temperature; $\nu_0 = 100$ Mc/sec. According to Yoshino and Komiyama (*155*), the various resonance lines are due to the central methylene proton of the following tactic tetrads: A = *rmr*, B = *mmr* + *mmm*, C = *mmm*, D = *mmr*, E = *rmr*, F = *mrr*, G = *mrm* + *rrr*, and H = *mrr*. [Reproduced by permission of Wiley-Interscience.]

the α-deuterio polymers, would concentrate the resonance absorption near the average shielding value. This effect would make detection of the geminal shielding difference much more difficult than in the absence of the geminal coupling. Thus, the shielding variations among methylene protons in PVC should be detected more easily by PMR spectra of the α,β-dideuterio polymers which possess neither vicinal nor geminal proton–proton spin couplings.

Yoshino and Komiyama have shown that spectra of poly(α-*cis*-β-d_2-vinyl chloride) (Fig. 13) exhibit 8 of the 10 methylene proton resonances that may occur if the protons of each of the central, heterosteric methylene groups of tactic tetrads have nonequivalent shieldings (*155*). According to their assignments (Fig. 13), such shielding variations do exist, but the shieldings of the less shielded central methylene protons of *mmr* and *mmm* tetrads are accidentally the same, and the shieldings of the central methylene protons of homosteric *mrm* and *rrr* tetrads are accidentally the same. Of the heterosteric methylene groups, only that in the center of *rmr* tetrads was interpreted by Yoshino and Komiyama to have protons with substantially different shieldings (about 0.23 ppm). Yoshino and Komiyama's results show that the average shieldings of all the meso methylene protons are nearly the same and also that the shieldings of all the racemic methylene protons are nearly the same.

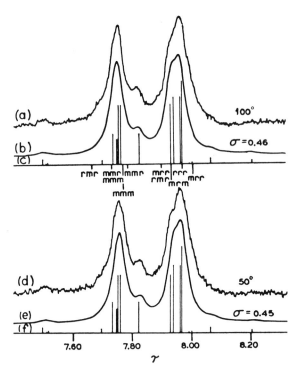

Fig. 14. Experimental and calculated PMR spectra of poly(α-d_1-vinyl chlorides) prepared with free-radical initiator in 10 vol.% cyclohexanone solutions at (a–c) 100°C and (d–f) 50°C; (a, d) experimental spectra for about 10–15 vol.% polymers in chlorobenzene solutions at 150°C and $\nu_0 = 60$ Mc/sec; (b, e) calculated spectra for Bernoullian distributions of tactic placements, $\sigma \equiv (m)$, and line widths of 2.5 cps; (c, f) calculated "stick" spectra corresponding to b and e, respectively. [Reproduced from F. A. Bovey, F. P. Hood, E. W. Anderson, and R. L. Kornegay, *J. Phys. Chem.*, **71**, 312 (1967), by permission of the American Chemical Society.]

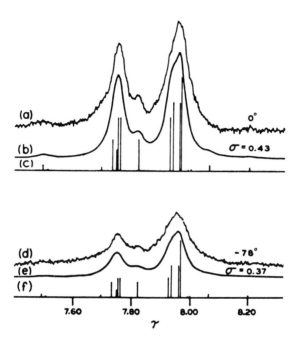

Fig. 15. Experimental and calculated PMR spectra of poly(α-d_1-vinylchlorides) prepared via ^{60}Co γ-irradiation in 10 vol. % cyclohexanone solutions at (a–c) 0°C and (d–f) −78°C; (a, d) experimental spectra for about 10–15 vol. % polymers in chlorobenzene solutions at 150°C and $v_0 = 60$ Mc/sec; (b, e) calculated spectra for Bernoullian distributions of tactic placements, $\sigma \equiv (m)$, and line widths of 2.5 and 3.2 cps, respectively; (c, f) calculated "stick" spectra corresponding to b and c, respectively. [Reproduced from F. A. Bovey, F. P. Hood, E. W. Anderson, and R. L. Kornegay, *J. Phys. Chem.*, **71**, 312 (1967), by permission of the American Chemical Society.]

Bovey and co-workers (*160*) recently have obtained much higher resolution PMR spectra of poly(α-d_1-vinyl chlorides) than those described (*148,152*) earlier. These newer spectra were in very good agreement with those calculated on the basis of slight modifications of Yoshino and Komiyama's chemical-shift assignments and Bernoullian distributions of tactic placements; see Figs. 14 and 15.† The results $\sigma \equiv (m)$ obtained from Figs. 14 and 15 show that PVC prepared at 100°C is nearly atactic

† Schaefer (*158*) and Ramey (*159*) have recently obtained vicinally spin-decoupled PMR spectra of PVCs under conditions of higher resolution than those described (*152, 153*) earlier. These more recent spectra of PVCs, particularly Ramey's, appear to be in good accord with the spectra in Fig. 14 of the α-deuterio polymers.

and that decreasing the polymerization temperature increases the syndio-tactic placement content by only a small amount. The temperature dependence of (m) yields the values $\Delta H_m^\ddagger - \Delta H_r^\ddagger = 310 \pm 20$ cal/mole and $\Delta S_m^\ddagger - \Delta S_m^\ddagger = 0.6 \pm 0.01$ e.u./mole (160). This value of $\Delta H_m^\ddagger - \Delta H_r^\ddagger$ is substantially lower than earlier estimates by Fordham et al. (170) and Germar et al. (171) but higher than that made by Bovey and Tiers (148).

It is well known that the glass-transition temperature, the size and/or perfection of crystallites, and, apparently, the magnitude of the crystal-lizability of PVC all increase quite markedly with decreasing polymeriza-tion temperature (see e.g., $170,172$). These variations in properties cannot be explained quantitatively in terms of presently available data on the dependence of tacticity, branching ($173–176$), and molecular weight on polymerization temperature. More extensive determinations of structural variables, particularly those describing branching, and more rigorous analyses of crystallinity–temperature characteristics in terms of improved melting theories (see e.g., $48–51$) appear to be needed.

6. *Polypropylene*

Syntheses and characterizations of structurally regular polypropylenes with different tacticities have been described in numerous papers, par-ticularly in those by Natta and collaborators ($177–189$). Their X-ray infrared, and dilatometric studies, and those of other investigators ($48,49, 190–196$), have proved the existence of highly isotactic, highly syndiotactic, practically atactic, and stereoblock polypropylenes. A still clearer account of the steric isomerism of polypropylenes has been obtained from PMR spectral studies ($105c,197–211$).

Figure 16 shows that the PMR spectra of both highly isotactic and highly syndiotactic polypropylenes are very complex. Relatively strong vicinal methine–methylene and methine–methyl proton spin couplings split the methine proton resonances into complex multiplets. These multi-plets are located in the regions of about 80–120 cps of Fig. 16. The vicinal methine–methyl proton spin couplings split the relatively intense methyl proton resonances into asymmetrical doublets which are located in the regions of about 49–55 and 47–53 cps in Figs. 16(a) and (b), respectively. As expected from first approximations, the vicinal methine–methylene proton spin couplings split the racemic methylene proton resonance of the highly syndiotactic polymer into an asymmetrical triplet. This triplet is located in the region of about 57–70 cps in Fig. 16(b). The methylene proton resonances of the highly isotactic polymer are much more com-plicated and are located in the region of about 37–80 cps in Fig. 16(a).

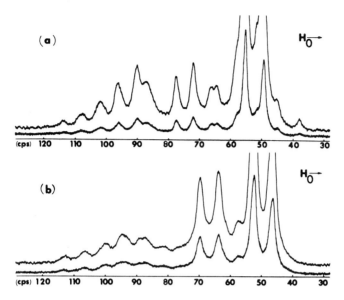

Fig. 16. PMR spectra of (a) very highly isotactic and (b) very highly syndiotactic polypropylenes prepared with Ziegler–Natta type catalysts; about 8 vol. % polymers in *o*-dichlorobenzene solutions at 150°C; $\nu_0 = 60$ Mc/sec; line positions are in cps downfield from dissolved HMDS as internal reference. [Reproduced from J. C. Woodbrey, *J. Polymer Sci.*, **B2**, 315 (1964), by permission of Wiley-Interscience.]

Satoh et al. proposed (*197*) that the methylene proton resonances of highly isotactic polypropylenes are complicated by magnetic nonequivalence and geminal coupling of protons in each heterosteric meso methylene group. Stehling showed that such nonequivalence does indeed exist (*198, 199*). He found that boiling-*n*-heptane-insoluble poly(2,3,3,3-d_4-propene) with high crystallizability due to isotactic sequences gives rise to the characteristic AB-type quartet (e.g., see Fig. 17). On the basis of spectra obtained at 40 and 60 Mc/sec, it was shown that the shielding difference between the meso methylene protons is about 0.39 ppm and that the geminal coupling constant is about 13.2 cps in magnitude (*198,199*). Stehling also showed that boiling-ether-soluble, amorphous, so-called atactic poly(2,3,3,3-d_4-propene) gives rise to a singlet in addition to the AB-type quartet. This singlet, which is located near the center of the quartet, is characteristic of protons of homosteric, racemic methylene groups. Stehling estimated that the relative intensities of the singlet and quartet for his particular noncrystallizable 2,3,3,3-d_4 polymer were comparable. Thus, if the tactic placements were distributed randomly, the

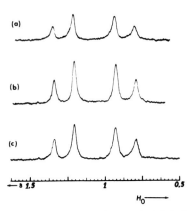

Fig. 17. PMR spectra of very highly isotactic poly(2,3,3,3-d_4-propenes): (a) whole polymer prepared with $TiCl_3$ (violet)–$Al(C_2H_5)_2I$ catalyst; (b) boiling-*n*-heptane-soluble fraction; and (c) boiling-*n*-heptane-insoluble fraction; about 2–10 vol.% polymers in *o*-dichlorobenzene solutions at 150°C; $\nu_0 = 100$ Mc/sec; line positions are in ppm downfield from dissolved HMDS as internal reference. [Reproduced from G. Natta, E. Lombardi, A. L. Segre, A. Zambelli, and A. Marinangeli, *Chim. Ind. (Milan)*, **47**, No. 4, 378 (1965), by permission of La Chimica e l'Industria.]

polymer would be practically atactic as concluded by previous investigators from crystallinity measurements on similar polypropylenes. Since the singlet was not detected in the spectra of the 2,3,3,3-d_4 polymer having high crystallizability due to isotactic sequences, Stehling concluded that the polymer was indeed very highly isotactic. He estimated that (*m*) must be greater than about 0.95. Stehlings results have been confirmed by Natta et al. (*207,208*). These investigators obtained 100-Mc/sec PMR spectra of the 2,3,3,3-d_4 polymers having very high isotacticity (Fig. 17) and very high syndiotacticity.

The absence of lines in Fig. 17 characteristic of protons in homosteric, racemic methylene groups indicates that the polymers have extremely high isotacticity. Such high isotacticities appear to be in conflict with those suggested by comparisons of experimental and calculated unperturbed dimensions of highly isotactic polymer chains such as $-\!\!+\!CH_2-\!CHR\!+\!_n$, where R = CH_3, CH_3CH_2, $CH_3CH_2CH_2$, etc. Flory and co-workers have calculated the unperturbed dimensions for such chains possessing variously biased Bernoullian distributions of tactic placements (*212,213*). The calculations were made in terms of the interdependent-rotation model (*214*), bond torsion potentials, and repulsions and dispersion attractions between nonbonded atoms. The calculated mean unperturbed chain dimensions for purely isotactic chains were much larger than experimental values (215,216a) for highly crystallizable, isotactic poly(α-olefins) prepared with Ziegler–Natta type catalysts. The calculations showed that small amounts of syndiotactic placements distributed randomly in the otherwise isotactic chains have a precipitous effect in reducing unperturbed chain dimensions. It was found (212,213) that the calculated unperturbed chain dimensions could be brought into agreement with the higher experimental values (215) if at least 5–10% syndiotactic placements were distributed randomly in the otherwise isotactic chains. This indication that highly isotactic polyolefins have 5–10% syndiotactic placements distributed randomly has important bearings on interpretations of polymerization mechanisms, modes of crystallization, and PMR spectra of such chains. Because of the high crystallizabilities and narrow melting ranges of polymers such as highly isotactic polypropylenes, many of the syndiotactic defects would have to be incorporated into crystallites of otherwise isotactic sequences.† Flory and collaborators were well aware of this requirement, and they proposed (213) plausible modes for the incorporation of the syndiotactic defects.

Subsequently, Flory and Baldeschwieler recognized (210) that if the protons of homosteric, racemic methylene groups in . . . $m_x r m_y$ . . . sequences have the same magnetic shielding as those in the centers of . . . r_{x+y+1} . . . sequences, where $x, y, = 1, 2, 3, . . . $, as few as 2% syndiotactic placements should give rise to a noticeable singlet near the center of each quartet in Fig. 17. They pointed out that the average main-chain conformations in the centers of these tactic sequences should be markedly different and that the magnetic shieldings in general should differ accordingly. They suggested that this shielding difference might be as large as the 0.39-ppm shift between the protons of a meso-methylene group in polypropylene.§ Flory and Baldeschwieler proposed (210) that the singlet due to protons of (presumably 5–10%) homosteric, racemic methylene groups in sequences such as . . . $m_x r m_y$ . . . may be obscured by one of the components of the quartets in Fig. 17. However, if the polymers characterized by Fig. 17 contain as few as 5% syndiotactic placements, then the total intensity of the two high-field components in each quartet of Fig. 17

---

† Such incorporations of tactic defects would virtually destroy the value of melting theories [see, e.g., Refs. (48,49)] for characterizing the steric structures of partially crystalline homopolymers.

§ As illustrated in Figs. 7, 13, and 14(a), the shielding difference between the central methylene protons in *mrm* and *rrr* sequences in poly(methyl methacrylate) and poly(vinyl chloride) are thought to be smaller than about 0.13 ppm.

must differ by 10% from that of the two low-field components. Also, the intensity of one of the inner components in each quartet would have to be 16% greater than that of the other inner component, or the intensity of one of the outer components in each quartet would have to be 31% greater than that of the other outer component. Measurements show that the total intensity of the two high-field components in each quartet of Fig. 17 differ from that of the two low-field components by less than 7%. Intensities of corresponding inner components differ by less than 7%, and intensities of corresponding outer components differ by less than 17% (*216b*).† Thus, it appears that the syndiotactic placement contents are about 3% or less for all the polymers characterized by Fig. 17. Ferguson has found from 200-Mc/sec PMR spectra that an isotactic polypropylene may contain about 2% syndiotactic placements (*211a*). Moreover, extremely high isotacticities have been indicated for boiling–*n*-octane-insoluble and boiling–xylene-soluble fractions of poly(1,1-d_2-propenes) having high crystallizabilities due to isotactic sequences. PMR spectra of these polymers revealed no resonances characteristic of central methyl protons in heterotactic or syndiotactic triads (*151,203*). The nature of such methyl proton resonances are discussed later in this chapter.

The balance of available experimental PMR results indicates that carefully extracted, highly isotactic polypropylenes prepared with Ziegler–Natta type catalysts have values of (*m*) equal to 0.97 or greater. Such results appear to impose a large discrepancy between the calculated (*213*) and experimental (*215,216a*) unperturbed chain dimensions. Possibly the experimental chain dimensions were determined for samples having unusually low isotacticities, or possibly the calculated chain dimensions are too high because of the approximate nature of the potential functions employed. In any case, the tactic placement contents of highly isotactic poly(2,3,3,3-d_4-propenes) should be measured more accurately from spectra obtained under conditions of higher signal-to-noise ratios with the aid of a computer of average transients.

Several investigators have attempted to calculate various parts of the complex PMR spectra of nondeuterated, isotactic, and syndiotactic polypropylenes (*197,200,201,203–205,207–209*). Satoh et al. proposed (*197*) that the methyl, methylene, and methine proton resonances of the syndiotactic polymer could be interpreted in terms of the A_3 part of A_3B, the A_2 part of A_2B_2, and the C part of A_3B_4C spin systems (*34–36*), respectively. Tincher initially attempted to interpret the 60-Mc/sec methylene

† Relative intensities were determined via integrations of photographically enlarged copies of the spectra in Fig. 17.

proton resonances of the isotactic polymer in terms of the AB parts of an ABC_2 spin system (200).

However, the isolated methylene proton resonances in Fig. 16 for the iso- and syndiotactic polymers could not be reproduced exactly by the AB parts of $ABCC'$ and the A_2 part of A_2B_2 spin systems, respectively (201,203).† The inadequacy of these spin systems was particularly apparent in the case of the isotactic polymer where the methylene protons undergo geminal in addition to vicinal spin couplings. It was mentioned (201,203) that model systems with such small numbers of mutually coupled spins should be inadequate for molecules such as polypropylenes because of the effects of virtual coupling (217).

The resonances due to any particular pair of methylene protons in polypropylene, which are affected by the spin couplings of the methylene protons to the methine protons in the vicinal positions (with $|J_{vic}| \approx 6\text{--}7$ cps), can be additionally affected by vicinal couplings of the vicinal methine protons to methyl and other methylene protons. In this sense, all the protons of a polypropylene molecule can be mutually or virtually coupled, even though only the vicinal couplings have finite spin-coupling constants. The perturbations due to the effects of virtual coupling are large for strongly coupled systems and small and insignificant for weakly coupled systems. Since the main-chain vicinal spin couplings in polypropylenes are relatively strong at $\nu_0 = 60$ Mc/sec (i.e., $|\Delta\nu_{vic}|/|J_{vic}| \approx 3\text{--}7$), the effects of virtual coupling on the 60-Mc/sec spectra should be substantial.

Tincher interpreted the 60-Mc/sec methylene proton resonances of polypropylenes in terms of third-order§ types of approximations which account for some of the effects of virtual coupling (209). He used six-spin systems corresponding to hypothetical cyclic dimers such as $\overline{+\text{CH}_2\text{---}}$ $\overline{\text{CHR}+}_2$. All the main-chain vicinal and geminal proton spin couplings were included, but the vicinal methine-methyl proton spin couplings were neglected because of the limitations of the computed program employed. Similar third-order types of approximations have been used to calculate the

† Ohnishi and Nukada have confirmed the inadequacy of the AB parts of an $ABCC'$ spin system in describing the 60-Mc/sec methylene proton resonances of isotactic polypropylene (204).

§ Here, first-order types of approximations are considered to be those based on the rules for weak coupling (see Sect. IIH), e.g., the A_2 part of an A_2X_2 spin system for the methylene proton resonances of syndiotactic polypropylene. Second-order types of approximations are considered to be those which account for deviations from weak coupling but neglect altogether effects due to virtual coupling, e.g., the A_2 part of an A_2B_2 spin system for the methylene proton resonances of syndiotactic polyproplylene.

main-chain 60-Mc/sec proton resonances of isotactic poly(isopropyl acry-
late) (*128*), where $|\Delta\nu_{\text{vic}}|/|J_{\text{vic}}| \approx$ 4–8, and of isotactic polystyrene (*169*),
where $|\Delta\nu_{\text{vic}}|/|J_{\text{vic}}| \approx$ 6.3. Among the polypropylenes and the last two
polymers, only in the case of isotactic polystyrene did the third-order,
cyclic-dimer type of approximation yield calculated spectra in good agreement with the observed spectra. In this instance, the agreement apparently
resulted from the relatively low spectral resolution (i.e., line widths of
3 cps) and the relatively weaker coupling.
    Some of the important spectral effects due to virtual coupling in poly-
mers having relatively strong vicinal coupling across every main-chain

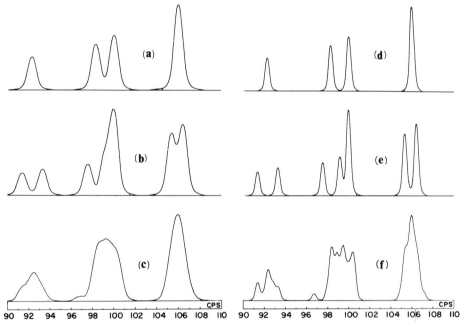

Fig. 18. Calculated A, AA', and $AA'A''$ parts of PMR spectra for the hypothetical
(a, d) open-chain segment —CH_BY—CH_AX—$CH_{B'}Y$—, (b, e) cyclic dimer

—CH_AX—CH_BY—$CH_{A'}X$—$CH_{B'}Y$—, and (c, f) cyclic trimer

—CH_AX—CH_BY—$CH_{A'}X$—$CH_{B'}Y$—$CH_{A''}X$—$CH_{B''}Y$—,

respectively; $\Delta\nu_A = \Delta\nu_{A'} = \Delta\nu_{A''} = 100$ cps, $\Delta\nu_B = \Delta\nu_{B'} = \Delta\nu_{B''} = 128$ cps, $J_{\text{vic}} =$
7 cps or $|\Delta\nu_{\text{vic}}|/|J_{\text{vic}}| = 4$, $J_{\text{nonvic}} = 0$; all components have Lorentzian line shapes
with line widths of 1 cps in (a–c) and 0.5 cps in (d–f).

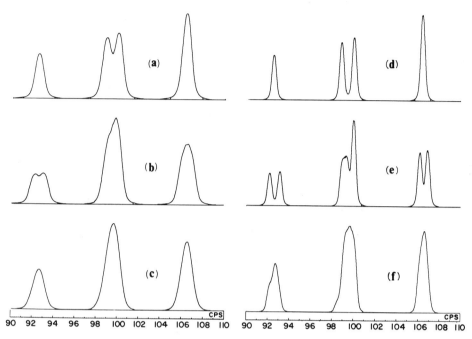

Fig. 19. Same as Fig. 18 except that $\Delta\nu_B = \Delta\nu_{B'} = \Delta\nu_{B''} = 156$ cps or $|\Delta\nu_{vic}|/|J_{vic}| = 8$.

bond are illustrated in Figs. 18 and 19. There it is shown that substantial differences exist among the A, AA', and $AA'A''$ spectra for the respective second-order ABB' open-chain, third-order $AA'BB'$ cyclic-dimer, and fourth-order $AA'A''BB'B''$ cyclic-trimer types of approximations for long linear polymer chains such as $+$ CHX—CHY $+_n$. The cyclic-trimer model undoubtedly gives a better approximation than the cyclic-dimer model for the linear polymers having relatively strong vicinal couplings. Thus, it is readily understood why the cyclic dimer model does not yield calculated spectra in good agreement with experimental, high-resolution 60-Mc/sec PMR spectra of polymers such as polypropylene and poly(isopropyl acrylate), where $|\Delta\nu_{vic}|/|J_{vic}| \approx 3$–8. Ohnishi and Nukada have found that the 100-Mc/sec methylene proton resonances of isotactic polypropylene can be matched rather well by the AB parts of an $ABCC'$ spin system (*204*). This agreement between experiment and the second-order type of approximation probably is due to the weaker coupling at $\nu_0 = 100$ Mc/sec (where $|\Delta\nu_{vic}|/|J_{vic}| \approx 6$–12) and the relatively low spectral resolution obtained (i.e., linewidths of about 3 cps).

The relative tactic placement contents of polypropylenes can be determined from the methylene proton resonances obtained at 60 Mc/sec. Woodbrey found that the isolated methylene proton resonances of numerous fractions with widely different tactic placement contents and stereoblock characters could be matched exactly with the corresponding resonances observed for appropriate mixtures of the very highly iso- and syndiotactic polymers characterized by Fig. 16 (*201–203*). Thus, the form of the methylene proton resonances depends only on the tactic placement content and not observably on their distribution in the polymer chains. In order to determine directly the absolute tactic placement contents in unknowns, (*m*), it is necessary to know the exact forms of the methylene proton resonances for the 100% iso- and 100% syndiotactic polymers. As mentioned earlier, these could not be calculated for $\nu_0 = 60$ Mc/sec. The relative tactic placement contents of unknowns were determined, therefore, by a method which, in effect, matches portions of the experimental methylene proton resonances with linear combinations of those observed for the very highly iso- and syndiotactic samples characterized by Fig. 16. Figure 16 shows that the intensity of resonance absorption in the region of about 75–80 cps is large for iso- and small for syndiotactic polymers, respectively. The reverse is true in the region of about 60–68 cps. The variation of the ratio of intensities in these two regions, $R \equiv (A_{74.4–79.3}/A_{59.6–67.5})$, with the relative tactic placement content α is shown in Fig. 20. This curve was obtained via electronic integration of the spectra of standard mixtures of the polymers characterized by Fig. 16(a) and (b), by assuming that these very highly tactic polymers were 100% iso- and 100% syndiotactic, respectively. Relative tactic placement contents of unknowns, α, were determined precisely from Fig. 20 and the ratios R obtained experimentally as illustrated in Fig. 21 for a fraction of polypropylene having $\alpha = 0.71 \pm 0.1$.† The balance of available evidence shows that the isotactic polymer characterized by Fig. 16(a) has (*m*) > ca. 0.95 (and probably much higher than 0.95) and that the syndiotactic polymer characterized by Fig. 16(b) has (*m*) < ca. 0.07–0.09 (*203*). Thus, the relative tactic placement contents α of samples with intermediate tacticities are nearly the same as the absolute values (*m*).

From the PMR spectra of highly isotactic and predominantly syndiotactic fractions of poly(1,1-d_2-propenes) and poly(1,1,3,3,3-d_5-propenes), Woodbrey determined the chemical shift for the methine protons and

---

† A somewhat similar method for determinations of relative tactic placement contents in polypropylenes has been described by Natta and co-workers (*207,208*).

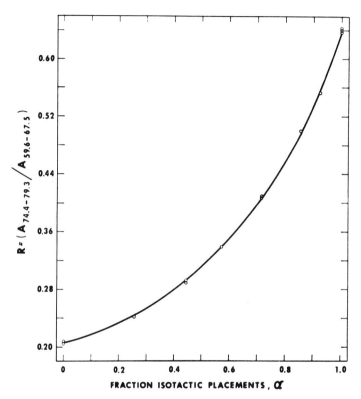

Fig. 20. Calibration curve for the determination of relative tactic placement contents, $\alpha \approx (m)$, in polypropylenes from portions of the 60-Mc/sec methylene proton resonances. [Reproduced from J. C. Woodbrey and Q. A. Trementozzi, *J. Polymer Sci.*, **C8**, 113 (1965), by permission of Wiley-Interscience.]

showed that it is virtually invariant with changes in tacticity (*151,202,203*). These findings were confirmed by other investigators (*207–209*).

Woodbrey has shown that central methyl protons in the different tactic triads of polypropylenes have different magnetic shieldings and, consequently, the stereoblock characters of the polymers with intermediate tacticities can be assessed directly (*201–203*). As mentioned earlier, the methyl proton resonances in polypropylenes appear as asymmetrical doublets because of vicinal methyl–methine proton couplings. It is shown by Fig. 16 that the doublet due to central methyl protons in syndiotactic triads (in the syndiotactic polymer) occurs at higher fields (0.044_2 ppm)

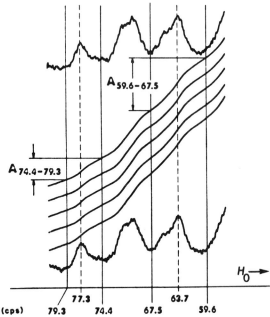

Fig. 21. Partial PMR spectra and integrals of a boiling-acetone-insoluble, boiling-*n*-heptane-soluble fraction of a highly isotactic polypropylene whole polymer prepared with Ziegler–Natta type catalyst; about 8 vol.% polymer in *o*-dichlorobenzene solution at 150°C; $\nu_0 = 60$ Mc/sec; line positions are in cps downfield from dissolved HMDS as internal reference. [Reproduced from J. C. Woodbrey and Q. A. Trementozzi, *J. Polymer Sci.*, **C8**, 113 (1965), by permission of Wiley-Interscience.]

than that due to central methyl protons in isotactic triads (in the isotactic polymer). These resonances are clearly resolvable in the 60-Mc/sec PMR spectra of stereoblock polypropylenes† [e.g., Fig. 22(a)], whereas the resonances due to central methyl protons in heterotactic triads are not directly discernible. The position of the resonance doublet due to hetero-tactic triads occurs between those due to iso- and syndiotactic triads. This assignment was indicated by approximate shielding calculations for different tactic sequences in different conformations (*203*). The assignment was confirmed by spectra such as Fig. 22(b) and proved by spectra such as

† The stereoblock polypropylenes, such as that characterized by Fig. 22(a), are rare examples for which there is substantial proof that the polymers are true stereoblock macromolecules rather than mixtures of highly iso- and syndiotactic polymer molecules (*185,203*).

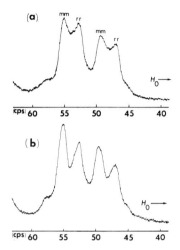

Fig. 22. Partial PMR spectra of (a) a stereoblock, boiling-*n*-pentane-insoluble, boiling-*n*-hexane-soluble fraction of polypropylene having 56% isotactic placements and (b) a mixture containing 56% of the isotactic and 44% of the syndiotactic polypropylenes characterized by Fig. 16; about 8 vol.% polymers in *o*-dichlorobenzene solutions at 150°C; $\nu_0 = 60$ Mc/sec; line positions are in cps downfield from dissolved HMDS as internal reference. [Reproduced from J. C. Woodbrey, *J. Polymer Sci.*, **B2**, 315 (1964), by permission of Wiley-Interscience.]

Fig. 23. Figure 22(b) is the spectrum of a mixture of the very highly iso- and syndiotactic polymers characterized by Fig. 16. The mixture of highly tactic polymers has the same tactic placement content as the stereoblock polymer and has virtually no heterotactic triads. The resolution between the high- and low-field components of the resonance doublets due to iso- and syndiotactic triads observed for the mixture [Fig. 22(b)] is much better than that for the stereoblock polymer [Fig. 22(a)]. This observation indicates the presence of small amounts of heterotactic triads in the stereoblock polymer. The resonance doublet due to the heterotactic triads in the stereoblock polymer is resolved clearly in 100-Mc/sec PMR spectra such as Fig. 23; this weak doublet occurs halfway between the more intense resonance doublets due to iso- and syndiotactic triads. Since this weak doublet was not observed in 100-Mc/sec PMR spectra of the corresponding mixture of the highly iso- and syndiotactic polymers (*203*), the assignment for heterotactic triads appears to be well established. Natta and co-workers (*207,208*) have confirmed the assignments given in the foregoing, and they also have resolved the three doublets corresponding

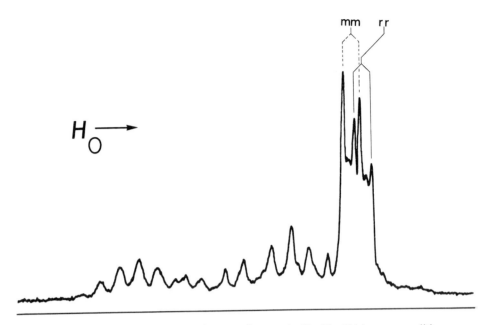

Fig. 23. PMR spectrum of same polymer as characterized by Fig. 22(a); same conditions as in Fig. 22, except that $\nu_0 = 100$ Mc/sec. [Reproduced from J. C. Woodbrey, *J. Polymer Sci.*, **B2**, 315 (1964), by permission of Wiley-Interscience.]

to the tactic triads in polypropylenes having much more random distributions of tactic placements than that revealed by Figs. 22(a) and 23 for the stereoblock polymer.

7. *Other Addition-Type Homopolymers*

Unique structural information about many other homopolymers made by addition-type reactions has been obtained by high-resolution NMR. Direct estimates of the tactic triad contents in poly(1,1-d_2-styrenes) have shown (*221*) that the polymers made with cationic, anionic, and free-radical catalysts are predominantly syndiotactic. The cationic polymer appears to be somewhat less syndiotactic than the anionic and free-radical polymers. Commercially important polystyrene made with free-radical catalyst appears to be about 80% syndiotactic (*169*).

Tactic triad contents in poly(vinyl methyl ethers) can be measured quantitatively by PMR spectroscopy (*152,237–241*). Recent results (*240, 241*) for these polymers demonstrate that completely different factors control the steric structure when different catalysts are used. For example, the tactic triad contents of poly(vinyl methyl ethers) made with BF_3–$O(C_2H_5)_2$ catalyst show that the polymerizations are non-Bernoullian. This result indicates a penultimate effect and control of the steric structure by the terminal and penultimate main-chain sites of steric isomerism. Conversely, the tactic triad contents of the polymers made with heterogeneous sulfuric acid-aluminum sulfate catalysts are in very good agreement with enantiomorphically paired Bernoullian distributions of main-chain steric configurations; i.e., Eq. (13) is obeyed. Such results show that the steric structures are controlled by the nature (probably the asymmetries) of the heterogeneous catalyst sites.

Fluorine magnetic resonance and PMR spectra of poly(vinyl fluorides) and poly(vinylidene fluorides) have revealed substantial amounts of structural irregularities in these polymers (247–249). Analyses of the spectra show that 10–12 and 26–32 % head-to-head type of addition occurs in the free-radical polymerizations of vinylidene fluoride and vinyl fluoride, respectively (248).

References to published high-resolution NMR studies of addition-type homopolymers not mentioned in the preceding sections are listed in Table 3. Since these studies are similar in many respects to those described in the preceding or following sections, they will not be discussed here. The papers listed include high-resolution NMR studies of structural, steric, and conformational isomerism in the homopolymers and their model compounds.

B. Direction of Addition in Vinyl Polymerization

It was shown in the preceding section that determinations of relative configurations at neighboring α-carbon atoms in vinyl-type polymers give unique information about certain aspects of the propagation steps in the addition polymerizations. The nature of these propagation steps can be further illuminated by determinations of the direction of addition of the active chain end to the double bond of the monomer during propagation, i.e., by determinations of whether the double bond opens in an apparently *cis* or *trans* fashion. Such determinations often can be made by NMR for isotactic-type polymerizations if the β-carbon atoms become sites of steric isomerism in the polymer, as, e.g., in the polymers made from *cis* or *trans* monomers such as CHR=CHR′, where R, R′ $\neq$ H. Polymers of this type can be obtained from β-*cis*-d_1 or β-*trans*-d_1 vinyl-type monomers. The polymerizations of such monomers may yield *erythro* diisotactic, *threo* diisotactic, or syndiotactic polymers; e.g., see structures (6) and (7) of Sect. IIB. The terminology of *erythro* and *threo* for ditactic polymers has

TABLE 3

Polymer	Ref.
Polyethylene	*105b,211b,251b*
Polystyrene	*132,169,218–223*
Poly(4-vinylbiphenyl)	*236b*
Poly(1-vinylnaphthalene)	*236b*
Poly(2-vinylnaphthalene)	*236b*
Poly(vinyl acetate)	*101,152,224–228*
Poly(vinyl bromide)	*235b*
Poly(vinyl trifluoroacetate)	*226,227,229, 230*
Poly(vinyl formate)	*225,231*
Poly(vinyl alcohol)	*166,227–229,232–235a*
2,4-Pentanedithiol	*236a*
Poly(vinyl methyl ether)	*152,237–241*
Poly(vinyl-*t*-butyl ether)	*226,240a,242*
Poly(vinyl ethyl ether)	*242*
Poly(vinyl isopropyl ether)	*242*
Poly(α-methylvinyl methyl ether)	*243*
Polyacetaldehyde	*244–246,268*
Poly(vinyl fluoride)	*152,247,248*
Poly(vinylidene fluoride)	*247–249*
Polytrifluoroethylene	*247*
Polytrifluorochloroethylene	*247,250*
Poly(2-vinylpyridine)	*251*
Polyisoprene	*211a,252–256,269,276b*
Polybutadiene	*254,256*
Polychloroprene	*105b–c,211a,257*
Polycyclopentadienes	*258,259*
Poly(ethylene oxide)	*260*
Poly(propylene oxide)	*261*
Poly(alkylene oxides) (miscellaneous)	*262,263*
Polyolefins (miscellaneous, prepared with cationic catalysts)	*264–267*

been extended by calling the proton on the β-carbon atom of the *erythro* polymer the "*erythro* proton" and the proton on the β-carbon atom of the *threo* polymer the "*threo* proton" (*106*). It can be shown with molecular models that the *cis* monomer gives the *erythro* proton on *cis* opening and the *threo* proton on *trans* opening of the double bond. Conversely, the *trans* monomer gives the *erythro* proton on *trans* opening and the *threo* proton on *cis* opening.

Yoshino et al. have studied the nature of the double-bond opening in free-radical and in anionic, LiAlH$_4$-catalyzed polymerizations of methyl acrylate in toluene at 50 and $-78°C$, respectively (*129*). The polymers used were made from the $\alpha,\beta\text{-}d_2$ monomers. The polymer made with the free-radical catalyst gave three methylene proton resonances due to racemic, *erythro* meso, and *threo* meso groups. The relative intensities of these lines showed that the polymer had about the same number of meso and racemic groups, which is in agreement with the findings for many other vinyl-type polymers made with free-radical catalysts. The number of *erythro* meso and *threo* meso groups was about the same, which shows that the apparently *cis* and *trans* openings have about the same probability of occurrence in the isotactic, free-radical additions. The spectrum of the polymer made with anionic LiAlH$_4$ catalyst showed that the polymer was highly diisotactic and that one of the meso methylene proton resonances was much larger than the other. Without assignments for the *erythro* meso and *threo* meso methylene proton resonances, it could only be concluded that one type of double-bond opening (*cis* or *trans*) occurred in high preference to the other. Shuerch et al. (*128*) proposed assignments for the meso proton resonances which demanded that the double-bond opening be predominantly *trans*. Later, the assignments suggested by Schuerch et al. were proved to be correct by Yoshino et al. (*130*) on the basis of PMR measurements on model compounds. This finding that the isotactic, LiAlH$_4$-catalyzed polymerization of methyl acrylate occurs via predominantly *trans* opening is in contrast to the *cis* openings found for cationic polymerizations of alkyl β-chlorovinyl ethers (*270*) and Ziegler–Natta type polymerizations of propylene (*183,187,188,271,272*) and ethylene (*273*). Natta and co-workers have shown (*207,208*) on the basis of PMR spectra of diisotactic poly(1-d_1-propenes) prepared with Ziegler–Natta type catalysts that the mode of double-bond opening is indeed almost exclusively *cis* or *trans*. Using independent evidence (*183, 187,188,271,272*) that the mode of addition is *cis*, they were able to assign the low-field doublets in Fig. 17 to *threo* meso methylene protons and the high-field doublets to *erythro* meso methylene protons.

Schuerch et al. (*128*) have found that poly(isopropyl-α-*cis*-β-d_2-acrylate) prepared with nearly ether-free C$_6$H$_5$MgBr in toluene at $-78°$C had very high diisotacticity. The methylene proton resonances of the polymer consisted of two equally intense lines characteristic of *erythro* meso and *threo* meso protons; see Fig. 24(b). No resonance characteristic of racemic methylene protons was observed. The assignments for the methylene proton resonances were proposed by Schuerch et al. on the basis of known shielding effects in somewhat analogous small molecules. Subsequently, their proposed assignments were proved to be correct by Yoshino and co-workers (*130*). The equal intensity of the two lines in Fig. 24(b) shows that equal numbers of *cis* and *trans* openings of the monomer molecules occurred in the polymerization. The C_6H_5MgBr used in this polymerization contained small amounts of residual diethyl ether. When the ether was removed entirely from the catalyst, the polymer characterized by Fig. 24(c) was obtained (*106*). This spectrum shows that a large predominance of *cis* opening occurred during polymerization in the absence of ether. The polymerization with a 10:1 mole ratio of ether to

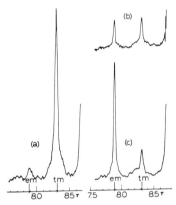

Fig. 24. Methylene proton resonances of poly(isopropyl-α-*cis*-β-d_2-acrylate) prepared in toluene at −78°C with phenyl magnesium bromide and (a) a large molar excess of diethyl ether, (b) partial removal of diethyl ether, and (c) rigorous removal of diethyl ether. [Reproduced from F. A. Bovey, to be published in *J. Pure Appl. Chem.*, by permission of Butterworth (London).]

C_6H_5MgBr gave the polymer characterized by Fig. 24(a) (*106*). This spectrum reveals the occurrence of almost exclusive *trans* addition. Thus, variation in the ether concentration effects large changes in the configurations at the β-carbon atoms without any apparent changes in the configurations at the α-carbon atoms.

The nature of the distribution of the *erythro* and *threo* protons in the phenyl Grignard-initiated polymers such as that characterized by Fig. 24(b) has been described by Yoshino and Kuno (*131*). Using poly(isopropyl-*trans*-β-d_1-acrylate), they showed from the vicinal spin-coupling multiplets that essentially all the *threo* units have *threo* units as neighbors and that essentially all the *erythro* units have *erythro* units as neighbors; i.e., both the *erythro* and *threo* sequences are long. Thus, some catalyst sites produce only *cis* opening and others only *trans* opening, or the catalyst sites interconvert between states producing *cis* and *trans* openings at rates slow compared to the rate of propagation. The latter possibility appears to be analogous to the multistate mechanism suggested by Coleman and Fox (*62,65*) which, in general, gives non-Markoffian statistical distributions of tactic placements.† As mentioned in Sect. IVA1, another indication of such a mechanism in phenyl Grignard polymerizations is Bovey's finding (*106*) that poly(methyl methacrylate) made with C_6H_5MgBr in toluene at −78°C has a nonsimple Markoffian distribution of tactic placements. Yoshino and Komiyama have studied the *erythro* and *threo* structures of poly(isopropyl-α,β-d_2-acrylates) made with phenyl Grignard catalysts under various conditions of solvent, temperature, and time of polymerization (*134*). The polymerizations gave some rather puzzling results which are not completely understood. Probably the complications are related to the heterogeneous nature of the polymerization system.§

Bovey (*106*) and Fowells et al. (*274*) have found an effect of ether concentration on the anionic, 9-fluorenyllithium-catalyzed (9-FLi) polymerizations of isopropyl acrylate and methyl and ethyl methacrylates in toluene which is similar but opposite to that found for the phenyl Grignard-catalyzed polymerization of isopropyl acrylate. Increasing the concentration of tetrahydrofuran (THF) in the 9-FLi systems caused *cis* double-bond opening to increase relative to the *trans* opening. In the cases of the methacrylate monomers, use of THF solvent with no toluene (i.e., very high mole ratio of THF/catalyst) affected the configurations of the α-carbon atoms; these polymers were found to be predominantly syndiotactic. The 9-FLi-catalyzed polymerizations appear to be much less complex than the phenyl Grignard-catalyzed polymerizations (probably because of the more heterogeneous nature of the latter systems). Bovey (*106*) and Fowells et al. (*274*) have been able to draw several interesting conclusions about probable reactive species present in the 9-FLi systems under various conditions of solvent and temperature, i.e., about contact ions, solvated ion pairs, and solvent-separated ion pairs.

C. Conformational Isomerism

One of the important applications of high-resolution NMR spectroscopy is the estimation of relative energies of conformational (rotational) isomers in substituted ethanes having an asymmetric carbon atom. In some cases, the relative energies can be evaluated directly from the intensities of the

---

† The relationships between the statistics for the formations of tactic placements, which are determined by the relative configurations at α-carbon atoms, and those for the formations of *erythro* and *threo* protons, which are determined by the configurations at the β-carbon atoms, have not been established.

§ By PMR characterizations of the stereochemical structures of dead oligomers, Yoshino and co-workers recently have described in detail the nature of some of the phenyl Grignard polymerizations of isopropyl acrylate (*317,318*).

separate spectra of conformers obtained under conditions of negligible (or slow) rotational (exchange) averaging at low temperatures. At room temperature and above, however, rapid internal rotation causes complete rotational averaging of the conformer spectra of virtually all substituted ethanes and vinyl-type polymers. This rotational averaging simplifies the spectra but reduces the informational content. Nevertheless, valuable information about relative energies of the lower-energy conformers of some substituted ethanes can be obtained from the rotationally averaged spectra. The method (39) is based on the fact that vicinal coupling constants and magnetic shieldings usually are dependent on the molecular conformation. The experimental, rotationally averaged values of the spectral parameters are population–weight averages of the values for the various conformers. If there are only two lower-energy conformers, and if the specific spectral parameters for these conformers are different and known, then the relative populations of the conformers (thus their relative energies also) can be estimated from measurements of the rotationally averaged spectral parameters. In general, the populations of more than two conformers may be significant. Since the temperature dependence of the relative populations is determined by the relative free energies of the conformers, measurement of the temperature dependence of the rotationally averaged spectral parameters† yields additional experimental information which aids in the solutions of most problems. This type of study has been extended to polymer model compounds where rotation about more than one bond must be considered (132,136,161,162,166,168,169).

McMahon and Tincher have studied the conformations of racemic- and meso-2,4-dibromo-, dichloro-, dicyano-, and dihydroxypentanes via calculations of relative conformational energies from potential functions for interactions among nonbonded atoms and through analyses of the vicinal proton spin couplings and proton chemical shifts at different temperatures (166). In the cases of the (dl) racemic- dibromo-, dichloro-, and dicyano-pentanes, they concluded that only the (tt) and (g⁺g⁺) conformers have sufficiently low energies to affect the PMR spectra.§ The energy difference between the (tt) and (g⁺g⁺) conformers were estimated for each of these three compounds. For the racemic- dibromo- and dichloropentanes, McMahon (166b) concluded that the (tt) conformer is the one having

---

† Measurements of coupling constants are normally preferable, because they are less affected by molecular association.

§ Here, the symbolism described by Flory and co-workers (212,213) is used. Parentheses enclose conformational designations for main-chain bonds between main-chain sites of steric isomerism.

lowest energy. In the cases of the (dd) meso-dibromo-, dichloro-, and dicyanopentanes, McMahon and Tincher concluded that the two equi-energy conformers (tg^-) and (g^+t) are the only ones having energy low enough to affect the PMR spectra ($166a$). The conformational analyses of the dihydroxypentanes were complicated by the existence of several low-energy conformers and by intra- and intermolecular hydrogen bonding.

Shimanouchi and co-workers ($161,162$) and Doskočilová and co-workers (168) have confirmed the results just described for racemic- and meso-2,4-dichloropentanes and have extended the study of vicinal proton spin couplings to the three stereoisomeric 2,4,6-trichloroheptanes (TCHs). Both groups of investigators found that the $(tt)(tt)$ form is the most stable conformer of syndiotactic TCH and that the equienergy $(tg^-)(tg^-)$ and $(g^+t)(g^+t)$ forms are the most stable conformers of the (ddd) isotactic TCH. Doskočilová et al. concluded that the energies of the more stable conformers of (dll) heterotactic TCH increase in the order $(tt)(tg^+) > (tt)(g^-t) \gg (g^+g^+)(tg^+)$ (168). Shimanouchi et al. concluded that (dll) heterotactic TCH has only one of the last three conformers mentioned in high population at normal temperatures; their infrared and dipole-moment data indicate that it is $(tt)(tg^+)$ ($161,162$). The PMR results for the poly(vinyl chloride) model compounds described in the foregoing appear to be in rather good agreement with the results from numerous infrared studies of this polymer [Refs. ($161,162,168$) and the references cited therein].

Doskočilová and Schneider (132) and Bovey et al. (169) have studied the conformations of racemic- and meso-2,4-diphenylpentanes through analyses of the vicinal methine–methylene proton spin couplings. They concluded that the equienergy (tg^-) and (g^+t) forms are the most stable conformers of the (dd) meso-2,4-diphenylpentane. The (tt) form was found to be the most stable conformer of the racemic compound at room temperature, but, due to an entropy factor, the (g^+g^+) conformer (of the dl compound) predominates at elevated temperatures.

Doskočilová et al. ($132,136$) also have studied the vicinal proton spin couplings in racemic- and meso-methyl-2,4-pentanedicarboxylates (MPDCs) and in the three stereoisomeric methyl-2,4,6-heptanetricarboxyl-ates (MHTCs). Although the (tt) conformers in the (dl) syndiotactic dyads of racemic-MPDC and heterotactic and syndiotactic MHTCs were found to be more stable than the (g^+g^+) conformers, the energy difference was much smaller than that obtained for the poly(vinyl chloride) model compounds. This variation might be due to interactions of the pendant carbomethoxy groups which have more degrees of rotational freedom than pendant chlorine atoms. However, the temperature dependence of the spin-coupling patterns indicated a small value of the entropy factor in the poly(methyl acrylate) model compounds. As in model compounds for other vinyl-type polymers, Doskočilová et al. found that the most stable conformers in (dd) isotactic dyads of the poly(methyl acrylate) model compounds are the equienergy forms (tg^-) and (g^+t).

Yoshino and co-workers (*135*) have determined the relative populations of main-chain *trans* and *gauche* conformers in isotactic poly(methyl-β-d_1-acrylate) and in isotactic poly(isopropyl-β-d_1-acrylate) from the rotationally averaged vicinal proton coupling constants. The coupling constants for specific *trans* and *gauche* conformers were determined from PMR spectra of trimethyl-*cis*-hexahydrotrimesate as a model compound with fixed geometry. Relative populations P of the main-chain conformers were somewhat dependent on the solvent used, but these populations were in the ranges $P(t) \approx 0.5$, $P(g) \approx 0.24$–0.33, and $P(g') \approx 0.18$–0.30, where t, g, and g' designate the conformers illustrated by structures (**12**), (**13**), and (**14**), respectively. The relative populations found for the g' conformer are

(**12**)   (**13**)   (**14**)

$$[R = CO_2CH_3, CO_2CH(CH_3)_2]$$

surprisingly high. Such conformers usually are considered to be relatively high in energy. Apparently, interactions between groups (probably carboalkoxy groups) separated by many bonds in the isotactic polyacrylate chains increase the potential energies of sequences rich in the t and g conformers more than that due to analogous interactions in other types of vinyl polymers with smaller pendant substituents.

V. STRUCTURAL STUDIES OF ADDITION-TYPE COPOLYMERS AND CONDENSATION-TYPE POLYMERS

Structural studies of numerous addition-type copolymers and a few condensation-type polymers have been performed by high-resolution PMR and fluorine magnetic resonance. These studies include analyses for monomer-unit contents of addition- and condensation-type polymers; determinations of monomer-unit sequence probabilities in copolymers;

characterizations of structural, steric, and conformational isomerism in polymers; and functional-group analyses of polymers. The results from these studies have given unique information about (1) reactivity ratios and penultimate effects in addition-type copolymerizations, (2) reactions which lead to different isomeric units in polymers, and (3) chemical functionality of polymers. Some illustrative examples will be described briefly.

Ferguson has shown that fluorine magnetic resonance gives unique information about the structures of vinylidene fluoride–hexafluoropropylene copolymers (105b,298). As usual, the fluorine chemical-shift differences in these copolymers are larger than proton shift differences. The copolymers give eight separate fluorine resonance lines which are characteristic of the fluorine atoms F in the following types of structural fragments:

$$-CF_2CF(CF_3)CH_2-, \quad -CH_2CF_2CF_2-, \quad -CF_2CF_2CF(CF_3)-,$$

$$-CF_2CF(CF_3)CH_2-, \quad -CF_2CF(CF_3)CF_2-, \quad -CH_2CF_2CF(CF_3)-,$$

$$-CH_2CF_2CH_2-, \text{ and } -CH_2CF_2CF_2CH_2-.$$

By using the intensities of the characteristic resonance lines observed for the copolymers, Ferguson showed that (1) little or no chain branching and homopolymerization of hexafluoropropylene occur in the copolymerizations and (2) the copolymers have the general structure

$$\{[-CH_2CF_2CF_2CF(CF_3)-]_{0.93}[-CH_2CF_2CF(CF_3)CF_2-]_{0.07}\}_{1-n}-$$

$$\{[-CH_2CF_2CH_2CF_2-]_{0.95}[-CH_2CF_2CF_2CH_2-]_{0.05}\}_{n/2}$$

where the structural repeat units in brackets are distributed randomly in the copolymer chains and $n \equiv (x - 50)/x$; x is the mole fraction of vinylidene fluoride in the copolymer, which can be determined from the experimental intensities of characteristic resonance lines. These results show that a small amount of backwards addition occurs during the copolymerizations. This phenomenon was found later in homopolymerizations of vinylidene fluoride (see Sect. IVA7).

Chen (276a) and Mochel (276b) have shown that PMR spectroscopy is unique in providing a means to characterize the structures of isoprene–butadiene copolymers. These copolymers give eight separate proton resonance lines which are characteristic of the hydrogen atoms in different types of structural fragments. By using the intensities of the observed resonance lines, the relative amounts of all five possible structural isomeric units resulting from 1,2, 3,4, and 1,4 additions can be determined, i.e.,

$$-CH_2-C(CH_3)(CH=CH_2)-, \quad -CH[C(CH_3)=CH_2]-CH_2-,$$
$$-CH_2-C(CH_3)=CH-CH_2-, \quad -CH_2-CH(CH=CH_2)-,$$

and

$$-CH_2-CH=CH-CH_2-.$$

The principles involved in NMR determinations of monomer-unit sequence probabilities in copolymers are very similar to those described earlier for determinations of tactic placement, triad, and tetrad contents in vinyl and related types of homopolymers. Kinsinger et al. (295,296) and Hellwege et al. (297) have studied the PMR spectra of copolymers made via free-radical copolymerizations of vinylidene chloride and isobutylene. These copolymers are particularly well suited for PMR determinations of monomer-unit sequence probabilities. No chain branching or backwards additions occur in the copolymerizations. The copolymers have no sites of steric isomerism, and the PMR spectra of the copolymers are free of complications due to proton–proton spin couplings. The chlorine atoms of the vinylidene chloride base unit, $-CH_2-CCl_2-$, have large deshielding effects on protons situated along the chains. Hellwege et al. (297) have shown that these effects induce resolvable chemical-shift differences among the central methylene protons of the different monomer-unit sequences with even numbers of units up to six in length and among the central methyl protons of the different sequences with odd numbers of monomer units up to five in length. Kinsinger et al. have interpreted experimental intensities of the PMR lines characteristic of tetrads of monomer units in terms of copolymerization theory with penultimate effects included (296). Their interpretations gave the reactivity ratios $r_1 \equiv k_{AAA}/k_{AAB} = 2.95$, $r_1' \equiv k_{BAA}/k_{BAB} = 6.22$, $r_2 \equiv k_{BBB}/k_{BAA} = 0.15$, and $r_2' \equiv k_{ABB}/k_{ABA} = 0.02$, where A is vinylidene chloride and B is isobutylene. These results reveal a penultimate effect in the free-radical copolymerizations of A and B.

Schaefer has studied the PMR spectra of ethylene–vinyl chloride (158), ethylene–vinyl acetate (158), propylene oxide–maleic anhydride (261,299), and propylene oxide–citraconic anhydride (299) copolymers. The PMR spectra of the two types of ethylene copolymers are complicated by proton–proton spin couplings and by main-chain sites of steric isomerism. The spectra of the two types of propylene oxide (PO) copolymers are complicated by spin couplings and structural isomerism (backwards additions) of the PO and citraconic anhydride (CA) units. Nevertheless, by using multiple-resonance experiments to remove complications due to spin couplings, and by using higher PMR frequencies (220 Mc/sec) to enhance experimental shift differences in the case of the PO–CA copolymers, Schaefer was able to determine a number of monomer-unit sequence probabilities for all the copolymers. The results of the studies on the PO copolymers made with various metal–halide or metal–alkyl catalysts were quite unusual. PMR showed that the modes of addition (i.e., head-to-tail, head-to-head, and tail-to-tail) of PO are randomly distributed with respect to maleic anhydride (MA) (or CA). Depending on the catalyst used, Markoffian copolymerization statistics (*60*) of order 1, 2, or 3 were required in order to account for the monomer-unit sequence probabilities determined by PMR. These PMR results were confirmed and superseded by independent determinations of the PO sequence probabilities for sequences up to 11 units in length (*299*). These latter probabilities were determined via vapor-phase chromatographic (VPC) analyses for the oligoetherglycols obtained upon hydrolyses of the copolymers. The VPC results for copolymers made with some of the catalysts were consistent with Markoffian copolymerization statistics of high order. These findings show that, in effect, the probability for the event of adding a monomer to the copolymer chain is dependent on the results of several prior events. Apparently, this phenomenon results from preassociation of both co-monomers around a coordination sphere formed by the catalyst and the growing chain end, or from coordination of several units of the terminal sequence of residues in the chain around the catalyst.

One advantage of higher-radiofrequency spectra in NMR studies of polymers is demonstrated by Figs. 25 and 26. These figures show 60-, 100-, and 220-Mc/sec PMR spectra of the methyl groups in PO units of the same PO–CA copolymer. The spectra consist of five overlapping doublets which arise from the central methyl groups in nine different triads of monomer units as shown in Table 4. The doublet patterns are the result of vicinal methyl–methine proton spin coupling. Because of the nature of the overlaps among the five doublets in the 60- and 100-Mc/sec spectra (Fig. 25), the relative intensities of the doublets could not be determined uniquely. At 220 Mc/sec (Fig. 26), the experimental shift differences have increased sufficiently to allow determination of unique and rather accurate relative intensities with the aid of the Du Pont 310 Curve Resolver.

The structures of soluble phenol–formaldehyde condensation polymers can be characterized rather thoroughly by PMR spectroscopy (*305,306*). Hirst et al. have shown that the fraction of diphenylmethane-type methylene bridges which are p,p' to phenolic hydroxyl groups in novolac-type resins can be determined from the methylene-bridge proton resonances (*306*). Woodbrey and co-workers have studied the PMR spectra of both

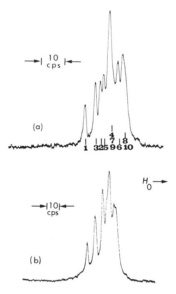

Fig. 25. Methyl proton resonances of propylene oxide monomer units in a propylene oxide–citraconic anhydride copolymer prepared with $(C_2H_5)_2Zn$ catalyst; about 25 vol.% copolymer in deuteriochloroform solution at 30°C; (a) $\nu_0 = 60$ Mc/sec; line assignments are given in Table 4; and (b) $\nu_0 = 100$ Mc/sec. [Reproduced from J. Schaefer, R. J. Kern, and R. J. Katnik, *Polymer Preprints*, **8**(2), 1037 (1967), by permission of the American Chemical Society, Division of Polymer Chemistry.]

nonacetylated and acetylated novolac- and resole-type resins (*305*). These investigators have shown that benzyl-type hemiformal groups make substantial contributions to the structures of many resole-type resins and that these functionalities exhibit surprisingly high stability under certain conditions of initial cure. In addition, it was shown that the following structural features can be determined for the nonacetylated resins which have no bridges of the diphenyl ether type: (1) the average number of aromatic-ring protons per aromatic ring, (2) the average number of benzyl-type hemiformal groups per aromatic ring, (3) the average number of hydroxymethyl groups per aromatic ring, (4) the average number of diphenylmethane-type methylene bridges per aromatic ring, (5) the ratio of the numbers of ortho- to para-hydroxymethyl groups, and (6) the ratio of the numbers of p,p'- to o,p'- plus o,o'-diphenylmethane-type methylene bridges. Provided that the methylene bridges do not connect the aromatic-ring units into cyclic structures, the average number of aromatic rings per molecule and the number-average molecular weights can be determined

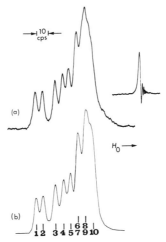

Fig. 26. Methyl proton resonances of propylene oxide monomer units in the same copolymer characterized by Fig. 25; about 25 vol.% copolymer in deuteriochloroform solution at about 20°C; (a) experimental spectrum at $\nu_0 = 220$ Mc/sec; the spectral resolution is indicated by the line inserted to the right, which is due to the internal TMS reference; (b) a 10-channel simulation of the spectrum in (a) made with a Du Pont 310 Curve Resolver; line assignments are given in Table 4. [Reproduced from J. Schaefer, R. J. Kern, and R. J. Katnik, *Polymer Preprints*, **8**(2), 1037 (1967), by permission of the American Chemical Society, Division of Polymer Chemistry.]

TABLE 4

Line Assignments for the Methyl Proton Resonances
in Figs. 25 and 26 (*299*)

Line numbers	Monomer-unit sequence[a]	
1, 2	BA(A),	(A)A*B*
3, 4	B*A(A),	(A)A*B
5, 6	BA*(A),	(A)AB*
7, 8	B*A*(A),	(A)AB
9, 10	(A)(A)(A)	

[a] $A \equiv -CH(CH_3)CH_2O-$, $A^* \equiv -CH_2CH(CH_3)O-$, $B \equiv -COC(CH_3)=CHCO_2-$, $B^* \equiv -COCH=C(CH_3)CO_2-$, and monomer units within parentheses can have either sense of direction.

TABLE 5

Polymer	Ref.
Poly(acrylonitrile–*co*-ethyl acrylate)	275
Poly(acrylonitrile–*co*-methacrylonitrile)	275
Poly(acrylonitrile–*co*-stryrene)	275
Poly(butadiene–*co*-isoprene)	276
Poly(butadiene–*co*-styrene)	3,276b
Poly(ethylene–*co*-propylene)	211b,277
Poly(ethylene–*co*-vinyl acetate)	158
Poly(ethylene–*co*-vinyl chloride)	158
Poly(methyl acrylate–*co*-1,1-diphenylethylene)	278
Poly(methyl acrylate–*co*-methyl methacrylate)	279
Poly(methyl acrylate–*co*-α-methyl styrene)	311b
Poly(methyl acrylate–*co*-styrene)	280,311b
Poly(methyl methacrylate–*co*-butyl acrylate)	279
Poly(methyl methacrylate–*co*-ethyl acrylate)	279
Poly(methyl methacrylate–*co*-propyl acrylate)	279
Poly(methyl methacrylate–*co*-ethyl methacrylate)	279
Poly(methyl methacrylate–*co*-α-methylstyrene)	281,311b
Poly(methyl methacrylate–*co*-styrene)	281–289,311b,320
Poly(α-methylstyrene–*co*-*p*-methyl-α-methylstyrene)	311a
Poly(propylene–*co*-styrene)	290
Poly(tetrafluoroethylene–*co*-hexafluoropropylene)	291
Poly(vinyl chloride–*co*-vinyl acetate)	292
Poly(vinyl chloride–*co*-vinylidene chloride)	149,293,294,312
Poly(vinylidene chloride–*co*-isobutylene)	295–297
Poly(vinylidene chloride-*co*-vinyl acetate)	319,320
Poly(vinylidene fluoride–*co*-hexafluoropropylene)	105b,298
Poly(propylene oxide–*co*-citraconic anhydride)	299
Poly(propylene oxide–*co*-maleic anhydride)	261,299
Poly(propylene glycol–*co*-4,4′-methylenediphenylene diisocyanate)	300
Poly(propylene glycol–*co*-2,4-tolylene diisocyanate)	300
Poly(propylene glycol–*co*-2,6-tolylene diisocyanate)	300
Polyurethanes (miscellaneous)	301,302
Polybenzyl	303
Poly(α-methyl benzyl)	303
Poly(ethylene–1,4-cyclohexanedicarboxylate)	304
Poly(ethylene terephthalate)	314
Poly(ethylene isophthalate)	314
Poly(ethylene orthophthalate)	314
Poly(ethylene sebacate)	314
Poly(ethylene *trans*-hexahydroterephthalate)	314
Poly(recorsine terephthalate)	314
Poly(ethylene terephthalate–*co*-isophthalate)	314
Poly(ethylene terephthalate–*co*-orthophthalate)	314

TABLE 5 (*Continued*)

Polymer	Ref.
Poly(ethylene terephthalate–*co*-sebacate)	*314*
Poly(ethylene–*co*-recorcine terephthalate)	*314*
Poly(ester–acetals), from cyclic acetals of	
azelaaldehydate	*315*
Polyglutarimide, from β-carboxymethyl caprolactam	*316*
Phenol-formaldehyde polymers	*305,306*
Poly(vinyl formal)	*307*
D-Glucopyranose polymers	*308*
Carbohydrates	*309*
Biopolymers (a review)	*310*

also. These last two types of structural features and the first four mentioned above, *and* the average number of bridges of the diphenyl ether type per aromatic ring, can be determined from the PMR spectra of the acetylated resins. Such information about the structures of phenol–formaldehyde condensates is very difficult, if not impossible, to obtain by other methods, particularly for the higher molecular weight prepolymers.

References to most of the published high-resolution NMR studies of addition-type copolymers and condensation-type polymers are listed in Table 5.

VI. SUMMARY

The present chapter has pointed out those features of high-resolution NMR which make it an excellent method for the study of a wide variety of problems concerning the structures of synthetic polymers. The broad applicability and some of the limitations of the method have been demonstrated by the numerous examples cited. In addition, the chapter has attempted to bring the reader up to date in a field of research which is progressing rapidly. NMR studies of biopolymers have not been discussed, because this field of research was reviewed recently by Kowalsky and Cohn (*310*). It should be pointed out that the applications of NMR to both synthetic and biopolymers are expected to progress as long as improvements in instrumentation continue. The future exploitation of increased magnetic fields, recently made accessible through use of superconducting solenoids, should give more informative proton spectra and lead to new applications of other nuclei such as ^{13}C to polymer problems.

ACKNOWLEDGMENT

The author is indebted to Dr. J. E. Kurz for reading this chapter and for his helpful suggestions.

REFERENCES

1. W. P. Slichter, *Fortschr. Hochpolym. Forsch.*, **1**, 35 (1958).
2. J. G. Powles, *Polymer*, **1**, 219 (1960); J. A. Sauer and A. E. Woodward, *Rev. Mod. Phys.*, **32**, 88 (1960).
3. F. A. Bovey and G. V. D. Tiers, *Fortschr. Hochpolym. Forsch.*, **3**, 139 (1963).
4. D. W. McCall and W. P. Slichter, in *Newer Methods of Polymer Characterization*, (B. Ke, ed.), Wiley (Interscience), New York, 1964, Chap. 8.
5. F. A. Bovey, *Chem. Eng. News*, **43**(35), 98 (1965).
6. L. M. Jackman, *Applications of Nuclear Magnetic Resonance in Organic Chemistry*, Pergamon Press, Oxford, 1959.
7. J. D. Roberts, *Nuclear Magnetic Resonance, Applications to Organic Chemistry*, McGraw-Hill, New York, 1959.
8. N. S. Bhacca and D. H. Williams, *Applications of NMR Spectroscopy to Organic Chemistry*, Holden-Day, San Francisco, 1964.
9. S. Brownstein, *Chem. Rev.*, **59**, 463 (1959).
10. W. D. Phillips, in *Determination of Organic Structures by Physical Methods*, Vol. 2 (F. C. Nachod and W. D. Phillips, eds.), Academic Press, New York, 1962, Chap. 6.
11. P. C. Lauterbur, in *Determination of Organic Structures by Physical Methods*, Vol. 2 (F. C. Nachod and W. D. Phillips, eds.), Academic Press, New York, 1962, Chap. 7.
12. J. B. Stothers, *Quart. Rev. London*, **19**(2), 144 (1965).
13. J. S. Waugh (ed.), *Advances in Magnetic Resonance*, Vol. 1, Academic Press, New York, 1965.
14. J. A. Pople, W. G. Schneider, and H. J. Bernstein, *High Resolution Nuclear Magnetic Resonance*, McGraw-Hill, New York, 1959.
15. J. W. Emsley, J. Feeney, and L. H. Sutcliffe, *High Resolution Nuclear Magnetic Resonance Spectroscopy*, Vols. 1 and 2, Pergamon Press, Oxford, 1965 and 1966.
16. E. R. Andrew, *Nuclear Magnetic Resonance*, Cambridge Univ. Press, New York, 1956.
17. G. E. Pake, *Solid State Phys.*, **2**, 1 (1956).
18. A. Abragam, *The Principles of Nuclear Magnetism*, Oxford Univ. Press (Clarendon), London, 1961.
19. N. Bloembergen, *Nuclear Magnetic Relaxation*, Benjamin, New York, 1961.
20. R. E. Richards, in *Determination of Organic Structures by Physical Methods*, Vol. 2 (F. C. Nachod and W. D. Phillips, eds.), Academic Press, New York, 1962, Chap. 8.
21. C. P. Slichter, *Principles of Magnetic Resonance*, Harper & Row, New York, 1963.
22. A. G. Redfield, in *Advances in Magnetic Resonance*, Vol. 1 (J. S. Waugh, ed.), Academic Press, New York, 1965, pp. 1–32.
23. See Ref. *14*, Chap. 7.
24. See Ref. *15*, Vol. 1, Chaps. 3 and 4.

25. See Ref. *14*, Chaps. 11 and 12.
26. N. S. Bhacca, L. F. Johnson, and J. S. Shoolery, *NMR Spectra Catalog*, Vol. 1, Varian Associates, Palo Alto, Calif., 1962; N. S. Bhacca, D. P. Hollis, L. F. Johnson, and E. A. Pier, *NMR Spectra Catalog*, Vol. 2, Varian Associates, Palo Alto, Calif., 1963.
27. (*a*) *Sadtler NMR Spectra*, Sadtler Research Laboratories, Inc., Philadelphia, Pa.; (*b*) H. A. Szymanski and R. Yelin, *NMR Band Handbook*, Plenum, New York, 1967.
28. See Ref. *15*, Vol. 2.
29. See Ref. *14*, Chap. 8.
30. M. Barfield and D. M. Grant, in *Advances in Magnetic Resonance*, Vol. 1, (J. S. Waugh, ed.), Academic Press, New York, 1965, pp. 149–193.
31. See Ref. *15*, Vol. 1, Chaps. 3 and 5.
32. S. Sternhell, *Rev. Pure Appl. Chem.*, **14**, 15 (1964).
33 A. A. Bothner-By, in *Advances in Magnetic Resonance*, Vol. 1, (J. S. Waugh, ed.), Academic Press, New York, 1965, pp. 195–316.
34. See Ref. *14*, Chap. 6.
35. P. L. Corio, *Chem. Rev.*, **60**, 363 (1960); *Structure of High-Resolution NMR Spectra*, Academic Press, New York, 1966.
36. See Ref. *15*, Vol. 1, Chap. 8.
37. J. D. Baldeschwieler and E. W. Randall, *Chem. Rev.*, **63**, 81 (1963).
38. See Ref. *14*, Chap. 10.
39. See Ref. *15*, Vol. 1, Chap. 9.
40. C. S. Johnson, Jr., in *Advances in Magnetic Resonance*, Vol. 1 (J. S. Waugh, ed.), Academic Press, New York, 1965, pp. 33–102.
41. M. L. Huggins, G. Natta, V. Desreux, and H. Mark, *Pure Appl. Chem.*, **12**(1–4), 645 (1966).
42. B. D. Coleman, *J. Polymer Sci.*, **31**, 155 (1958).
43. F. A. Bovey and G. V. D. Tiers, *J. Polymer Sci.*, **44**, 173 (1960).
44. F. A. Bovey, *Pure Appl. Chem.*, **12**(1–4), 525 (1966).
45. M. Goodman, see (*a*) footnote on p. 526 of Ref. *44* and (*b*) H. L. Frisch, C. L. Mallows, and F. A. Bovey, *J. Chem. Phys.*, **45**, 1565 (1966).
46. T. G. Fox, B. S. Garrett, W. E. Goode, S. Gratch, J. F. Kincaid, A. Spell, and J. D. Stroupe, *J. Am. Chem. Soc.*, **80**, 1768 (1958).
47. F. Gornick, PhD. thesis, *Thermodynamic Properties of Polymers in Relation to Their Stereochemical Structure*, University of Pennsylvania, Philadelphia, 1959.
48. S. Newman, *J. Polymer Sci.*, **47**, 111 (1960).
49. R. L. Miller, *J. Polymer Sci.*, **57**, 975 (1962).
50. F. Gornick and J. L. Jackson, *J. Chem. Phys.*, **38**, 1150 (1963).
51. S. L. Aggarwal, L. Marker, W. L. Kollar, and R. Geroch, *Polymer Preprints*, **5**(2), 1136, (1964); **6**(2), 541 (1965).
52. F. R. Mayo and F. M. Lewis, *J. Am. Chem. Soc.*, **66**, 1594 (1944).
53. T. Alfrey and G. Goldfinger, *J. Chem. Phys.*, **12**, 205, 244 (1944).
54. E. Merz, T. Alfrey, and G. Goldfinger, *J. Polymer Sci.*, **1**, 75 (1946).
55. J. W. L. Fordham, *J. Polymer Sci.*, **39**, 321 (1959).
56. G. E. Ham, *J. Polymer Sci.*, **45**, 169 (1960).
57. A. Miyake and R. Chûjô, *J. Polymer Sci.*, **46**, 163 (1960).
58. R. L. Miller and L. E. Nielsen, *J. Polymer Sci.*, **46**, 303 (1960).

59. U. Johnsen, *Kolloid-Z.*, **178**, 161 (1961).
60. F. P. Price, *J. Chem. Phys.*, **36**, 209 (1962).
61. L. Peller, *J. Chem. Phys.*, **36**, 2976 (1962).
62. B. D. Coleman and T. G. Fox, *J. Chem. Phys.*, **38**, 1065 (1963).
63. B. D. Coleman and T. G. Fox, *J. Polymer Sci.*, **A1**, 3183 (1963).
64. B. D. Coleman and T. G. Fox, *J. Am. Chem. Soc.*, **85**, 1241 (1963).
65. B. D. Coleman and T. G. Fox, *J. Polymer Sci.*, **C4**, 345 (1963).
66. H. K. Frensdorff and R. Pariser, *J. Chem. Phys.*, **39**, 2303 (1963).
67. R. Chûjô, S. Satoh, and E. Nagai, *J. Polymer Sci.*, **A2**, 895 (1964).
68. T. Fueno and J. Furukawa, *J. Polymer Sci.*, **A2**, 3861 (1964).
69. S. L. Aggarwal, *Polymer Preprints*, **5**(2), 1130 (1964).
70. T. Fueno, R. A. Sheldon, and J. Furukawa, *J. Polymer Sci.*, **A3**, 1279 (1965).
71. R. A. Sheldon, T. Fueno, T. Tsunetsugu, and J. Furukawa, *J. Polymer Sci.*, **B3**, 23 (1965).
72. L. Peller, *J. Chem. Phys.*, **43**, 2355 (1965).
73. K. Ito and Y. Yamashita, *J. Polymer Sci.*, **A3**, 2165 (1965).
74. K. Tada, T. Fueno, and J. Furukawa, *J. Polymer Sci.*, **A4**, 2981 (1966).
75. R. Chûjô, paper presented at the *I.U.P.A.C. International Symposium on Macromolecular Chemistry, Tokyo-Kyoto, 1966*.
76. A. Yamada and M. Yamagita, paper presented at the *I.U.P.A.C. International Symposium on Macromolecular Chemistry, Tokyo-Kyoto, 1966;* J. Furukawa, *Polymer Preprints*, **8**(1), 39 (1967).
77. M. Reinmöller and T. G. Fox, *Polymer Preprints*, **7**(2), 987 (1966).
78. W. R. Krigbaum, in *Newer Methods of Polymer Characterization* (B. Ke, ed.), Wiley (Interscience), New York, 1964, Chap. 1.
79. T. G. Fox, W. E. Goode, S. Gratch, C. M. Hugget, J. F. Kincaid, A. Spell, and J. D. Stroupe, *J. Polymer Sci.*, **31**, 173 (1958).
80. J. D. Stroupe and R. E. Hughes, *J. Am. Chem. Soc.*, **80**, 2341 (1958).
81. A. Nishioka, H. Watanabe, I. Yamaguchi, and H. Shimizu, *J. Polymer Sci.*, **45**, 232 (1960).
82. A. Nishioka, H. Watanabe, K. Abe, and Y. Sono, *J. Polymer Sci.*, **48**, 241 (1960).
83. F. A. Bovey, *J. Polymer Sci.*, **46**, 59 (1960).
84. U. Johnsen and K. Tessmar, *Kolloid-Z.*, **168**, 160 (1960).
85. S. Okamura and T. Higashimura, *J. Polymer Sci.*, **46**, 593 (1960).
86. D. M. Wiles and S. Bywater, *Polymer*, **3**, 175 (1962).
87. T. G. Fox and H. W. Schnecko, *Polymer*, **3**, 575 (1962).
88. R. L. Miller, *J. Polymer Sci.*, **56**, 375 (1962).
89. A. Nishioka, Y. Kato, T. Uetake, and H. Watanabe, *J. Polymer Sci.*, **61**, 532 (1962).
90. D. Braun, M. Herner, U. Johnsen, and W. Kern, *Makromol. Chem.*, **51**, 15 (1962).
91. C. Walling and D. D. Tanner, *J. Polymer Sci.*, **A1**, 2271 (1963).
92. D. L. Glusker, R. A. Galluccio, and R. A. Evans, *J. Am. Chem. Soc.*, **86**, 187 (1964).
93. D. M. Wiles and S. Bywater, *J. Phys. Chem.*, **68**, 1983 (1964).
94. Y. Kato and A. Nishioka, *Bull. Chem. Soc. (Japan)*, **37**, 1614 (1964).
95. Y. Oshumi, T. Higashimura, and S. Okamura, *J. Polymer Sci.*, **A3**, 3729 (1965).
96. D. M. Wiles and S. Bywater, *Trans. Faraday Soc.*, **61**, 150 (1965).
97. Y. Kato and A. Nishioka, *J. Polymer Sci.*, **B3**, 739 (1965).
98. H. Abe, K. Imai, and M. Matsumoto, *J. Polymer Sci.*, **B3**, 1053 (1965).

99. Y. Kato and A. Nishioka, *J. Chem. Soc. Japan, Ind. Chem. Sect.*, **68**, 1461 (1965).
100. S. Brownstein and D. M. Wiles, *Can. J. Chem.*, **44**, 153 (1966).
101. K. C. Ramey and J. Messick, *J. Polymer Sci.*, **A4**, 155 (1966).
102. T. Tsuruta, T. Makimoto, and H. Kanai, *J. Macromol. Chem.*, **1**, 31 (1966).
103. T. Otsu, B. Yamada, M. Imoto, *J. Macromol. Chem.*, **1**, 61 (1966).
104. D. Lím, J. Čoupek, K. Jůzl, J. Báča, S. Sýkora, and B. Schneider, paper presented at the *I.U.P.A.C. International Symposium on Macromolecular Chemistry, Tokyo-Kyoto, 1966.*
105. (a) T. Higashimura, Y. Ohsumi, and S. Okamura, paper presented at the *I.U.P.A.C. International Symposium on Macromolecular Chemistry, Tokyo-Kyoto, 1966;* (b) R. C. Ferguson and W. D. Phillips, *Science*, **157**(3786), 257 (1967); (c) R. C. Ferguson, *Trans. N.Y. Acad. Sci.*, **29**(4) (1967); (d) K. C. Ramey, *Polymer Preprints*, **8**(2), 1017 (1967).
106. F. A. Bovey, paper presented at the *I.U.P.A.C. International Symposium on Macromolecular Chemistry, Tokyo-Kyoto, 1966;* to be published in *Pure Appl. Chem.*
107. M. Reinmöller and T. G. Fox, *Polymer Preprints*, **7**(2), 999 (1966).
108. B. D. Coleman, T. G. Fox, and M. Reinmöller, *J. Polymer Sci.*, **B4**, 1029 (1966).
109. F. A. Bovey and G. V. D. Tiers, *J. Polymer Sci.*, **47**, 479 (1960).
110. J. C. H. Hwa, *J. Polymer Sci.*, **60**, S12 (1962).
111. W. L. Miller, W. S. Brey, Jr., and G. B. Butler, *J. Polymer Sci.*, **54**, 329 (1961).
112. M. Reinmöller and T. G. Fox, *Polymer Preprints*, **7**(2), 1005 (1966).
113. H. Sobue, K. Matsuzaki, and S. Nakano, *J. Polymer Sci.*, **A2**, 3339 (1964).
114. K. Matsuzaki, N. Tateno, and T. Watanabe, paper presented at the *I.U.P.A.C. International Symposium on Macromolecular Chemistry, Tokyo-Kyoto, 1966.*
115. H. Sobue, T. Uryu, K. Matsuzaki, and Y. Tabata, *J. Polymer Sci.*, **B1**, 409 (1963).
116. K. Matsuzaki and T. Uryu, *J. Polymer Sci.*, **B4**, 255 (1966); Y. Kotake, T. Yoshihara, H. Sata, N. Yamada, and Y. Joh, *J. Polymer Sci.*, **B5**, 163 (1967).
117. A. Crawshaw and G. B. Butler, *J. Am. Chem. Soc.*, **80**, 5464 (1958).
118. J. F. Jones, *J. Polymer Sci.*, **33**, 15 (1958).
119. C. S. Marvel, *J. Polymer Sci.*, **48**, 101 (1960).
120. G. B. Butler, *J. Polymer Sci.*, **48**, 279 (1960).
121. J. C. H. Hwa and L. Miller, *J. Polymer Sci.*, **55**, 197 (1961).
122. J. Mercier and G. Smets, *J. Polymer Sci.*, **57**, 263 (1962).
123. W. T. Gibbs and J. T. Murray, *J. Polymer Sci.*, **57**, 141 (1962).
124. K. Yokota and Y. Ishii, *J. Polymer Sci.*, **B3**, 771 (1965).
125. (a) D. M. Wiles and S. Brownstein, *J. Polymer Sci.*, **B3**, 951 (1965); (b) W. M. Lee, *Polymer Preprints*, **8**(2), 1030 (1967).
126. A. L. Segre, F. Ciampelli, and G. Dall'Asta, *J. Polymer Sci.*, **B4**, 633 (1966); K. Ishigure, Y. Tabata, and K. Oshima, *J. Polymer Sci.*, **B4**, 669 (1966).
127. K. Matsuzaki, T. Uryu, A. Ishida, and T. Ohki, *J. Polymer Sci.*, **B2**, 1139 (1964).
128. C. Schuerch, W. Fowells, A. Yamada, F. A. Bovey, F. P. Hood, and E. W. Anderson, *J. Am. Chem. Soc.*, **86**, 4481 (1964).
129. T. Yoshino, J. Komiyama, and M. Shinomiya, *J. Am. Chem. Soc.*, **86**, 4482 (1964).
130. T. Yoshino, M. Shinomiya, and J. Komiyama, *J. Am. Chem. Soc.*, **87**, 387 (1965).
131. T. Yoshino and K. Kuno, *J. Am. Chem. Soc.*, **87**, 4404 (1965).
132. D. Doskočilová and B. Schneider, *J. Polymer Sci.*, **B3**, 213 (1965).
133. K. Matsuzaki, T. Uryu, and A. Ishida, paper presented at the *I.U.P.A.C. International Symposium on Macromolecular Chemistry, Prague, 1965.*

134. T. Yoshino and J. Komiyama, *J. Am. Chem. Soc.*, **88**, 176 (1966).

135. T. Yoshino, Y. Kikuchi, and J. Komiyama, *J. Phys. Chem.*, **70**, 1059 (1966).

136. D. Doskočilová, S. Sýkora, H. Pivcová, B. Obereigner, and D. Lím, paper presented at the *I.U.P.A.C. International Symposium on Macromolecular Chemistry, Tokyo-Kyoto, 1966.*

137. K. Matsuzaki, T. Uryu, and M. Takeuchi, *J. Polymer Sci.*, **B3**, 835 (1965).

138. R. Yamadera and M. Murano, *J. Polymer Sci.*, **B3**, 821 (1965).

139. K. Matsuzaki, T. Uryu, K. Ishigure, and M. Takeuchi, *J. Polymer Sci.*, **B4**, 93 (1966).

140. K. Matsuzaki, T. Uryu, M. Okada, K. Ishigure, T. Ohki, and M. Takeuchi, *J. Polymer Sci.*, **B4**, 487 (1966).

141. J. Bargon, K.-H. Hellwege, and U. Johnsen, *Kolloid-Z.*, **212**, 51 (1966).

142. H. G. Clark, *Makromol. Chem.*, **63**, 69 (1963).

143. S. Brownstein, S. Bywater, and D. J. Worsfold, *Makromol. Chem.*, **48**, 127 (1961).

144. Y. Sakurada, M. Matsumoto, K. Imai, A. Nishioka, and Y. Kato, *J. Polymer Sci.*, **B1**, 633 (1963).

145. D. Braun, G. Heufer, U. Johnsen, and K. Kolbe, *Ber. Bunsenges. Physik. Chem.*, **68**(10), 959 (1964).

146. K. C. Ramey and G. L. Statton, *Makromol. Chem.*, **85**, 287 (1965).

147. U. Johnsen, *J. Polymer Sci.*, **54**, S8 (1961).

148. F. A. Bovey and G. V. D. Tiers, *Chem. Ind. (London)*, **(1962)** 1826.

149. R. Chûjô, S. Satoh, T. Ozeki, and E. Nagai, *J. Polymer Sci.*, **61**, S12 (1962).

150. W. C. Tincher, *J. Polymer Sci.*, **62**, S148 (1962).

151. J. C. Woodbrey, unpublished results, 1963.

152. F. A. Bovey, E. W. Anderson, D. C. Douglass, and J. A. Manson, *J. Chem. Phys.*, **39**, 1199 (1963).

153. S. Satoh, *J. Polymer Sci.*, **A2**, 5221 (1964).

154. W. C. Tincher, *Makromol. Chem.*, **85**, 20 (1965).

155. T. Yoshino and J. Komiyama, *J. Polymer Sci.*, **B3**, 311 (1965).

156. (*a*) J. Bargon, K.-H. Hellwege, and U. Johnsen, *Makromol. Chem.*, **86**, 43 (1966); (*b*) U. Johnsen and K. Kolbe, *Kolloid-Z. Z. Polymere*, **221**, 64 (1967); (*c*) O. C. Böckman, *J. Polymer Sci.*, **A3**, 3399 (1965).

157. B. Schneider, J. Štokr, D. Doskočilová, M. Kolínský, S. Sýkora, and D. Lím, paper presented at the *I.U.P.A.C. International Symposium on Macromolecular Chemistry, Prague, 1965.*

158. J. Schaefer, *J. Phys. Chem.*, **70**, 1975 (1966).

159. K. C. Ramey, *J. Phys. Chem.*, **70**, 2525 (1966).

160. F. A. Bovey, F. P. Hood, E. W. Anderson, and R. L. Kornegay, *J. Phys. Chem.*, **71**, 312 (1967).

161. T. Shimanouchi, M. Tasumi, and Y. Abe, *Makromol. Chem.*, **86**, 43 (1965).

162. Y. Abe, M. Tasumi, T. Shimanouchi, S. Satoh, and R. Chûjô, *J. Polymer Sci.*, **A4**, 1413 (1966).

163. See Ref. *15*, Vol. 1, Chap. 5, and Vol. 2, Chap. 10.

164. D. Doskočilová, *J. Polymer Sci.*, **B2**, 421 (1964).

165. D. Doskočilová and B. Schneider, *Collection Czech. Chem. Commun.*, **29**, 2290 (1964).

166. (*a*) P. E. McMahon and W. C. Tincher, *J. Mol. Spectry.*, **15**, 180 (1965); (*b*) P. E. McMahon, *J. Mol. Spectry.*, **16**, 221 (1965).

167. H. Pivcová and B. Schneider, *Collection Czech. Chem. Commun.*, **31**, 3154 (1966).

168. D. Doskočilová, J. Štokr, B. Schneider, H. Pivcová, M. Kolínský, J. Petránek, and D. Lím, paper presented at the *I.U.P.A.C. International Symposium on Macromolecular Chemistry, Prague, 1965.*

169. F. A. Bovey, F. P. Hood, III, E. W. Anderson, and L. C. Snyder, *J. Chem. Phys.,* **42,** 3900 (1965).

170. J. W. L. Fordham, P. H. Burleigh, and C. L. Sturm, *J. Polymer Sci.,* **20,** 251 (1956); **41,** 73 (1959).

171. H. Germar, K.-H. Hellwege, and U. Johnsen, *Makromol. Chem.,* **60,** 106 (1963).

172. F. P. Reding, E. R. Walter, and F. J. Welch, *J. Polymer Sci.,* **56,** 225 (1962).

173. J. D. Cotman, Jr., *Ann. N.Y. Acad. Sci.,* **57,** 417 (1953).

174. G. Bier and H. Krämer, *Kunststoffe,* **46,** 498 (1956).

175. H. Batzer and A. Nisch, *Makromol. Chem.,* **22,** 131 (1957).

176. M. H. George, R. J. Grisenthwaite, and R. F. Hunter, *Chem. Ind. (London),* **(1958),** 1114; A. Nakajima, H. Hamada, and S. Hayashi, *Makromol. Chem.,* **95,** 40(1966).

177. G. Natta, *Atti Accad. Nazl. Lincei, Mem. Classe Sci. Fis. Mat. Nat., Sez. II,* **4,** 61 (1955).

178. G. Natta, *J. Polymer Sci.,* **16,** 143 (1955).

179. G. Natta, P. Pino, P. Corradini, F. Danusso, E. Mantica, G. Mazzanti, and G. Moraglio, *J. Am. Chem. Soc.,* **77,** 1708 (1955).

180. G. Natta, P. Corradini, and M. Cesari, *Atti Accad. Nazl. Lincei, Rend., Classe Sci. Fis. Mat. Nat.,* **21,** 365 (1956).

181. G. Natta, P. Corradini, and M. Cesari, *Atti Accad. Nazl. Lincei, Rend., Classe Sci. Fis. Mat. Nat.,* **22,** 11 (1957).

182. G. Natta, G. Mazzanti, B. Crespi, and G. Moraglio, *Chim. Ind. (Milan),* **39,** 275 (1957).

183. G. Natta, M. Farina, and M. Peraldo, *Atti Accad. Nazl. Lincei, Rend., Classe Sci. Fis. Mat. Nat.,* **25,** 424 (1958).

184. G. Natta, M. Peraldo, and P. Corradini, *Atti Accad. Nazl. Lincei, Rend., Classe Sci. Fis. Mat. Nat.,* **26,** 14 (1959).

185. G. Natta, I. Pasquon, P. Corradini, M. Peraldo, M. Pegoraro, and A. Zambelli, *Atti Accad. Nazl. Lincei, Rend., Classe Sci. Fis. Mat. Nat.,* **28,** 539 (1960).

186. G. Natta, M. Farina, and M. Peraldo, *Chim. Ind. (Milan),* **42,** 255 (1960).

187. G. Natta and M. Farina, *Chim. Ind. (Milan),* **42,** 1349 (1960).

188. G. Natta, I. Pasquon, and A. Zambelli, *J. Am. Chem. Soc.,* **84,** 1488 (1962).

189. A. Zambelli, G. Natta, and I. Pasquon, *J. Polymer Sci.,* Č4, 411 (1963).

190. J. P. Luongo, *J. Appl. Polymer Sci.,* **3,** 302 (1960).

191. J. J. Brader, *J. Appl. Polymer Sci.,* **3,** 370 (1960).

192. J. P. Siblia and R. C. Winklhofer, *J. Appl. Polymer Sci.,* **5,** 556 (1962).

193. P. G. Schmidt, *J. Polymer Sci.,* **A1,** 2317 (1963).

194. R. N. Hughes, *Polymer Preprints,* **4**(2), 697 (1963).

195. C. Y. Liang, in *Newer Methods of Polymer Characterization* (B. Ke, ed.), Wiley (Interscience), New York, 1964, Chap. 2.

196. T. Miyazawa, in *Stereochemistry of Macromolecules* (A. D. Ketley, ed.), Dekker, New York, 1968, Vol. 3, Chap. 3.

197. S. Satoh, R. Chûjô, T. Ozeki, and E. Nagai, *J. Polymer Sci.,* **62,** S101 (1962).

198. S. Stehling, *Polymer Preprints,* **3**(1), 278 (1962).

199. S. Stehling, *J. Polymer Sci.,* **A2,** 1815 (1964).

200. W. C. Tincher, *Polymer Preprints*, **3**(2), 142* (1962).

201. J. C. Woodbrey, *J. Polymer Sci.*, **B2**, 315 (1964).

202. J. C. Woodbrey and Q. A. Trementozzi, *Polymer Preprints*, **5**(2), 1071 (1964).

203. J. C. Woodbrey and Q. A. Trementozzi, *J. Polymer Sci.*, **C8**, 113 (1965).

204. S. Ohnishi and K. Nukada, *J. Polymer Sci*, **B3**, 179 (1965).

205. S. Ohnishi and K. Nukada, *J. Polymer Sci.*, **B3**, 1001 (1965).

206. P. Pino, S. Pucci, E. Benedetti, and P. Bucci, *J. Am. Chem. Soc.*, **87**, 3263 (1965).

207. G. Natta, E. Lombardi, A. L. Segre, A. Zambelli, and A. Marinangeli, *Chim. Ind. (Milan)*, **47**(4), 378 (1965).

208. E. Lombardi, A. Segre, A. Zambelli, A. Marinangeli, and G. Natta, paper presented at the *I.U.P.A.C. International Symposium on Macromolecular Chemistry Prague, 1965*.

209. W. C. Tincher, *Makromol. Chem.*, **85**, 34 (1965).

210. P. J. Flory and J. D. Baldeschwieler, *J. Am. Chem. Soc.*, **88**, 2873 (1966).

211. (a) R. C. Ferguson, *Chem. Eng. News*, **44**(37), 46 (1966); (b) R. C. Ferguson, *Polymer Preprints*, **8**(2), 1026 (1967).

212. P. J. Flory, J. E. Mark, and A. Abe, *J. Polymer Sci.*, **B3**, 973 (1965).

213. P. J. Flory, J. E. Mark, and A. Abe, *J. Am. Chem. Soc.*, **88**, 639 (1966).

214. P. J. Flory and R. L. Jernigan, *J. Chem. Phys.*, **42**, 3509 (1965); and references cited therein.

215. J. E. Mark, and P. J. Flory, *J. Am. Chem. Soc.*, **87**, 1423 (1965).

216. (a) H. Inagaki, T. Miyamoto, and S. Ohta, *J. Phys. Chem.*, **70**, 3420 (1966); (b) J. C. Woodbrey, unpublished results, 1967.

217. See Ref. *15*, Vol. 2, Chap. 10, pp. 815–816.

218. F. A. Bovey, G. V. D. Tiers, and G. Filipovich, *J. Polymer Sci.*, **38**, 73 (1959).

219. D. W. McCall and F. A. Bovey, *J. Polymer Sci.*, **45**, 530 (1960).

220. R. J. Kern and J. V. Pustinger, *Nature*, **185**, 236 (1960).

221. S. Brownstein, S. Bywater, and D. J. Worsfold, *J. Phys. Chem.*, **66**, 2067 (1962).

222. K.-J. Liu and R. Ullman, *Polymer*, **6**, 100 (1965).

223. D. Lím, M. Kolinský, J. Petránek, D. Doskočilová, and B. Schneider, *J. Polymer Sci.*, **B4**, 645 (1966).

224. K. C. Ramey and N. D. Field, *J. Polymer Sci.*, **B3**, 69 (1965).

225. K. Fujii, Y. Fujiwara, and S. Fujiwara, *Makromol. Chem.*, **89**, 278 (1965).

226. S. Murahashi, S. Nozakura, and M. Sumi, *J. Polymer Sci.*, **B4**, 65 (1966).

227. S. Murahashi, S. Nozakura, M. Sumi, H. Yuki, and K. Hatada, *Kobunshi Kagaku*, **23**, 605 (1966).

228. K. C. Ramey and D. C. Lini, *J. Polymer Sci.*, **B5**, 39 (1967).

229. K. C. Ramey and N. D. Field, *J. Polymer Sci.*, **B3**, 63 (1965).

230. J. G. Pritchard, R. L. Vollmer, W. C. Lawrence, and W. B. Black, *J. Polymer Sci.* **A4**, 707 (1966).

231. K. C. Ramey, D. C. Lini, and G. L. Statton, *J. Polymer Sci.*, **A5**, 257 (1967).

232. W. C. Tincher, *Makromol. Chem.*, **85**, 46 (1965).

233. J. Bargon, K.-H. Hellwege, and U. Johnsen, *Makromol. Chem.*, **85**, 291 (1965).

234. D. Doskočilová, J. Stokr, E. Votavová, B. Schneider, and D. Lím, paper presented at the *I.U.P.A.C. International Symposium on Macromolecular Chemistry, Prague, 1965*.

235. (a) H. N. Friedlander, H. E. Harris, and J. G. Pritchard, *J. Polymer Sci.*, **A4**, 649 (1966); (b) M. Frata, G. Vidotto, and G. Talmini, *Chim. Ind. (Milan)*, **48**, 42 (1966).

236. (a) C. G. Overberger and T. Kurtz, *J. Org. Chem.*, **31**, 288 (1966); (b) J. Heller and D. B. Miller, *J. Polymer Sci.*, A5, 2323 (1967).
237. R. J. Kern, J. J. Hawkins, and J. D. Calfee, *Makromol. Chem.*, **66**, 126 (1963).
238. S. Brownstein and D. M. Wiles, *J. Polymer Sci.* A2, 1901 (1964).
239. K. C. Ramey, N. D. Field, and I. Hasegawa, *J. Polymer Sci.*, B2, 865 (1964).
240. Y. Ohsumi, T. Higashimura, and S. Okamura: (a) paper presented at the *I.U.P.A.C. International Symposium on Macromolecular Chemistry, Tokyo-Kyoto, 1966;* (b) *Kobunski Kagaku*, **23**, 613 (1966); (c) *J. Polymer Sci.*, A5, 849 (1967).
241. T. Higashimura, Y. Ohsumi, K. Kuroda, and S. Okamura, *J. Polymer Sci.*, A5, 863 (1967).
242. K. C. Ramey, N. D. Field, and A. E. Borchert, *J. Polymer Sci.*, A3, 2885 (1965).
243. M. Goodman, Y. Fan, *J. Am. Chem. Soc.*, **86**, 4922, 5712 (1964).
244. J. Brandup and M. Goodman, *J. Polymer Sci.*, B2, 123 (1964).
245. E. G. Brame, Jr., R. S. Sudol, and O. Vogl, *J. Polymer Sci.*, A2, 5337 (1964).
246. M. Goodman and J. Brandup, *J. Polymer Sci.*, A3, 327 (1965).
247. R. E. Naylor, Jr., and S. W. Lasoki, Jr., *J. Polymer Sci.*, **44**, 1 (1960).
248. C. W. Wilson, III, and E. R. Santee, Jr., *J. Polymer Sci.*, C8, 97 (1965).
249. C. W. Wilson, III, *J. Polymer Sci.*, A1, 1305 (1963).
250. G. V. D. Tiers and F. A. Bovey, *J. Polymers Sci.*, A1, 833 (1963).
251. (a) G. Geuskens, J. C. Lubikulu, and C. David, *Polymer*, **7**(1), 63 (1966); (b) K.-J. Liu, *Polymer Preprints*, **8**(2), 1098 (1967).
252. H. Y. Chen, *Anal. Chem.*, **34**, 1793 (1962).
253. D. J. Worsfold and S. Bywater, *Can. J. Chem.*, **42**, 2884 (1964).
254. J. L. Binder, *J. Polymer Sci.*, B4, 19 (1966).
255. H. Y. Chen, *J. Polymer Sci.*, B4, 891 (1966).
256. H. Y. Chen, *J. Polymer Sci.*, B4, 1007 (1966).
257. R. C. Ferguson, *J. Polymer Sci.*, A2, 4735 (1964).
258. A. G. Davies and A. Wasserman, *J. Polymer Sci.*, A4, 1887 (1966).
259. C. Aso, T. Kunitake, I. Kenji, and Y. Ishimoto, *J. Polymer Sci.*, B4, 701 (1966).
260. T. M. Connor and K. A. McLauchlan, *J. Phys. Chem.*, **69**, 1888 (1965).
261. R. J. Kern and J. Schaefer, *J. Am. Chem. Soc.*, **89**, 6 (1967).
262. J. D. Ingham, D. D. Lawson, S. L. Manatt, N. S. Rapp, and J. P. Hardy, *J. Macromol. Chem.*, **1**, 75 (1965).
263. H. Haubenstock and W. Naegele, *Makromol. Chem.*, **97**, 248 (1966).
264. W. R. Edwards and N. F. Chamberlain, *J. Polymer Sci.*, A1, 2299 (1963).
265. J. P. Kennedy and A. W. Langer, Jr., *Fortschr. Hochpolym. Forsch.*, **3**, 508 (1964).
266. J. P. Kennedy, P. Borzel, W. Naegele, and R. G. Squires, *Makromol. Chem.*, **93**, 191 (1966).
267. B. E. Hudson, Jr., *Makromol. Chem.*, **94**, 172 (1966).
268. E. G. Brame, Jr., and O. Vogl; *J. Macromol. Sci.*, A1, 277 (1967).
269. M. A. Golub, S. A. Fuqua, and N. S. Bhacca, *J. Am. Chem. Soc.*, **84**, 4981 (1962).
270. G. Natta, M. Peraldo, M. Farina, and G. Bressan, *Makromol. Chem.*, **55**, 139 (1962).
271. T. Miyazawa and Y. Ideguchi, *J. Polymer Sci.*, B1, 389 (1963).
272. H. Tadokoro, M. Ukita, M. Kobayashi, and S. Murahashi, *J. Polymer Sci.*, B1, 405 (1963).
273. M. Tasumi, T. Shimanouchi, H. Tanaka, and S. Ikeda, *J. Polymer Sci.*, A2, 1607 (1964).

274. W. Fowells, C. Schuerch, F. A. Bovey, and F. P. Hood, *J. Am. Chem. Soc.*, **89**, 1396 (1967).
275. W. M. Ritchey and L. E. Ball, *J. Polymer Sci.*, **B4**, 557 (1966).
276. (*a*) H. Y. Chen, *Anal. Chem.*, **34**, 1134 (1962); (*b*) V. G. Mochel, *Rubber Chem. Technol.*, **40**, 1200 (1967).
277. R. S. Porter, *J. Polymer Sci.*, **A4**, 189 (1966).
278. K. Ito and Y. Yamashita, *J. Polymer Sci.*, **A4**, 631 (1966).
279. N. Grassie, B. J. D. Torrance, J. D. Fortune, J. D. Gemmel, *Polymer*, **6**, 653 (1965).
280. K. Ito and Y. Yamashita, *J. Polymer Sci.*, **B3**, 637 (1965).
281. F. A. Bovey, *J. Polymer Sci.*, **62**, 197 (1962).
282. A. Nishioka, Y. Kato, and N. Ashikari, *J. Polymer Sci.*, **62**, S10 (1962).
283. N. Ashikari and A. Nishioka, *Bull. Chem. Soc. Japan*, **37**, 1630 (1964).
284. H. J. Harwood, *Angew. Chem.*, **4**, 1051 (1964).
285. H. J. Harwood and W. M. Ritchey, *J. Polymer Sci.*, **B3**, 419 (1965).
286. C. G. Overberger and N. Yamamoto, *J. Polymer Sci.*, **B3**, 569 (1965).
287. K. Ito and Y. Yamashita, *J. Polymer Sci.*, **B3**, 625, 631 (1965).
288. R. G. Bauer, H. J. Harwood, and W. M. Ritchey, *Polymer Preprints*, **7**(2), 973 (1966).
289. C. G. Overberger and N. Yamamoto, *Polymer Preprints*, **7**(1), 115 (1966).
290. S. Kobayashi, Y. Kato, H. Watanabe, and A. Nishioka, *J. Polymer Sci.*, **A4**, 245 (1966).
291. C. W. Wilson, III, *J. Polymer Sci.*, **56**, S12 (1962).
292. T. Takeuchi, M. Yamazaki, and S. Mori, *J. Polymer Sci.*, **B4**, 695 (1966).
293. R. Chûjô, S. Satoh, and E. Nagai, *J. Polymer Sci.*, **A2**, 895 (1964).
294. J. L. McClanahan and S. A. Previtera, *J. Polymer Sci.*, **A3**, 3919 (1965).
295. T. Fisher, J. B. Kinsinger, and C. W. Wilson, III, *J. Polymer Sci.*, **B4**, 379 (1966).
296. J. B. Kinsinger, T. Fisher, and C. W. Wilson, III, *Polymer Preprints*, **7**(2), 967 (1966); *J. Polymer Sci.*, **B5**, 285 (1967).
297. K.-H. Hellwege, U. Johnsen, and K. Kolbe, *Kolloid-Z.*, **214**, 45 (1966).
298. R. C. Ferguson, *J. Am. Chem. Soc.*, **82**, 2416 (1960).
299. J. Schaefer, R. J. Kern, and R. J. Katnick, *Polymer Preprints*, **8**(2), 1037 (1967).
300. M. Sumi, Y. Chokki, Y. Nakai, M. Nakabayashi, and T. Kanzawa, *Angew. Chem.*, **3**, 146 (1964).
301. M. Sumi, Y. Chokki, Y. Nakai, M. Nakabayashi, and T. Kanzawa, *Makromol. Chem.*, **78**, 146 (1964).
302. H. Okuto, *Makromol. Chem.*, **98**, 148 (1966).
303. J. P. Kennedy and R. B. Isaacson, *Polymer Preprints*, **7**(2), 419 (1966).
304. J. C. W. Chien and J. F. Walker, *J. Polymer Sci.*, **45**, 239 (1960).
305. J. C. Woodbrey, H. P. Higginbottom, and H. M. Culbertson, *J. Polymer Sci.*, **A3**, 1079 (1965).
306. R. C. Hirst, D. M. Grant, R. E. Hoff, and W. J. Burke, *J. Polymer Sci.*, **A3**, 2091, (1965)
307. K. Fujii, K. Shibatani, Y. Fujiwara, Y. Ohyanagi, J. Ukida, and M. Matsumoto, *J. Polymer Sci.*, **B4**, 787 (1966).
308. C. A. Glass, *Can. J. Chem.*, **43**, 2652 (1965).
309. R. W. Lenz and J. P. Heeschen, *J. Polymer Sci.*, **51**, 247 (1961).
310. A. Kowalsky and M. Cohn, *Ann. Rev. Biochem.*, **33**, 481 (1964).

311. (*a*) E. M. Banas and O. O. Juveland, *J. Polymer Sci.*, **A5**, 397 (1967); (*b*) K. Ito, S. Iwase, K. Umehara, and Y. Yamashita, *J. Macromol. Sci.*, **A1**, 891 (1967).
312. U. Johnsen, *Ber. Bunsenges Physik. Chem.*, **70**(3), 320 (1966).
313. R. J. Kern and J. Schaefer, *J. Polymer Sci.*, **B5**, 157 (1967).
314. R. Yamadera and M. Murano, *J. Polymer Sci.*, **A5**, 2259 (1967).
315. R. W. Lenz, J. Nelson, R. A. Awl, W. R. Miller, and E. H. Pryde, *Polymer Preprints*, **8**(2), 1084 (1967).
316. J. P. Siblia, H. M. Reimschuessel, and G. E. Babbitt, *Polymer Preprints*, **8**(2), 1109 (1967).
317. T. Yoshino, H. Iwanaga, and K. Kuno, *J. Am. Chem. Soc.*, **89**, 6773 (1967).
318. T. Yoshino, J. Komiyama, and H. Iwanaga, *J. Am. Chem. Soc.*, **89**, 6925 (1967).
319. Y. Yamashita, K. Ito, S. Ikuma, and H. Kada, *J. Polymer Sci.*, **B6** (1968), in press.
320. K. Ito and Y. Yamashita, *J. Polymer Sci.*, **B6** (1968), in press.

CHAPTER 3

Vibrational Analyses of the Infrared Spectra of Stereoregular Polypropylene

Tatsuo Miyazawa

INSTITUTE FOR PROTEIN RESEARCH
OSAKA UNIVERSITY
JOANCHO, KITA-KU, OSAKA, JAPAN

I. INTRODUCTION

The stereoregular polypropylenes, isotactic and syndiotactic, have been synthesized and their crystal and molecular structures have been established by Natta et al. (*1*). The systematic difference between the chemical structures of isotactic and syndiotactic polymers may readily be recognized in Fig. 1. In this figure, all the C—C bonds of the main chain are tentatively set in the *trans* form and accordingly the main chain is in the planar zigzag conformation. For isotactic polypropylene, all the methyl

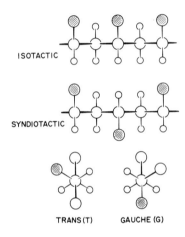

Fig. 1. Stereoregularities of isotactic and syndiotactic polymers and the *trans* and *gauche* forms (main-chain C—C bonds are drawn with heavy lines).

groups lie on the same side of the plane, whereas, for syndiotactic polypropylene, adjacent methyl groups are located alternately on opposite sides of the plane.

The infrared absorption bands of polymers arise from the vibrations of the polymer chains which depend upon the physical structure (or the arrangements of chain atoms) as well as upon the intramolecular force field. Detailed infrared studies of polypropylene have been expected to provide the basic knowledge necessary for vibrational analyses and structure studies of other stereoregular polymers. Therefore, the infrared spectra of isotactic polypropylene [—CH_2—$CH(CH_3)$—]$_p$ and deuterated derivatives have been measured and empirical vibrational assignments have been made (*2–9*). However, except for the bands due to the C—H and C—D stretching modes, the effects of isotopic substitutions upon the infrared spectra have been found to be quite complicated. Accordingly, for elucidating the nature of the infrared bands and also for studying the correlations with the chain structures, the treatment of the molecular vibrations have been found indispensable.

The intramolecular potential functions of hydrocarbon molecules have been extensively studied by Shimanouchi et al. (*10*) and Snyder and Schachtschneider (*11,12*). Subsequently, for treating the molecular vibrations of isotactic and syndiotactic polypropylene, the valence force field (*12*) has been used by Snyder and Schachtschneider (*13–15*) and the modified Urey–Bradley field (*10*) by Miyazawa et al. (*16–23*). The Urey–Bradley field (*24*) has been used by Tadokoro et al. (*25,26*). The nature of the infrared bands of isotactic and syndiotactic polypropylene have now been elucidated and the infrared spectra of amorphous polypropylene have also been analyzed in some detail. The infrared spectra and the vibrational analyses of stereoregular polypropylenes are expected to be useful for the interpretation of the infrared spectra of other stereoregular polymers.

II. CHAIN CONFORMATION OF STEREOREGULAR POLYPROPYLENES

A. Isotactic Polypropylene

For the isotactic polypropylene chain in the crystalline state, the *trans* and *gauche* forms (see Fig. 1) are alternately repeated along the main chain, so that the molecular chain is in the helical conformation with the threefold screw axis, as shown in Fig. 2. There are three chemical units —CH_2—$CH(CH_3)$— and one helical turn per fiber identity distance of 6.50 Å. Accordingly, the translation along the axis per unit is $d = 2.17$ Å and the rotation about the axis per unit is $\theta = 120°$ (*1*).

The helical parameters of the polymer chain ($-M_1-M_2-)_p$ have been derived as explicit functions of the bond lengths r, bond angles ϕ, and internal rotation angles t (*27*). For the particular case of isotactic vinyl polymers ($-CH_2-CHR-)_p$, the helical parameters d and θ may be expressed as

$$\cos \tfrac{1}{2}\theta = \sin^2 \tfrac{1}{2}\phi \cos \tfrac{1}{2}(t_{12} + t_{21}) - \cos^2 \tfrac{1}{2}\phi \cos \tfrac{1}{2}(t_{12} - t_{21}) \qquad (1)$$

$$d \sin \tfrac{1}{2}\theta = 2r \sin^2 \tfrac{1}{2}\phi \sin \tfrac{1}{2}(t_{12} + t_{21}) \qquad (2)$$

If the internal rotation angle of $t_{12} = 180°$ (*trans*) is substituted in Eq. (1), the parameter θ is equal to $\pi + t_{21}$. For the isotactic polypropylene chain, the internal rotation angle is then calculated as $-60°$ (*gauche*). With the bond length of $r = 1.54$ Å, the angle ϕ is calculated as $114°$ from the helical parameter of $d = 2.17$ Å. On the other hand, if reasonable values are assumed for the molecular parameters r and ϕ the internal rotation angles t_{12} and t_{21} may be calculated from the experimental values of d and θ.

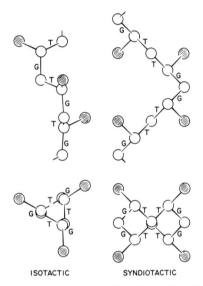

ISOTACTIC   SYNDIOTACTIC

Fig. 2. Helical conformations of isotactic and syndiotactic polypropylenes (*T*: *trans*; *G*: *gauche*).

B. Syndiotactic Polypropylene

Syndiotactic polypropylene has been prepared in two crystalline forms by Natta et al. (*1,28*). When the sample of syndiotactic polypropylene is quenched from the melt and is cold drawn, the molecular chain is in the zigzag form, with a fiber identity distance of 5.05 Å. However, if the sample in the zigzag form is kept at about 100° for several hours, the solid sample is transformed into the more stable crystalline form (Fig. 2) in which the main chain is in a helical form with the twofold screw axis. The internal rotation about the main chain C—C bonds are *trans*, *trans*, *gauche*, and *gauche*, as repeated throughout the chain. There are two repeating units [four —CH$_2$—CH(CH$_3$)— units] and one helical turn per fiber identity distance of 7.3 Å; and accordingly the helical parameters are $d = 3.65$ Å and $\theta = 180°$.

The helical parameters d and θ for polymer chains of the type $(-M_1-M_2-M_3-M_4-)_p$ have also been derived as explicit functions of the molecular parameters (27). For syndiotactic polypropylene, the molecular parameters may be assumed to be $r = 1.54$ Å and $\phi = 114°$, and then the internal rotation angles for the *trans* and *gauche* C—C bonds are calculated as 189° and 57°, respectively.

III. MOLECULAR VIBRATIONS OF HELICAL POLYMER CHAINS

A. Phase Difference

In the infrared absorption spectra of helical polymer chains consisting of many units, the effects of the end groups are not significant. Accordingly, in analyzing the infrared spectra, the chemical units may be regarded as repeating infinitely. Then the vibrational displacements of the whole chain may be specified with the phase difference δ between the corresponding atoms in adjacent units.

Take, as a simple example, a polymer chain of the type $(-M-)_p$ with the threefold axis. In Fig. 3 the Cartesian symmetry displacements (vibrational modes) for the phase difference of $\delta = 120°$ are schematically shown. Only the atomic displacements of the plus first, zeroth, and minus first atoms are indicated. The displacements for S_1 (radial) and S_2 (tangential) are perpendicular to the axis, whereas the displacements for S_3 are parallel to the axis. The atomic displacements for S_{1a}, S_{2b}, and S_{3b} are proportional to $\cos n\delta$, while the displacements for S_{1b}, S_{2a}, and S_{3a} are proportional to $\sin n\delta$ (n: the indices of chain atoms). Thus the displacements of all the chain atoms may be specified with the phase difference δ and the atom indices n. Here it suffices to take the values of δ in the range of $0 \leq \delta \leq 180°$.

For any given phase difference ($\delta \neq 0, \pi$), there are six vibrational modes, as shown in Fig. 3. However, the vibrational modes S_b may be derived from S_a simply by a shift in the phase angle of 90°; accordingly, S_a and S_b form three pairs of vibrational modes. The vibrational kinetic and potential energies for the whole chain are identical in terms of S_a and in terms of S_b. Accordingly, for a polymer chain of the type $(-M-)_p$, there are three pairs of degenerate vibrations. Generally, for

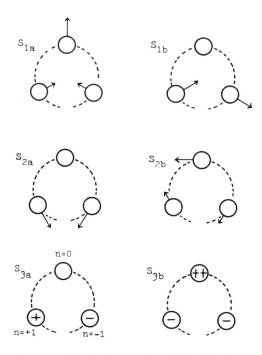

Fig. 3. Vibrational modes of a helical chain ($\delta = 120°$). The plus and minus signs for S_3 denote upward and downward displacements, respectively.

a polymer chain consisting of repeating units with m atoms, there are $3m$ pairs of degenerate vibrations.

B. Selection Rule

For a helical chain, the translational and rotational modes of the whole chain may also be specified with phase differences. As shown in Fig. 4, the rotational mode about the axis R_z and the translational mode along the axis T_z are expressed with the modes $S_2(0)$ and $S_3(0)$, respectively, with the phase difference of $\delta = 0$. In Fig. 3 are also shown the pair of translational modes T_x and T_y perpendicular to the helix axis. The modes $S_1(2\pi/3)$ and $S_2(2\pi/3)$, as given in Fig. 4, are obtained by the transformations of the modes s_1 and s_2 (shown in Fig. 3) such that:

$$S_1 = 2^{-1/2}(s_1 - s_2) \tag{3}$$

$$S_2 = 2^{-1/2}(s_1 + s_2) \tag{4}$$

In general, for any helical chain, the translational modes perpendicular to the helix axis are expressed with $S_1(\theta)$.

In the infrared absorption, the molecular vibrations are active only if they belong to the same symmetry types as the translational modes.

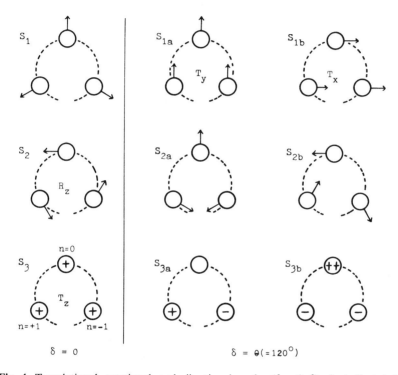

Fig. 4. Translational, rotational, and vibrational modes ($\delta = 0$, θ) of a helical chain. The plus and minus signs denote upward and downward displacements.

Since the phase difference is $\delta = 0$ for the translational mode T_z, the chain vibrations with $\delta = 0$ (the A species) are active. The transition moments of the A vibrations are parallel to the axis, giving rise to parallel infrared bands (the absorption intensity is maximum when the electric vector of the incident infrared beam is parallel to the direction of orientation of the chain axis). On the other hand, the $E(\theta)$ vibrations with $\delta = \theta$ are also active in the infrared absorption and they give rise to perpendicular bands.

C. Treatment of Helical Chain Vibrations

A general method for treating the chain vibrations of helical polymers was studied first by Higgs (*29*). The *GF* matrix method (*30*) was then developed by Miyazawa et al. (*16,31*) and all the numerical calculations may now be carried out with electronic computers. The internal symmetry coordinates for the phase difference δ are constructed from the bond-stretching, angle-bending, and internal-rotation coordinates. The inverse kinetic energy matrix $G(\delta)$ and the potential energy matrix $F(\delta)$ are then expressed in terms of symmetry coordinates. The vibrational frequencies are calculated from the characteristic values of the $G(\delta)F(\delta)$ matrix and the vibrational modes are obtained from the characteristic vectors. For elucidating the nature of observed infrared bands, the distributions of the vibrational potential energy among the symmetry coordinates may also be calculated from the $F(\delta)$ matrix and the characteristic vector of the molecular vibration concerned.

IV. INFRARED SPECTRA AND VIBRATIONAL ASSIGNMENTS OF ISOTACTIC POLYPROPYLENE

A. Treatment of Isotactic Chain Vibrations

For the isotactic polypropylene chain, the repeating unit —CH_2—CH-(CH_3)— contains nine atoms and accordingly there are 25 *A* vibrations and 26 pairs of $E(2\pi/3)$ vibrations. In treating the chain vibrations, 27 internal symmetry coordinates may be constructed; they are denoted as shown below (see also Figs. 5, 6, and 7).

CH_3	ν_s	symmetric stretching
	ν_a'	asymmetric stretching in the H—C—CH_3 plane
	ν_a''	asymmetric stretching out of the H—C—CH_3 plane
	δ_s	symmetric deformation
	δ_a^{ax}	asymmetric deformation (axial)
	δ_a^{eq}	asymmetric deformation (equatorial)
	rock^{ax}	rocking (axial)
	rock^{eq}	rocking (equatorial)
CH_2	ν_s	symmetric stretching
	ν_a	antisymmetric stretching
	bend	bending
	wag	wagging
	twist	twisting
	rock	rocking

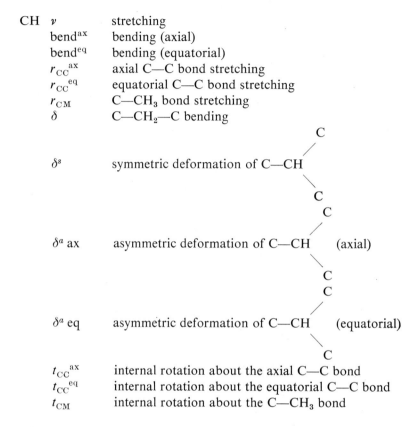

CH ν — stretching
bend^{ax} — bending (axial)
bend^{eq} — bending (equatorial)
$r_{CC}{}^{ax}$ — axial C—C bond stretching
$r_{CC}{}^{eq}$ — equatorial C—C bond stretching
r_{CM} — C—CH$_3$ bond stretching
δ — C—CH$_2$—C bending

δ^s — symmetric deformation of C—CH (with C / \ C C structure)

δ^a ax — asymmetric deformation of C—CH   (axial)

δ^a eq — asymmetric deformation of C—CH   (equatorial)

$t_{CC}{}^{ax}$ — internal rotation about the axial C—C bond
$t_{CC}{}^{eq}$ — internal rotation about the equatorial C—C bond
t_{CM} — internal rotation about the C—CH$_3$ bond

For the isotactic polypropylene chain, there are two types of main-chain C—C bonds. The *trans* C—C bonds are parallel to the helix axis, while the *gauche* C—C bonds are nearly perpendicular to the axis; these will be denoted as the axial and equatorial bonds, respectively.

The inverse kinetic energy matrices G for the A ($\delta = 0$) and E ($\delta = 2\pi/3$) vibrations may be expressed in terms of the 27 symmetry coordinates. In deriving the potential energy matrices F, the modified Urey–Bradley force field (*10*) has been used by Miyazawa et al. The principal terms in this force field are:

$\frac{1}{2}K(\Delta r)^2$ — bond stretching terms
$\frac{1}{2}H(\Delta \phi)^2$ — angle bending terms
$\frac{1}{2}F(\Delta q)^2$ — repulsion terms for nonbonded atom pairs
$\frac{1}{2}Y(\Delta t)^2$ — internal rotation terms.

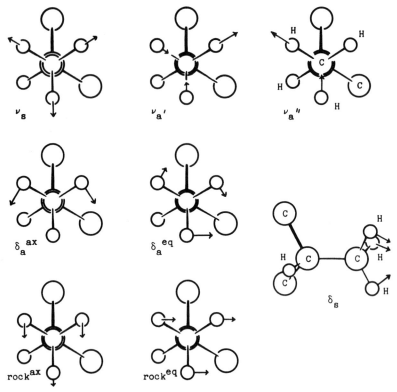

Fig. 5. Vibrational modes of the CH_3 group. Axial C—C bonds are drawn with heavy lines.

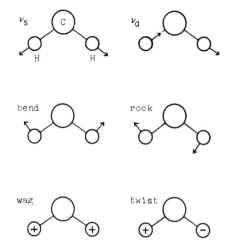

Fig. 6. Vibrational modes of the CH_2 group.

156

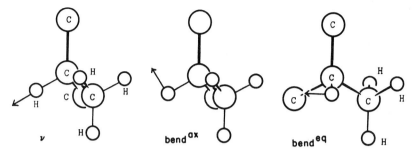

Fig. 7. Vibrational modes of the CH group. Axial C—C bonds are drawn with heavy lines.

A total of 25 potential constants (K, H, F, Y, and others) has been adjusted by the method of least squares ($17,19,20$) with reference to a total of about 150 infrared frequencies of

$$[-CH_2-CH(CH_3)-]_p, \qquad [-CH_2-CD(CH_3)-]_p,$$
$$[-CD_2-CH(CH_3)-]_p, \quad \text{and} \quad [-CH_2-CH(CD_3)-]_p$$

(2) and far infrared frequencies of $[-CH_2-CH(CH_3)-]_p$ ($16,18$). By the use of the potential constants, the frequencies calculated for these four isotopic species agreed closely with the observed frequencies; the root-mean-squared deviations for the vibrations above 650 cm^{-1} are 0.9, 0.9, 0.8, and 1.0%, respectively. Therefore the potential energy distributions have also been calculated for elucidating the nature of the infrared bands. The calculated results (19) are shown in Table 1, together with the observed frequencies (and dichroism).

B. C—H and C—D Stretching Modes

The infrared spectra of isotactic polypropylene and deuterated derivatives in the region 3000–2000 cm^{-1} have been discussed by Peraldo and Farina (2), Krimm (3), Liang et al. (5), and McDonald and Ward (8). These spectra have been restudied by Miyazawa ($19,20$) with reference to the calculated frequencies. The frequencies observed by Peraldo (2) will be cited here.

The infrared band at 2868 cm^{-1} is assigned to the $\nu_s(CH_3)$ mode. The parallel band at 2959 cm^{-1} and the perpendicular band at 2950 cm^{-1} are assigned to the $\nu_a(CH_3)$ modes. The bands due to the CD$_3$ group appear at 2215 cm^{-1} ($\parallel$) and 2204 cm^{-1} ($\perp$) (asymmetric stretching) and at 2066 cm^{-1} ($\parallel$) and 2067 cm^{-1} ($\perp$) (symmetric stretching).

TABLE 1

Infrared Frequencies (cm^{-1}) and Potential Energy Distributions (%) of Isotactic Polypropylene

Frequencies		Potential energy distributions[b]
Observed[a]	Calculated[b]	
1365 (∥)	ν_{11}^A 1367	CH$_2$ wag 40, CH bend^{ax} 30
1360 (⊥)	ν_{11}^E 1365	CH bend^{eq} 30, CH$_2$ twist 20
1330 (⊥)	ν_{12}^E 1344	CH$_2$ wag 35, CH bend^{ax} 35
1326 (∥)	ν_{12}^A 1332	CH bend^{eq} 60
1304 (∥)	ν_{13}^A 1304	CH$_2$ wag 50, CH$_2$ twist 25
1296 (⊥)	ν_{13}^E 1301	CH$_2$ wag 50, CH bend^{ax} 20, bend^{eq} 20
1254 (∥)	ν_{14}^A 1264	CH$_2$ twist 35, CH bend^{ax} 20
1220 (⊥)	ν_{14}^E 1195	CH$_2$ twist 25, r_{CC}^{eq} 20
1168 (∥)	ν_{15}^A 1165	r_{CC}^{ax} 40, CH$_3$ rock^{ax} 25
1155 (⊥)	ν_{15}^E 1166	r_{CM} 20
1103 (⊥)	ν_{16}^E 1112	CH$_3$ rock^{ax} 20, r_{CC}^{ax} 25
1045 (∥)	ν_{16}^A 1051	r_{CM} 35, r_{CC}^{eq} 30
1034 (⊥)	ν_{17}^E 1021	r_{CM} 30
998 (∥)	ν_{17}^A 996	CH$_3$ rock^{eq} 35, r_{CM} 35, CH bend 15
973 (∥)	ν_{18}^A 950	CH$_3$ rock^{ax} 50, r_{CC}^{ax} 20, r_{CC}^{eq} 20
941 (⊥)	ν_{18}^E 930	CH$_3$ rock^{ax} 35, r_{CC}^{ax} 35
899 (⊥)	ν_{19}^E 892	CH$_3$ rock^{eq} 35, CH$_2$ rock 20
	ν_{19}^A 862	CH$_3$ rock^{eq} 25, r_{CC}^{eq} 30
842 (∥)	ν_{20}^A 833	CH$_2$ rock 75
809 (⊥)	ν_{20}^E 818	CH$_2$ rock 35, r_{CM} 25, r_{CC}^{eq} 20

[a] By Peraldo and Farina (2)
[b] By Miyazawa and Ideguchi (19)

The nondichroic band at 2838 cm^{-1} is assigned to the ν_s(CH$_2$) mode and the perpendicular band at 2879 cm^{-1} is assigned to the ν_a(CH$_2$) mode. The bands due to the CD$_2$ stretching modes are observed at 2085 cm^{-1} (∥) and 2092 cm^{-1} (⊥) (symmetric) and at 2169 cm^{-1} (∥) and 2171 cm^{-1} (⊥) (antisymmetric).

The strong perpendicular band at 2921 cm^{-1} is assigned to the C—H stretching mode. The bands due to the C—D stretching mode are observed at 2162 cm^{-1} (⊥) and 2154 cm^{-1} (∥).

The C—H stretching modes of the CH$_3$, CH$_2$, and CH groups are highly localized in each group and accordingly the C—H stretching frequencies are little affected by stereoregularities or by chain conformations. In fact, for syndiotactic polypropylene (32) the C—H stretching bands have been observed at 2868 cm^{-1} [ν_s(CH$_3$)], 2950 and 2960 cm^{-1} [ν_a(CH$_3$)], 2840 cm^{-1} [ν_s(CH$_2$)], 2882 cm^{-1} [ν_a(CH$_2$)], and 2920 cm^{-1} [ν(CH)].

C. CH$_3$ Deformation Modes and CH$_2$ Bending Mode

The bands due to the asymmetric deformation modes of the methyl group are observed at 1460 cm^{-1} ($\perp$) and 1454 cm^{-1} ($\parallel$). The strong perpendicular band at 1377 cm^{-1} and the parallel band at 1378 cm^{-1} are assigned to the symmetric deformation modes of the methyl group (*A* and *E* species, respectively).

The infrared band of polypropylene at 1435 cm^{-1} is assigned to the CH$_2$ bending vibration. For [—CH$_2$—CH(CD$_3$)—]$_p$, the corresponding band is split into the parallel component at 1440 cm^{-1} and the perpendicular component at 1438 cm^{-1}.

D. CH$_2$ Wagging and Twisting Modes and CH Bending Modes

In the region 1370–1200 cm^{-1}, the CH$_2$ wagging and twisting frequencies and the CH bending frequencies are expected. For [—CH$_2$—CD(CH$_3$)—]$_p$, the bands primarily due to the CH$_2$ wagging modes are observed (*2*) at 1342 cm^{-1} ($\parallel$) and 1334 cm^{-1} ($\perp$) and the bands primarily due to the CH$_2$ twisting modes are observed at 1291 cm^{-1} ($\parallel$) and 1273 cm^{-1} ($\perp$). On the other hand, for [—CD$_2$—CH(CH$_3$)—]$_p$, the bands primarily due to the CH bending modes (axial and equatorial) are observed (*2*) at 1327 cm^{-1} ($\parallel$), 1325 cm^{-1} ($\perp$), 1313 cm^{-1} ($\parallel$), and 1303 cm^{-1} ($\perp$). Thus the intrinsic frequencies of all these modes lie in the region of 1300 cm^{-1}. For [—CH$_2$—CH(CH$_3$)—]$_p$, there are the CH$_2$ and CH groups in each repeating unit and, accordingly, the vibrational modes of these groups are strongly coupled. The bands of polypropylene (Fig. 8) in the region 1370–1200 cm^{-1} arise from the hybridized modes of the CH$_2$ wagging and twisting modes and the CH bending modes. The potential energy distributions are shown in Table 1.

E. CH$_3$ and CH$_2$ Rocking Modes and C—C Stretching Modes

In the region 1200–700 cm^{-1}, the infrared bands of polypropylene are due to the hybridized vibrations of the methyl rocking modes (axial and equatorial), main chain C—C stretching modes (axial and equatorial), C-methyl stretching mode, and the CH$_2$ rocking mode. The nature of these bands may be discussed with reference to the potential energy distributions (Table 1).

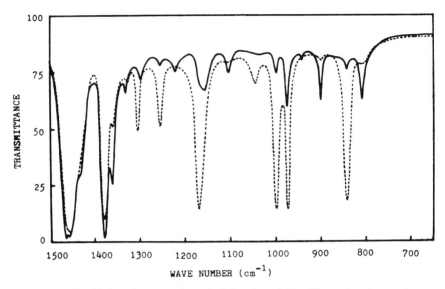

Fig. 8. Polarized infrared spectra of a uniaxially oriented film of isotactic polypropylene; the solid curve was measured with the electric vector perpendicular and the broken curve with the electric vector parallel to the direction of orientation. Data of Peraldo and Farina. [Redrawn from Fig. 2 of Ref. (2).]

In the infrared spectra of polypropylene, four prominent parallel bands are observed at 1168, 998, 973, and 842 cm^{-1} (Fig. 5). The band at 998 cm^{-1} is due to the coupled vibration of the equatorial rocking mode of the methyl group and the C-methyl stretching mode. On the other hand, the bands at 973 and 1168 cm^{-1} are due to the ν_a and ν_b vibrations

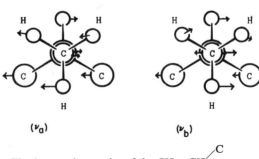

Fig. 9. ν_a and ν_b modes of the $CH_3{-}CH{\Big\langle}{}^C_C$ group.

(33) i.e., the coupled vibrations of the methyl rocking modes and the stretching of the main chain C—C bonds (see Fig. 9). In these vibrations, the methyl rocking modes are antisymmetric with respect to the H—C-methyl plane. The axial and equatorial C—C bonds of the main chain stretch or contract alternately throughout the chain. These ν_a and ν_b vibrations will also be discussed later, together with the corresponding bands of syndiotactic polypropylene.

F. CD Bending Modes

The CD bending modes of $[-CH_2-CD(CH_3)-]_p$ are strongly coupled with the CH_3 and CH_2 rocking modes and the C—C and C-methyl stretching modes and give rise to bands in the region 1250–700 cm^{-1}. No single band is exclusively due to the CD bending modes, and the effects of the deuterium substitution of the CH group of polypropylene $[-CH_2-CH(CH_3)-]_p$ are quite complicated. The nature of the infrared bands have been elucidated by the treatment of the chain vibrations *(13,14,17,19,20)*.

G. CD$_2$ Deformation Modes

The infrared bands due to the CD$_2$ bending vibrations of

$$[-CD_2-CH(CH_3)-]_p$$

are observed at 1058 ($\parallel$) and 1051 cm^{-1} ($\perp$). The bands due to the CD$_2$ rocking modes are observed at 691 ($\parallel$) and 715 cm^{-1} ($\perp$) *(2)*.

The CD$_2$ wagging and twisting modes are strongly coupled with the CH$_3$ rocking modes and the C—C and C-methyl stretching modes and give rise to infrared bands in the region 1200–800 cm^{-1}. Because of these couplings, the nature of the infrared bands of $[-CD_2-CH(CH_3)-]_p$ in the region below 1200 cm^{-1} have been elucidated only after the treatment of the molecular chain vibrations *(13,14,17,19,20)*.

H. CD$_3$ Deformation and Rocking Modes

For $[-CH_2-CH(CD_3)-]_p$, the strong parallel band at 1051 cm^{-1} and the strong perpendicular band at 1054 cm^{-1} *(2)* are assigned to the asymmetric deformation modes of the CD$_3$ group. The CD$_3$ symmetric deformation mode is strongly coupled with the C—C or C-methyl stretching modes and gives rise to the parallel bands at 1115 and 989 cm^{-1} and the perpendicular band at 1081 cm^{-1}. The parallel bands at 791 and 703 cm^{-1} and the perpendicular bands at 759 and 743 cm^{-1} are assigned primarily to the rocking modes of the CD$_3$ group *(14,20)*.

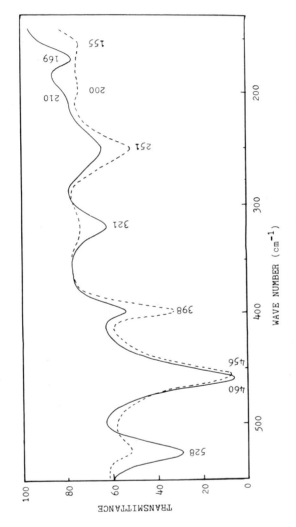

Fig. 10. Polarized far infrared spectra of a uniaxially oriented film of isotactic polypropylene; the solid curve was measured with the electric vector perpendicular and the broken curve with the electric vector parallel to the direction of orientation. Data of Miyazawa et al. [Redrawn from Fig. 1 of Ref. (*16*) and Fig. 2 of Ref. (*18*).]

I. Far Infrared Bands

The far infrared bands of isotactic polypropylene (Fig. 10) are due to the C—C—C bending modes (δ^s, δ^a, and δ) and the internal rotation modes (t_{CC}^{ax}, t_{CC}^{eq}, and t_{CM}) (Table 2).

TABLE 2

Far Infrared Frequencies (cm^{-1}) and Potential Energy
Distributions of Isotactic Polypropylene

Frequencies		Potential energy distributions[b]
Observed[a]	Calculated[b]	
528 ($\perp$)	ν_{21}^{E} 509	δ^a 40, δ 25
460 ($\perp$)	ν_{22}^{E} 445	δ^s 65
456 ($\parallel$)	ν_{21}^{A} 473	δ^a 75
398 ($\parallel$)	ν_{22}^{A} 392	δ^s 35, δ^a 40
321 ($\perp$)	ν_{23}^{E} 314	δ^a 60
251 ($\parallel$)	ν_{23}^{A} 272	δ^s 40, δ^a 20
210 ($\perp$)	ν_{24}^{E} 207	t_{CM} 95
200 ($\parallel$)	ν_{24}^{A} 203	t_{CM} 85
169 ($\perp$)	ν_{25}^{E} 162	δ^a 40, δ 30
155 ($\parallel$)	ν_{25}^{A} 157	δ 40, t_{CC}^{eq} 35
106	ν_{26}^{E} 90	t_{CC}^{ax} 70

[a] By Miyazawa et al. (*16, 18*).
[b] By Miyazawa and Ideguchi (*19*).

The weak parallel band at 200 cm^{-1} and the perpendicular band at 210 cm^{-1} are assigned to the internal rotation of the methyl group (t_{CM}). From the potential constant for the internal rotation, the potential barrier for the methyl group is calculated to be as high as 2.9 kcal/mole (*19*).

The band primarily associated with the internal rotation of the equatorial C—C bond is observed at 155 cm^{-1} ($\parallel$) and the band due to the internal rotation of the axial C—C bond is observed at 106 cm^{-1} (*18*).

V. *CIS*-OPENING POLYMERIZATION OF PROPYLENE

A. Polymerization Scheme of Diisotactic Polymers

For stereoregular polymers (—CH$_2$—CHR—)$_p$, the configurations about the CHR groups have been discussed in Section I. For the stereoregular polymers of the type (—CHR'—CHR—)$_p$, the configurations

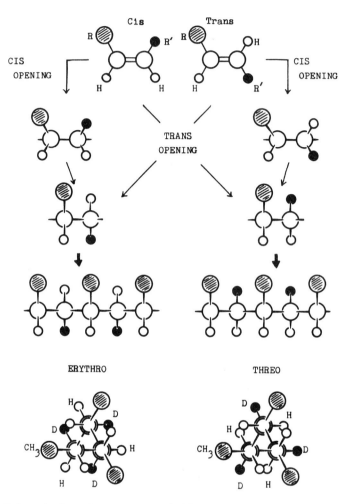

Fig. 11. Polymerization scheme, stereoregularities, and chain conformation of *erythro* and *threo* diisotactic poly(propylene-1-*d*).

about the CHR′ groups are concerned as well as the configurations about the CHR groups. There are two types of diisotactic polymers, namely *erythro* and *threo*, as shown in Fig. 11, where the main chain is tentatively set in the planar zigzag conformation. For these polymers, the R groups lie on the same side of the plane, while the R′ groups themselves lie on the same side of the plane. For the *erythro* polymer, the adjacent R and

R′ groups lie alternately on opposite sides of the plane, whereas for the *threo* polymer the adjacent R and R′ groups lie on the same side of the plane (*1*).

Separate formation of the diisotactic polymers, *erythro* and *threo*, from the *cis* and *trans* monomers indicates that the double bond of the monomer RCH=CHR′ is regularly opened (either *cis* or *trans*) in the stereospecific head-to-tail polymerization. As shown in Fig. 11, for the *cis*-opening polymerization, the *erythro* polymer forms from the *cis* monomer and the *threo* polymer from the *trans* monomer. On the other hand, if the *trans*-opening polymerization occurs, the *erythro* polymer forms from the *trans* monomer and the *threo* polymer from the *cis* monomer. Natta et al. (*34*) have previously analyzed the structure of diisotactic poly(*trans*-propenylisobutyl ether) by the X-ray diffraction method and have found that this polymer is *threo* diisotactic. Accordingly, the polymerization of alkenyl alkyl ethers occurs through the *cis*-opening of the double bond.

B. Molecular Structures of Poly(propylene-1-*d*)

For studying the catalytic reaction mechanism, it is also important to elucidate the opening scheme of propylene in stereospecific polymerization and, for this, the structure analyses of diisotactic poly(propylene-1-*d*) [—CHD—CH(CH$_3$)—]$_p$ are useful (*35*). The chain conformations (as viewed along the helix axis) of the *erythro* and *threo* polymers are shown in Fig. 11. In these two structures, the hydrogen and deuterium atoms of the CHD group are exchanged; this structural difference does not show up in the X-ray diffraction. However, since the molecular vibrations of polymer molecules depend upon the spatial arrangements of atoms, the *threo* and *erythro* polymers are expected to exhibit different infrared spectra. In fact, Natta et al. (*35*) have synthesized poly(propylene-1-*d*-*cis*) [poly-*cis*] and poly(propylene-1-*d*-*trans*) [poly-*trans*] and have found that the infrared spectra of these polymers are distinctly different from each other.

The polarized infrared spectra (4000–650 cm^{-1}) of poly-*cis* and poly-*trans* have been measured by Peraldo and Farina (*2*) and accordingly the observed parallel and perpendicular bands are assigned to the A and $E(\theta)$ vibrations, respectively. Subsequently, the A and E vibrations of the *erythro* and *threo* diisotactic structures (Fig. 11) have been treated by Miyazawa and Ideguchi (*21*) with the intrachain force field as refined by the method of least squares (*19*). The chain vibrations have also been treated by Tadokoro et al. (*26*) with the Urey–Bradley field.

The molecular structures of poly-*cis* and poly-*trans* have been elucidated with reference to the frequencies of the A and $E(\theta)$ vibrations calculated for the *erythro* and *threo* structures. In studying the correspondences between the two structures and the observed spectra, the nine vibrations as listed in Table 3 have been used (*21*). These vibrations are observed distinctly for both poly-*cis* and poly-*trans*, and the calculated frequency difference between the *erythro* and *threo* forms is greater than 15 cm^{-1}.

TABLE 3

Observed and Calculated Infrared Frequencies (cm^{-1}) of Diisotactic Poly(propylene-1-*d*)

Observed frequencies[a]			Calculated frequencies[b]	
Poly-*cis*	Poly-*trans*		*Erythro*	*Threo*
1360(s)	1340(w)	ν_{10}^{E}	1365 ± 4	1348 ± 3
1173(s)	1180(s)	ν_{14}^{A}	1166 ± 7	1182 ± 7
1121(s)	1076(m)	ν_{15}^{A}	1121 ± 9	1087 ± 5
1045(w)	1080(w)	ν_{16}^{E}	1047 ± 4	1073 ± 4
1033(m)	1038(m)	ν_{16}^{A}	1041 ± 10	1022 ± 10
990(w)	950(w)	ν_{17}^{E}	964 ± 7	941 ± 5
873(s)	894(m)	ν_{18}^{A}	887 ± 7	896 ± 4
746(s)	719(m)	ν_{20}^{A}	741 ± 7	722 ± 6
736(m)	749(m)	ν_{20}^{E}	731 ± 6	750 ± 5

[a] By Peraldo and Farina (*2*); intensity: s, strong; m, medium; and w, weak.
[b] By Miyazawa and Ideguchi (*21*).

The root-mean-squared deviations (%) for those nine vibrations are calculated as shown below in the two alternative correspondences.

(A) poly-*cis*:   *erythro*   1.1%⎫ 1.0%
      poly-*trans*:   *threo*   0.8%⎭

and

(B) poly-*trans*:   *erythro*   2.4%⎫ 2.5%
      poly-*cis*:   *threo*   2.7%⎭

For the first case (A), the deviation of 1.0% is as small as the deviation (1.0%) for the calculated frequencies of

$$[-CH_2-CH(CH_3)-]_p, \qquad [-CH_2-CD(CH_3)-]_p,$$
$$[-CD_2-CH(CH_3)-]_p, \qquad \text{and} \qquad [-CH_2-CH(CD_3)-]_p.$$

On the other hand, for the second case (B), the deviation of 2.5% is much greater than the deviation for the first case (A). Therefore it may be concluded that poly-*cis* and poly-*trans* are *erythro* and *threo* diisotactic, respectively (*21*). Accordingly, the polymerization of propylene (*35*) should have occurred by the *cis* opening of the double bond.

The infrared bands of poly-*cis* and poly-*trans* have been assigned on the bases of the frequencies and potential energy distributions calculated for the *erythro* and *threo* structures (*21*). Infrared bands due to the CH'D bending modes of $[—CH'D—CH(CH_3)—]_p$ are observed at 1273 cm^{-1} ($\parallel$) and 1286 cm^{-1} ($\perp$) for poly-*cis* and at 1281 cm^{-1} ($\parallel$), 1253 cm^{-1} ($\parallel$) and 1290 cm^{-1} ($\perp$) for poly-*trans*. The CH' bending modes (out of the CH'D plane) are coupled with the CH bending modes and give rise to the bands in the region 1370–1300 cm^{-1}. The $\nu_{20}{}^A$ and $\nu_{20}{}^E$ vibrations (Table 3) of $[—CH'D—CH(CH_3)—]_p$ are associated with the CH'D rocking modes. The C—C (axial and equatorial) and C-methyl stretching modes and CH$_3$ rocking modes (axial and equatorial) are coupled with the CH'D twisting or CD bending modes (out of the CH'D plane) and give rise to the bands in the region 1200–800 cm^{-1}. These couplings vary with the spatial arrangements of the CH'D group (see Fig. 11) and accordingly the bands as listed in Table 3 are useful for distinguishing the *erythro* and *threo* diisotactic structures.

VI. INFRARED SPECTRA AND VIBRATIONAL ASSIGNMENTS OF SYNDIOTACTIC POLYPROPYLENE

A. Zigzag Conformation

For the zigzag form of the syndiotactic polypropylene chain, the chain vibrations are classified into four species, as shown in Table 4. The symmetry elements include the twofold symmetry axes C_2 (parallel to the *x* axis), the glide plane $\sigma_v{}^g$ (parallel to the *xz* plane), and the symmetry planes σ_v (parallel to the *yz* plane) (Fig. 12). The transition moments

TABLE 4

Symmetry Species and Infrared Selection Rule (and Dichroism) for the Zigzag Form of Syndiotactic Polypropylene

	E	C_2	$\sigma_v{}^g$	σ_v	Infrared
A_1	+1	+1	+1	+1	$\perp$
A_2	+1	+1	−1	−1	Inactive
B_1	+1	−1	−1	+1	$\perp$
B_2	+1	−1	+1	−1	$\parallel$

(oscillating dipole moments) of the B_2 vibrations are parallel to the chain direction (z) and give rise to parallel bands. On the other hand, the transition moments of the A_1 and B_1 vibrations are parallel to the x and y axes, respectively, and they give rise to perpendicular bands. The A_2 vibrations are not active in the infrared absorption.

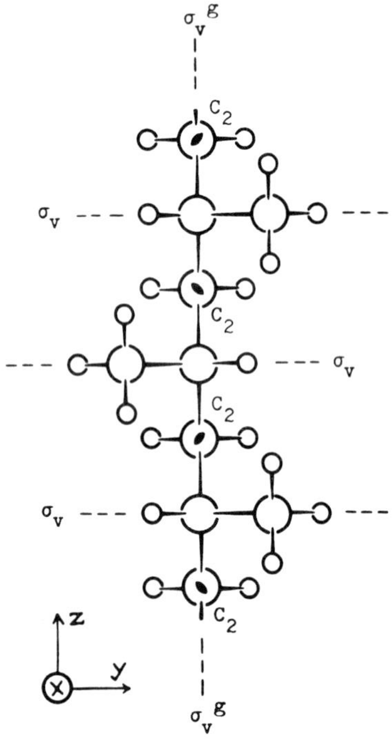

Fig. 12. The zigzag conformation and symmetry elements of syndiotactic polypropylene chain.

The polarized infrared spectra of the zigzag form of syndiotactic polypropylene have been reported by Natta et al. (28) and Peraldo and Cambini (32). The preparation of uniaxially oriented films for infrared measurements has also been described in detail (32).

The frequencies and potential energy distributions for the zigzag form have been calculated by Schachtschneider and Snyder (15) and Miyazawa and Ideguchi (22). The potential function has been transferred from isotactic polypropylene and the atomic displacements (the normal modes) have also been calculated as shown in Fig. 13 (22).

The nature of the infrared bands of the zigzag form may be discussed on the basis of the potential energy distributions (Table 5) and atomic displacements (Fig. 13). The strong parallel band of polypropylene at 1233 cm^{-1} is characteristic to the zigzag form (*32*). This band is due to the

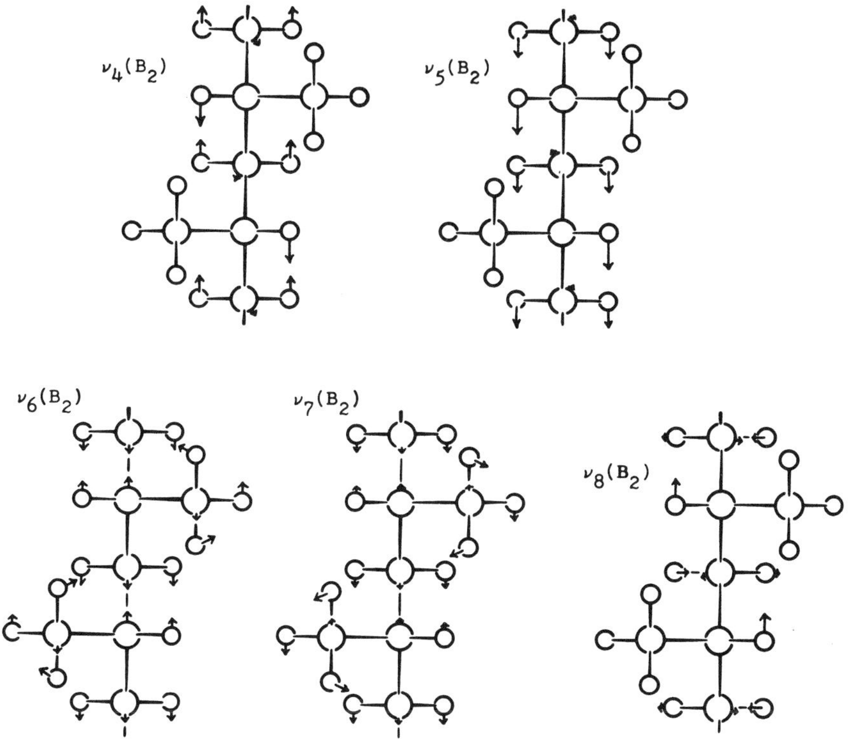

Fig. 13. Atomic displacements of the molecular vibrations of the zigzag form of syndiotactic polypropylene. The carbon and hydrogen atoms are drawn with larger and smaller circles, respectively.

hybridized $\nu_5(B_2)$ vibration of the CH_2 wagging and CH out-of-plane bending mode. As shown in Fig. 13, the hydrogen atoms of the CH_2 and CH groups all displace in phase along the chain axis in the same direction. The corresponding band is also observed at 1228 cm^{-1} for syndiotactic poly(vinyl chloride) in the zigzag form (*36*). On the other hand, for the $\nu_4(B_2)$ vibration of syndiotactic polypropylene calculated at 1360 cm^{-1}, the hydrogen atoms of the CH_2 group displace in the opposite direction to the displacements of the CH group. Although the $\nu_4(B_2)$ vibration has not been identified for polypropylene, the corresponding vibration of poly(vinyl chloride) has been observed as the weak parallel band at 1379 cm^{-1} (36).

The strong parallel bands at 1133 and 963 cm^{-1} are assigned to the ν_6 and $\nu_7(B_2)$ vibrations, respectively. For these vibrations (see Fig. 13),

TABLE 5

Infrared Frequencies (cm^{-1}) and Potential Energy Distributions (%) of the Zigzag Form of Syndiotactic Polypropylene

Frequencies		Potential energy distributions[b]
Observed[a]	Calculated[b]	
	$\nu_4(B_2)$ 1360	CH$_2$ wag 48, CH bend^o 20
	$\nu_7(B_1)$ 1344	CH$_2$ wag 79
1322 ($\perp$)	$\nu_8(B_1)$ 1326	CH bend^i 61, CH$_2$ wag 20
1233 ($\parallel$)	$\nu_5(B_2)$ 1259	CH$_2$ wag 54, CH bend^o 41
	$\nu_9(A_1)$ 1254	CH$_2$ twist 38, CH bend^i 20
1200 ($\perp$)	$\nu_{10}(A_1)$ 1198	r_{CC} 31, r_{CM} 20
1155 ($\perp$)	$\nu_9(B_1)$ 1157	CH$_2$ rock 33, r_{CM} 23, CH$_3$ rock^i 20
1133 ($\parallel$)	$\nu_6(B_2)$ 1139	r_{CC} 37, CH$_3$ rock^o 36
1075 ($\perp$)	$\nu_{10}(B_1)$ 1041	r_{CC} 55, r_{CM} 28
	$\nu_{11}(A_1)$ 959	CH$_3$ rock^i 52, CH bend^i 29, r_{CM} 21
963 ($\parallel$)	$\nu_7(B_2)$ 932	CH$_3$ rock^o 51, r_{CC} 46
899 ($\perp$)	$\nu_{11}(B_1)$ 907	CH$_3$ rock^i 51, r_{CC} 24
867 ($\perp$)	$\nu_{12}(A_1)$ 865	r_{CM} 51, CH$_3$ rock^i 19
830 ($\parallel$)	$\nu_8(B_2)$ 824	CH$_2$ rock 86, CH bend^o 21
828 ($\perp$)	$\nu_{12}(B_1)$ 827	r_{CM} 42, CH$_2$ rock 25, r_{CC} 19
492 ($\perp$)	$\nu_{13}(B_1)$ 469	δ^s 70

[a] By Peraldo and Cambini (32).

[b] By Miyazawa and Ideguchi (22); the superscripts i and o denote symmetric and antisymmetric modes, respectively, with respect to the H—C-methyl plane.

adjacent carbon atoms of the main chain are displaced in the opposite direction from each other and accordingly the main chain C—C bonds stretch or contract alternately throughout the chain. The rocking modes of the methyl groups are antisymmetric with respect to the H—C-methyl plane. Therefore these vibrations are associated with the ν_b and ν_a modes of the zigzag form.

The strong parallel band of syndiotactic polypropylene at 830 cm^{-1} is also observed at 833 cm^{-1} for poly(vinyl chloride). This is the CH$_2$ rocking vibration of the B_2 species as coupled with the CH out-of-plane bending mode (Table 5). The strong intensity may not be expected from the CH_2 rocking mode alone, but it is possibly due, at least in part, to the contribution of the CH bending mode, as shown in Fig. 13.

B. Helical Conformation

For the helical form of the syndiotactic polypropylene chain, the chain vibrations are classified into the four species shown in Table 6. The symmetry elements include the twofold screw axis $C_2^1(z)$ (parallel to the z axis) and two types of twofold axes, $C_2(y)$ (parallel to the y axis) and $C_2(x)$ (parallel to the x axis) (Fig. 14). The transition moments of the B_1,

TABLE 6

Symmetry Species and Infrared Selection Rule (and Dichroism)
for the Helical Form of Syndiotactic Polypropylene

	E	$C_2^1(z)$	$C_2(y)$	$C_2(x)$	Infrared
A	$+1$	$+1$	$+1$	$+1$	Inactive
B_1	$+1$	$+1$	-1	-1	$\|(z)$
B_2	$+1$	-1	$+1$	-1	$\perp(y)$
B_3	$+1$	-1	-1	$+1$	$\perp(x)$

B_2, and B_3 vibrations are parallel to the z, y, and x axes, respectively. The A vibrations are not active in the infrared absorption.

The polarized infrared spectra of doubly oriented films of syndiotactic polypropylene in the helical conformation have been published by Peraldo and Cambini (32), and the infrared bands for the helical form have been conclusively assigned to the B_1, B_2, and B_3 vibrations. The frequencies and potential energy distributions calculated by Miyazawa (23) for the helical form are shown in Table 6. The calculated frequencies agree closely with the observed frequencies; the root-mean-squared deviation is as small as 1.1% for the vibrations in the region 1500–650 cm^{-1}. The atomic displacements are shown in Fig. 15.

For the syndiotactic polypropylene chain in the helical form, there are two types of methylene groups, as shown in Fig. 14. The methylene group denoted as CH_2^T forms two *trans*-CH_2—CH bonds and the methylene group denoted as CH_2^G forms two *gauche*-CH_2—CH bonds, respectively, with adjacent CH groups. It may be remarked that the twofold axes, $C_2(y)$ and $C_2(x)$, pass through the CH_2^T and CH_2^G groups, respectively.

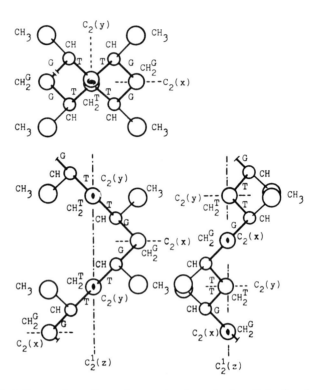

Fig. 14. The helical conformation and symmetry elements of syndiotactic polypropylene chain. [Reproduced from Fig. 2 of Ref. (*23*) with permission of the American Institute of Physics.]

The infrared bands observed in the region 1360–1200 cm^{-1} (see Table 7) are due to the coupled B_1 vibrations of the $CH_2{}^T$ and $CH_2{}^G$ wagging modes and the CH bending modes, the coupled B_2 vibrations of the $CH_2{}^T$ twisting, $CH_2{}^G$ wagging, and CH bending modes, and the coupled B_3 vibrations of the $CH_2{}^T$ wagging, $CH_2{}^G$ twisting, and CH bending modes. These vibrational couplings of the CH_2 and CH groups depend upon the internal rotation about the CH_2—CH bonds (and therefore upon the chain conformations) and the stereoregularities. The spectra in this region vary for the zigzag and helical forms of syndiotactic polypropylene and for the helical form of isotactic polypropylene.

The parallel band, $v_{13}(B_1)$, at 1264 cm^{-1} is associated with the CH out-of-plane bending mode and the $CH_2{}^T$ wagging mode; the hydrogen atoms of the —CH—CH$_2{}^T$—CH— group all move in the same direction.

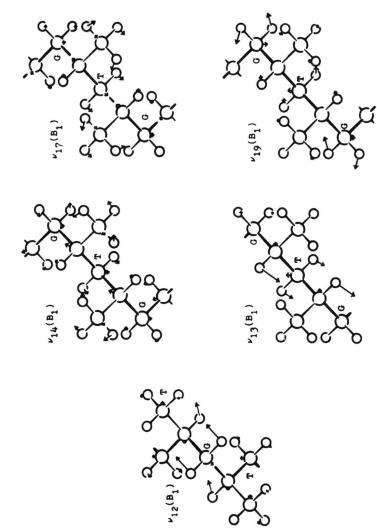

Fig. 15. Atomic displacements of the molecular vibrations of the helical form of syndiotactic polypropylene. The carbon and hydrogen atoms are drawn with larger and smaller circles, respectively, and the main-chain C—C bonds are drawn with heavy lines. Data of Miyazawa. [Redrawn from Figs. 3, 4, and 6 of Ref. (23).]

TABLE 7

Infrared Frequencies (cm^{-1}) and Potential Energy Distributions (%) of the Helical Form of Syndiotactic Polypropylene

Frequencies		Potential energy distributions[b]
Observed[a]	Calculated[b]	
	$\nu_{11}(B_2)$ 1366	CH bend 24, $CH_2{}^G$ wag 22, $CH_3 \delta_s$ 29
1360 (s, x)	$\nu_{11}(B_3)$ 1363	CH bend 34, $CH_2{}^T$ wag 24
1346 (s, z)	$\{\nu_{10}(B_1)$ 1355	$CH_2{}^T$ wag 37, $CH_2{}^G$ wag 29, CH bend 22
	$\{\nu_{11}(B_1)$ 1349	CH bend 35, $CH_2{}^T$ wag 29, $CH_2{}^G$ wag 21
	$\nu_{12}(B_3)$ 1345	CH bend 44, $CH_2{}^T$ wag 37
1332 (m, y)	$\nu_{12}(B_2)$ 1329	CH bend 36, $CH_2{}^G$ wag 35
1312 (m, x)	$\nu_{13}(B_3)$ 1287	$CH_2{}^T$ wag 36, CH bend 33
1294 (m, z)	$\nu_{12}(B_1)$ 1300	$CH_2{}^G$ wag 40, CH bend 31
1289 (w, y)	$\nu_{13}(B_2)$ 1289	CH bend 42, $CH_2{}^G$ wag 30
1264 (m, z)	$\nu_{13}(B_1)$ 1263	CH bend 50, $CH_2{}^T$ wag 23
1201 (w, x)	$\nu_{14}(B_3)$ 1195	$CH_2{}^G$ twist 26, CH bend 22
	$\nu_{14}(B_2)$ 1190	$CH_2{}^T$ twist 41, CH bend 33
1168 (s, z)	$\nu_{14}(B_1)$ 1147	CH_3 rock 30, $r_{CC}{}^T$ 26, $r_{CC}{}^G$ 17
1160 (w, x)	$\nu_{15}(B_3)$ 1148	$CH_2{}^G$ twist 37, CH bend 20
1152 (s, y)	$\nu_{15}(B_2)$ 1147	$r_{CC}{}^T$ 29
	$\nu_{16}(B_3)$ 1115	CH_3 rock 30, r_{CM} 22
$\begin{matrix}1088\\1082\end{matrix}$ (m, y)[c]	$\nu_{16}(B_2)$ 1113	CH_3 rock 30, $r_{CC}{}^G$ 29
1059 (w, z)	$\{\nu_{15}(B_1)$ 1062	$r_{CC}{}^G$ 26
	$\{\nu_{16}(B_1)$ 1057	r_{CM} 43
1032 (w, x)	$\nu_{17}(B_3)$ 1033	r_{CM} 28, $r_{CC}{}^T$ 22, CH_3 rock 20
1006 (m, y)	$\nu_{17}(B_2)$ 979	CH_3 rock 37, r_{CM} 36, CH bend 21
977 (s, z)	$\nu_{17}(B_1)$ 948	CH_3 rock 51, $r_{CC}{}^T$ 23, $r_{CC}{}^G$ 23
	$\nu_{18}(B_2)$ 939	CH_3 rock 43, $r_{CC}{}^G$ 36
935 (w, x)	$\nu_{18}(B_3)$ 929	CH_3 rock 53, $r_{CC}{}^T$ 20, $r_{CC}{}^G$ 20
905 (m, y)	$\nu_{19}(B_2)$ 901	$CH_2{}^G$ rock 37, CH_3 rock 28, r_{CM} 21
900 (w, z)	$\nu_{18}(B_1)$ 904	$CH_2{}^G$ rock 40, CH_3 rock 37
	$\nu_{19}(B_3)$ 883	CH_3 rock 41
867 (s, z)	$\nu_{19}(B_1)$ 873	$CH_2{}^G$ rock 31, $CH_2{}^T$ rock 25
	$\nu_{20}(B_1)$ 820	r_{CM} 31, $CH_2{}^T$ rock 29
812 (s, x)	$\nu_{20}(B_3)$ 826	$CH_2{}^T$ rock 46
	$\nu_{20}(B_2)$ 824	$CH_2{}^G$ rock 36, $r_{CC}{}^T$ 25
535 (w, y)	$\nu_{21}(B_2)$ 545	δ^a 50, C—$CH_2{}^T$—C bend 20
484 (w, x)	$\nu_{21}(B_3)$ 484	δ^a 45, δ^s 20
469 (w, z)	$\nu_{21}(B_1)$ 469	δ^s 68

[a] By Peraldo and Cambini (32); the relative intensities (s, strong; m, medium; and w, weak) and the direction of the transition moments are given in parentheses.

[b] By Miyazawa (23).

[c] Possibly the Fermi resonance doublet (32).

Also, the parallel band, $\nu_{12}(B_1)$, at 1294 cm^{-1} is associated with the CH bending mode and the CH$_2{}^G$ wagging mode; the hydrogen atoms of the —CH—CH$_2{}^G$—CH— group all move in the same direction (Fig. 15). These vibrations correspond to the $\nu_5(B_2)$ vibration of the zigzag form at 1233 cm^{-1}.

The parallel band, $\nu_{19}(B_1)$, at 866 cm^{-1} is associated with the CH$_2{}^T$ and CH$_2{}^G$ rocking modes (Table 7 and Fig. 15). This band has been found by Natta et al. (37) to be characteristic of syndiotactic polypropylene. It may be remarked that the perpendicular band of the zigzag form, $\nu_{12}(A_1)$, lies at about the same frequency. The band of syndiotactic polypropylene at 866–867 cm^{-1} is not specific to the helical form.

The strong parallel bands of the helical form at 977 and 1168 cm^{-1} are assigned to the $\nu_{17}(B_1)$ and $\nu_{14}(B_1)$ vibrations (Table 7). From the atomic displacements (Fig. 15), these vibrations are identified as the ν_a and ν_b modes of the helical form. As mentioned before, the corresponding bands are observed at 963 and 1130 cm^{-1} for the zigzag form of syndiotactic polypropylene and at 973 and 1168 cm^{-1} for the helical form of isotactic polypropylene.

VII. LIQUID SPECTRA OF POLYPROPYLENE

Polymer chains with regular chemical structures are usually found in regular chain conformations in the crystalline phase. However, if the polymer material is quenched from the melt, there is some large fraction of the amorphous phase where the chain conformations are somewhat similar to those in the liquid phase. The analyses of the liquid spectra will be useful for studying the chain conformations in the liquid and amorphous phases and also for studying the crystallization process of polymer materials.

The liquid spectra of isotactic polypropylene and deuterated derivatives (2) and syndiotactic polypropylene (32) have been observed by Peraldo et al. The infrared bands of the liquid phase have been analyzed in some detail by Miyazawa et al. (17,19,20,33) with reference to the frequencies, potential energy distributions, and atomic displacements as calculated for the crystalline phase.

A. CH$_3$ Deformation Modes and CH$_2$ Bending Mode

For polypropylene (isotactic and syndiotactic), strong bands due to the CH$_3$ symmetric and asymmetric deformation modes are observed at 1380 and 1460 cm^{-1}, respectively, in the liquid state. The infrared band of

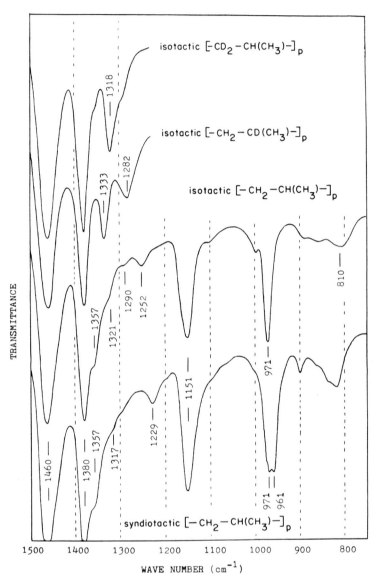

Fig. 16. Liquid spectra of polypropylene and deuterated derivatives. Data of Peraldo, Farina, and Cambini. [Redrawn from Fig. 1 of Ref. (*2*) and from Fig. 2 of Ref. (*32*).]

liquid $[—CH_2—CH(CD_3)—]_p$ at 1052 cm^{-1} is assigned to the asymmetric deformation mode of the CD_3 group.

The infrared band associated with the CH_2 bending mode in the liquid state is not observed distinctly for polypropylene, although it is clearly observed at 1446 cm^{-1} for $[—CH_2—CH(CD_3)—]_p$. The band due to the CD_2 bending mode of liquid $[—CD_2—CH(CH_3)—]_p$ is observed at 1057 cm^{-1}.

The infrared bands due to the CH_3 deformation and CH_2 bending mode are little affected on melting. In these vibrations, the vibrational displacements are highly localized in the CH_3 or CH_2 groups. Accordingly, the frequencies of these bands are not much affected by the transconformation of the main chain in the liquid state. The strong liquid bands are probably due to localized modes.

B. CH_2 Wagging, Twisting, and Rocking Modes and CH Bending Modes

As discussed in Section IVD, the CH_2 wagging mode of

$$[—CH_2—CD(CH_3)—]_p$$

is not coupled much with other vibrational modes. In fact, a strong band assignable to the CH_2 wagging mode is observed at 1333 cm^{-1} (2) for the liquid phase (Fig. 16). This frequency is not much different from the frequencies (1342 and 1334 cm^{-1}) for the crystalline phase. Similarly, the liquid band assignable to the CH_2 twisting mode is observed at 1282 cm^{-1}, corresponding to the bands (1291 and 1273 cm^{-1}) for the crystalline phase.

The CH bending modes of $[—CD_2—CH(CH_3)—]_p$ are not coupled much with other vibrational modes, as discussed in Section IVD. The strong liquid band at 1318 cm^{-1} (Fig. 16) may be assigned to the CH bending mode in the liquid state, corresponding to the bands (1327, 1325, 1313, and 1303 cm^{-1}) for the crystalline phase.

For isotactic polypropylene, $[—CH_2—CH(CH_3)—]_p$, in the liquid state, four bands are observed (2) at 1357, 1321, 1290, and 1252 cm^{-1}. These peaks are possibly associated with the CH_2 wagging and twisting modes and the CH bending modes. However, the two well-defined bands, 1357 and 1252 cm^{-1}, are distinctly shifted from the intrinsic liquid frequencies of the CH_2 wagging (1333 cm^{-1}), CH_2 twisting (1282 cm^{-1}), and CH bending modes (1318 cm^{-1}). The absorption curve of $[—CH_2—CH(CH_3)—]_p$ in this region is much different from the superposition of the bands due to the CH_2 wagging and twisting modes of

$[-CH_2-CD(CH_3)-]_p$ and the band due to the CH bending modes of $[-CD_2-CH(CH_3)-]_p$ (Fig. 16).

For syndiotactic polypropylene in the liquid state, four bands are observed (*32*) at 1357, 1317, 1295, and 1229 cm^{-1} (Fig. 16). Apparently, the band at 1229 cm^{-1} corresponds to the $\nu_5(B_2)$ band (1233 cm^{-1}) of the zigzag form in the solid phase and accordingly is assigned to the similar vibration of the zigzag segments in the liquid phase. The liquid bands of the syndiotactic polymer at 1357, 1317, and 1295 cm^{-1} correspond with the bands of the isotactic polymer at 1357, 1321, and 1290 cm^{-1}. Detailed analyses of these bands will be useful for studying the chain conformations in the liquid state.

The liquid bands of polypropylene at 1252 and 1229 cm^{-1} are considered by Peraldo and Cambini (*32*) to be correlated with the isotactic and syndiotactic segments, respectively. For atactic polypropylene with a random distribution of steric elements, these two bands are observed with similar intensities.

In the region 900–800 cm^{-1}, similar absorption curves are observed (*2,32*) for isotactic and syndiotactic polypropylene in the liquid state, although the relative peak intensities are slightly different. The peak at about 810 cm^{-1} is possibly assigned to the CH$_2$ rocking mode in the liquid state. For liquid isotactic $[-CD_2-CH(CH_3)-]_p$, the band due to the CD$_2$ rocking mode is observed at 706 cm^{-1}.

C. ν_a and ν_b Modes

For isotactic polypropylene in the liquid phase, two strong bands are observed at 971 and 1151 cm^{-1}. These two bands have previously been ascribed to a helical conformation of appreciable length (*6,38*).

The liquid bands at 971 and 1151 cm^{-1} apparently correspond to the ν_a (973 cm^{-1}) and ν_b bands (1168 cm^{-1}) of the solid phase. These vibrations have also been identified in the liquid and solid spectra of syndiotactic polypropylene. The ν_a bands of the crystalline phases (zigzag: 963 cm^{-1}; helical: 977 cm^{-1}) appear to persist on melting, possibly due to the zigzag segments (961 cm^{-1}), CH—CH$_2{}^T$—CH(CH$_3$)—CH$_2{}^T$—CH, and the non-zigzag segments (971 cm^{-1}), CH—CH$_2{}^T$—CH(CH$_3$)—CH$_2{}^G$—CH, in the liquid phase. On the other hand, the ν_b bands of the crystalline phases (zigzag: 1133 cm^{-1}; helical: 1168 cm^{-1}) are replaced with a single band at 1155 cm^{-1} for the liquid phase at the same frequency as the corresponding ν_b band of liquid isotactic polypropylene. Accordingly, as discussed previously (*33*), the ν_a and ν_b vibrations of polypropylene are characteristic of the alternate sequence of the CH$_2$ and CH(CH$_3$) groups but are not specific to particular conformations or stereoregularities. The corresponding ν_a and ν_b bands have also been identified for deuterated derivatives in the liquid phase; at 977 and 1198 cm^{-1} for $[-CH_2-CD(CH_3)-]_p$, at 981 and 1160 cm^{-1} (*erythro*), and at 992 and 1151 cm^{-1} (*threo*) for diisotactic $[-CHD-CH(CH_3)-]_p$.

The ν_a bands of a variety of polypropylenes (head to tail) have been studied by Peraldo and Cambini (*32*). The band observed at 968 cm^{-1} has been ascribed to heterotactic segments of the polypropylene chain.

It is remarkable to note that the intensity of the band of isotactic polypropylene at 998 cm^{-1} decreases markedly on melting. Apparently, this vibration is greatly disturbed by the disorder in the chain conformation and is considered to arise from isotactic helical segments of appreciable length (*33*). The relative intensity of the bands at 998 and 973 cm^{-1} has been used as a measure of crystallinity or tacticity (*39,40*). For syndiotactic polypropylene in the helical form, the corresponding vibration (with similar potential energy distribution; see Tables 1 and 7) is identified at 1006 cm^{-1} and the band intensity decreases markedly on melting. Possibly this band also arises from syndiotactic helical segments of appreciable length.

REFERENCES

1. G. Natta, *Makromol. Chem.*, **35**, 94 (1960).

2. M. Peraldo and M. Farina, *Chim. Ind.* (*Milan*), **42**, 1349 (1960).

3. S. Krimm, *Fortschr. Hochpolymer. Forsch.*, **2**, 51 (1960).

4. C. Y. Liang and F. G. Pearson, *J. Mol. Spectr.*, **5**, 290 (1960).

5. C. Y. Liang, M. R. Lytton, and C. J. Boone, *J. Polymer Sci.*, **47**, 139 (1960).

6. C. Y. Liang, M. R. Lytton, and C. J. Boone, *J. Polymer Sci.*, **54**, 523 (1961).

7. H. Tadokoro, T. Kitazawa, S. Nozakura, and S. Murahashi, *Bull. Chem. Soc. Japan*, **34**, 1209 (1961).

8. M. P. McDonald and I. M. Ward, *Polymer*, **2**, 341 (1961).

9. C. Y. Liang and M. R. Lytton, *J. Polymer Sci.*, **61**, S45 (1962).

10. T. Shimanouchi, *Pure Appl. Chem.*, **7**, 131 (1963).

11. J. H. Schachtschneider and R. G. Snyder, *Spectrochim. Acta*, **19**, 117 (1963).

12. R. G. Snyder and J. H. Schachtschneider, *Spectrochim. Acta*, **21**, 169 (1965).

13. R. G. Snyder and J. H. Schachtschneider, *Spectrochim. Acta*, **20**, 853 (1964).

14. J. H. Schachtschneider and R. G. Snyder, *J. Polymer Sci.*, **C7**, 99 (1964).

15. J. H. Schachtschneider and R. G. Snyder, *Spectrochim. Acta*, **21**, 1527 (1965).

16. T. Miyazawa, Y. Ideguchi, and K. Fukushima, *J. Chem. Phys.*, **38**, 2709 (1963).

17. T. Miyazawa and Y. Ideguchi, *Bull. Chem. Soc. Japan*, **36**, 1125 (1963).

18. T. Miyazawa, K. Fukushima, and Y. Ideguchi, *J. Polymer Sci.*, **B1**, 385 (1963).

19. T. Miyazawa and Y. Ideguchi, *Bull. Chem. Soc. Japan*, **37**, 1065 (1964).

20. T. Miyazawa, *J. Polymer Sci.*, **C7**, 59 (1964).

21. T. Miyazawa and Y. Ideguchi, *Makromol. Chem.*, **79**, 89 (1964).

22. T. Miyazawa and Y. Ideguchi, *Reports Progress Polymer Phys. Japan*, **8**, 49 (1965).

23. T. Miyazawa, *J. Chem. Phys.*, **43**, 4030 (1965).

24. T. Shimanouchi, *J. Chem. Phys.*, **17**, 243, 734, 848 (1949).

25. H. Tadokoro, M. Ukita, M. Kobayashi, and S. Murahashi, *J. Polymer Sci.*, **B1**, 405 (1963).

26. H. Tadokoro, M. Kobayashi, M. Ukita, K. Yasufuku, S. Murahashi, and T. Torii, *J. Chem. Phys.*, **42**, 1432 (1965).

27. T. Miyazawa, *J. Polymer Sci.*, **55**, 215 (1961).

28. G. Natta, M. Peraldo, and G. Allegra, *Makromol. Chem.*, **75**, 215 (1964).

29. P. Higgs, *Proc. Roy. Soc. (London)*, **A220**, 472 (1953).

30. E. B. Wilson, Jr., *J. Chem. Phys.*, **7**, 1047 (1939); **9**, 76 (1941).

31. T. Miyazawa, *J. Chem. Phys.*, **35**, 693 (1961).

32. M. Peraldo and M. Cambini, *Spectrochim. Acta*, **21**, 1509 (1965).

33. T. Miyazawa, *J. Polymer Sci.*, **B2**, 847 (1964).

34. G. Natta, M. Farina, M. Peraldo, P. Corradini, E. G. Bresson, and P. Ganis, *Atti Accad. Nazl. Lincei, Rend., Classe Sci. Fis. Mat. Nat.*, **28**(8), 442 (1960).

35. G. Natta, M. Farina and M. Peraldo, *Atti Accad. Nazl. Lincei, Rend., Classe Sci. Fis. Mat. Nat.*, **25**(8), 424 (1958).

36. T. Shimanouchi and M. Tasumi, *Bull. Chem. Soc. Japan*, **34**, 359 (1961).

37. G. Natta, I. Pasquon, P. Corradini, M. Peraldo, M. Pegoraro, and A. Zambelli, *Atti Accad. Nazl. Lincei, Rend., Classe Sci. Fis. Mat. Nat.*, **28**(8), 539 (1960).

38. V. L. Folt, J. J. Shipman, and S. Krimm, *J. Polymer Sci.*, **61**, S17 (1962).

39. K. Abe and K. Yanagisawa, *J. Polymer Sci.*, **36**, 539 (1959).

40. J. P. Luongo, *J. Appl. Polymer Sci.*, **3**, 302 (1960).

CHAPTER 4

Optically Active Stereoregular Polymers

Mario Farina

ISTITUTO DI CHIMICA INDUSTRIALE DEL POLITECNICO
MILANO, ITALY

Giancarlo Bressan

ISTITUTO DI RICERCHE G. DONEGANI, MONTECATINI EDISON, S.P.A.
MILANO, ITALY

I. INTRODUCTION

Optically active polymers have drawn much attention during recent years. Their study represents a new approach to the problems of polymeric structures and polymerization mechanisms. Macromolecular stereochemistry differs from classical organic stereochemistry owing to the different size of the molecules under examination. For a better understanding of this difference, the measurement of optical activity under different conditions (temperature, concentration, wavelength) is very useful.

Moreover, with regard to the reaction mechanisms, it is often possible to draw the stereochemical relationships existing among monomer, polymer, and catalyst; the examination of the relationship between rotatory power and polymerization conditions (e.g., concentration, temperature, time) or molecular weight can provide new and independent elements for the interpretation of the polymerization mechanism.

The preparation and properties of optically active polymers were recently reviewed by several authors. Among the most up-to-date and complete reviews, we mention those published by Schulz and Kaiser (1), Pino (2), and Goodman et al. (3). An interesting discussion of polymer stereochemistry was developed by Arcus (4). For systematic information in this field, we refer to the papers cited here.

In this chapter, we shall first lay stress on some aspects of symmetry in polymer chains. Then, some of the most important lines of research in this field will be briefly described.

II. CONDITIONS FOR OPTICAL ACTIVITY
IN MACROMOLECULAR SYSTEMS

Optical activity consists in the rotation of the plane of linearly polarized light around the propagation axis of the beam. This phenomenon occurs when light passes through some substances either in the solid, liquid, or gaseous states, and it can be explained as the interaction between matter and the two components in which the linearly polarized light can be resolved, namely, circularly polarized light of the d and l types.

When this interaction is not symmetrical, a different refractive index ($n_D \neq n_L$) and a different absorption coefficient ($\varepsilon_D \neq \varepsilon_L$) can be observed. The former causes the rotation of the plane of the linearly polarized light, while ellipticity of the radiation and the presence of a Cotton effect in the rotatory dispersion curve depend on the latter (circular dichroism). A more detailed description is given in the general treatises on stereochemistry (5–7). We will reiterate here only that optical activity or specific rotatory power is defined by $[\alpha]_\lambda^t = \alpha/ld$, where α is the angle in degrees measured by a polarimeter at the temperature t, using monochromatic light with wavelength λ, l is the thickness of the sample measured in decimeters, and d is the density of the compound in grams per milliliter. For solutions, d represents the concentration in grams per milliliter, or as equivalent, $d = c/100$, in which c is the concentration of the solution in grams per 100 ml. Molar rotatory power $[M]$ or $[\phi]$ is the value $[\alpha]MW/100$, MW being the molecular weight of the substance under examination. For macromolecular compounds, MW is the molecular weight of an exactly defined structural unit, which generally coincides with the monomeric unit.

The quantum mechanical aspect of optical activity will not be described here [see in this regard the papers by Tinoco (8) and Ullman (114)]. Our discussion will deal only with some relationships between this phenomenon and molecular structure.

The fundamental condition for optical activity concerns the type of symmetry existing in the compound under examination. The shape of the molecule must not possess mirror symmetry (dissymmetric molecule or, in particular cases, asymmetric molecule). This is the same as saying that the shape of the molecule must not present an improper axis of symmetry (alternating or rotoreflection axis). The most important alternating axes are the onefold, twofold, and fourfold alternating axes, where the onefold axis is equivalent to the plane of symmetry ($S_1 = \sigma$), the twofold is equivalent to the center of symmetry ($S_2 = i$), while the fourfold alternating axis S_4 and, in general, the $4n$-fold alternating axes cannot be reduced to other elements.

According to the point group theory, dissymmetric molecules belong exclusively to the $\mathbf{C_1}$, $\mathbf{C_n}$, and $\mathbf{D_n}$ groups (9,10). The first group does not contain an element of symmetry and is really "asymmetric"; the second contains, as the only element of symmetry, an n-fold rotation axis (C_n); the third contains only an n-fold axis (C_n) and n-twofold axes perpendicular to the main axis ($\mathbf{D_n} = C_n + nC_2$).

The second condition required so that a system consisting of many molecules shows optical activity is that the number of molecules having dissymmetric structure of a given type (e.g., D) differs from that of the molecules of the L type. Otherwise, although the single molecules may be optically active, their total effect will be zero, since the rotation caused by the D molecules will be balanced by an equal and opposite rotation caused by the L molecules.

Having set forth these general remarks, let us consider the shape of the macromolecules in the liquid state, in the melt, or in solution. The shape of the molecules in solution is studied in another chapter of this book. Here, we only wish to point out that a polymethylenic hydrocarbon chain presents a high conformational mobility and that the number of possible conformations is huge and exponentially increases with the molecular weight.

If we fix a given conformation of the macromolecule, the probability that it will possess a nondissymmetric shape is quite negligible when the molecular weight reaches moderately high values; the probability is equally negligible that, in an experimentally accessible volume, another macromolecule having an exactly enantiomorphous conformation could be found. These remarks should lead to the conclusion that a solution of high molecular weight polymethylene molecules has the same characteristics as optically active compounds and therefore it should rotate the plane of polarized light. However, this does not agree with the experimental evidence.

Therefore, further considerations must be introduced. The first concerns the effect of the conformational mobility of chains, such as those of polymethylene, which cause the molecules to assume different shapes at subsequent times. The second concerns the statistical aspect of optical activity, it being the sum in value and sign of the specific contributions of each molecule. According to what was stated above, the sum of the contributions of each conformation of a polymethylene molecule, calculated, e.g., according to the Brewster method (11), adds up to zero. This can be easily verified in simple cases (e.g., in n-butane).

An alternative method leading to the same conclusion consists of the examination of local symmetries. The effect of a structural asymmetry on the optical activity of a series of homologous compounds varies upon varying the length of the substituents but rapidly tends to constant values (possibly zero) (12). A wide variety of experimental evidence allows us to state that the influence of a site of asymmetry on the optical rotation of a compound, provided that cooperative effects do not occur, appears to be a short distance effect. It is therefore reasonable to shift the problem from the examination of the whole macromolecule to that of macromolecule segments of suitable length.

Examination of the symmetries of these segments allows us to conclude that there is statistical compensation among the contributions to the rotatory power of asymmetric segments of opposite sign existing in different macromolecules (intermolecular compensation) as well as in the same macromolecule (intramolecular compensation). Evidently, a mixture of polymethylene molecules (or even only one molecule) cannot be optically active: In fact, the statistical weights of the D- and L-type segments are equal.

Rigorously enantiomorphous situations, such as the two 3/1 helices of polypropylene, possess equal energy: according to the above statistical considerations, they are obtained with the same probability and may be isolated only when the potential barriers between enantiomeric conformations are very high (at room temperature: $\Delta E > 20$ kcal/mole). For example, a conveniently substituted polyphenylene could be resolved in conformational antipodes.

Locally enantiomorphous conformations, however, can have different energy when they form a diastereomeric system, i.e., when in the close vicinities of the dissymmetric conformation there exists a second site of asymmetry. When the second site is of configurational type (e.g., an asymmetric carbon atom), there is a more or less extensive stabilization of one of the two forms and therefore a more or less high predominance of one conformation on its (pseudo)antipode. This is the case with polypeptides, where the α-helix is largely stabilized with respect to other helices, and, in particular, to the helix of opposite sign, by the presence of asymmetric carbon atoms in the chain; these carbon atoms cause a favorable disposition of the side substituents and of the groups able to give hydrogen bonds.

The presence of configurational asymmetries causes conformational effects, such as those just seen, and influences the optical rotation in an indirect manner; however, the presence of such asymmetries is the geometric condition strictly required for the existence of optically active polymers. Only configurationally dissymmetric structures possess a non-zero resultant of the asymmetric conformational effects (when very high potential barriers between enantiomeric conformations are not present).

Therefore, before examining optically active polymers, we shall premise a configurational analysis of macromolecular structures.

III. PREDICTION OF CONFIGURATIONAL DISSYMMETRY IN MACROMOLECULAR STRUCTURES

As already stated, the lack of mirror symmetry is a necessary condition for the occurrence of optical activity. While for low molecular weight substances this precludes the presence of alternating axes of any order (in particular of planes and of center of symmetry and of fourfold alternating axes) (7,9,10), for macromolecular structures this condition must be suitably modified.

As to symmetry, a macromolecule can be reasonably considered as a structure of infinite length. This approximation is of the same type as that generally assumed in crystallography: Although a crystal has finite dimensions, it can be considered as consisting of an infinite tridimensional repetition of unit cells. An oriented stereoregular linear macromolecule can be considered as a monodimensional crystal. As such, its symmetry properties are more accurately described by the line symmetry than by the point symmetry. The possible line groups for macromolecular systems were recently determined by Corradini (*13*).

The symmetry operations that can be performed on a macromolecule not only comprise rotation, reflection, and/or inversion, but also translation along the chain axis. Translation is not an operation of mirror symmetry: therefore repetition by translation does not require a compound to be dissymmetric.† Translation combined with rotation around the same axis gives rise to the screw axis, which is intrinsically dissymmetric. On the contrary, translation combined with reflection on a plane that contains the translation axis originates a mirror glide plane, the existence of which involves a mirror symmetry.

In general, according to the line group theory, the lack of mirror symmetry requires the absence of alternating axes of any order, either alone or combined with a monodimensional translation.

As to rigid polymeric structures, the absence of all these elements is a necessary condition for the existence of enantiomorphous macromolecules. For polymeric structures where the rotation around the chain bonds is allowed, this condition is not effective: In fact, we have seen that such molecules are, in general, asymmetric due to the great number of possible conformations. In this case, it is convenient to consider the molecule as if it existed in only one conformation, either real or hypothetical, chosen in such a manner that it is among the most symmetric ones. The energetic level and therefore the probability of existence of such a conformation is of no importance in this connection.§ Of the two possible highly symmetric conformations, i.e., the zigzag planar (staggered) (**1**) and the Fischer (eclipsed) (**2**), we think that (**2**) is more convenient to our purpose.

(**1**)   (**2**)

† In some ways it can be considered as being similar to rotation (it is exactly a rotation along a circumference of infinite diameter). A study of polymeric chains in terms of cyclic models was recently published by Farina et al. (*14*): It allows us to consider the configurational properties of the polymers as properties of molecules of finite size and to express them in terms of the point group theory, which is more commonly known to organic chemists.

§ The presence of a mirror-symmetrical conformation, either stable or not, is a sufficient, although not necessary, condition for optical inactivity of a flexible compound (*15–17*).

Although (1) sometimes corresponds to a conformation of lowest energy (e.g., in polyethylene), by using (2) the configurational examination of the structures is simpler, due to the constant angle of view. On the contrary, in case (1) the chain angle $\widehat{CCC}$ is turned once toward the top and once toward the bottom. This fact leads to some confusion in the configurational determinations due to the different periodicity of the equivalent atoms, i.e., whether they are separated by an even or by an odd number of bonds (18).

Unless otherwise stated, we shall use Fischer projection formulas, in which the horizontal bonds project toward the viewer.

In the Fischer representation, the only symmetry elements to be considered for the prediction of optical activity are: the mirror planes perpendicular to the chain axis, the mirror plane containing the chain axis and perpendicular to the projection, and the mirror glide plane containing the chain axis and perpendicular to the projection (14).

The following analysis is partly based on the papers by Arcus (4,19,20) and, more extensively, by Farina et al. (14).

We define "intrinsically dissymmetric structure"† as the polymeric structure that, when represented in the Fischer projection, or in the planar zigzag one, does not contain mirror-symmetry elements, even if we do not take into account the possible asymmetries of the side substituents. We define "nonintrinsically dissymmetric structure" as the structure that can exist in enantiomorphous forms, only owing to the asymmetries of the side substituents.

Let us consider some typical examples of macromolecular structures. Isotactic polymers of nondissymmetric vinyl monomers have non-dissymmetric structures since they contain mirror planes perpendicular to the chain. We remind the reader that a Fischer projection formula can be rotated by 180° on the plane of the sheet without altering its configuration: Therefore, (3) is equal to its mirror image (4) (R is a nondissymmetric substituent). As might be expected, no asymmetric induction was observed in the polymerization of monomers of this type by optically active catalysts: the high-molecular-weight polymers which resulted were always inactive (21–24).

---

† The term "asymmetric" refers to structures that have no symmetry elements (not even rotation or translation axes). The term "dissymmetric" refers to structures having no mirror-symmetry elements, although they do contain rotation and/or translation axes. To be precise, ideal stereoregular polymers are dissymmetric and not asymmetric, due to the repetition by translation of the structural units. However, real polymers are generally asymmetric, due to the presence of statistically distributed irregularities.

Isotactic polymers of dissymmetric vinyl monomers show nonintrinsically dissymmetric structures: None of the mirror symmetry elements reported above is present here. In this case, (**5**) cannot be superimposed to its mirror image (**6**) because substituent D cannot be superimposed on L (D and L are generic enantiomeric substituents). On the other hand, polymers of propylene oxide are intrinsically dissymmetric, (**7**) being the nonsuperimposable mirror image of (**8**) (R is a nondissymmetric group).

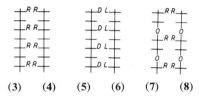

(3)   (4)   (5)   (6)   (7)   (8)

Syndiotactic polymers of nondissymmetric vinyl monomers are not dissymmetric: (**9**) contains planes perpendicular to the chain and a mirror glide plane; it can therefore be superimposed on (**10**). In their turn, syndiotactic polymers of dissymmetric vinyl monomers are nonintrinsically dissymmetric in that they do not contain mirror symmetry elements: (**11**) cannot be superimposed on (**12**). A syndiotactic polymer of propylene oxide contains a mirror glide plane. Therefore, it exists in a single isomer: (**13**) is equal to (**14**).

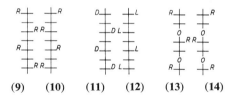

(9)   (10)   (11)   (12)   (13)   (14)

To examine polymers with a more complex tacticity, it is convenient to discuss the different types of structures separately.

Let us first consider the addition polymers obtained from noncyclic and nondissymmetric monoolefinic monomers of the CHA=CHB type. In this case, three ditactic, i.e., two diisotactic and one disyndiotactic, structures exist. Both diisotactic structures, *erythro* (**15**) and *threo* (**16**), possess mirror planes normal to the chain axis; the disyndiotactic structure (**17**) has the mirror glide plane as the only configurational symmetry element. None of the structures considered can be optically active.

To obtain intrinsically dissymmetric structures from monomers of this type, more complex tacticities are needed: they should possess at least six

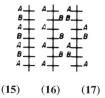

(15)   (16)   (17)

tertiary atoms in the chain for each structural repeat unit. The simplest structures among these are reported in (18), (19), and (20), where (20) is similar to (18) but has equal substituents at every C atom. (20) contains three monomeric units derived from monomers of the CHA=CHA type or six vinyl monomeric units (the presence of CH_2 groups in the chain does not modify the symmetry of this structure).

The existence of dissymmetric structures of this type was very simply deduced from the examination of the corresponding cyclic structures, according to what has already been described (14). The cyclic model of (20) is the active inositol (21), which is the simplest homosubstituted cyclic compound existing in enantiomorphous forms.

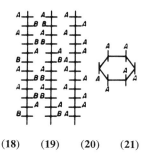

(18)   (19)   (20)   (21)

Optically active polytactic polymers from dissymmetric disubstituted olefins do not substantially differ from those previously described for dissymmetric vinyl monomers [see schemes (5), (6), (11), and (12)]: Their structures will be nonintrinsically dissymmetric.

A more complex and important case is given by the polymers having intrinsic dissymmetry. In this regard, we can distinguish two fundamental classes: the former consisting of linear polymers and the latter of polymers having cyclic monomeric units.

For the former, we consider a tertiary carbon atom —CHR—, i.e., a carbon atom bound to two chain portions, to a hydrogen atom and to a générical nondissymmetric R substituent (the following discussion also holds for tetrasubstituted atoms of the —CRR'— type). A succession of —CHR— groups can produce a dissymmetric structure by simple repetition rules [i.e., excluding complex structures like (20)], if the —CHR— group is bound to different substituents: —N—CHR—M—. In other words, the —CHR—M—N— succession must not be equal when observed from one or from the other side of the chain (M must differ from N). When the succession of the —CHR— groups is isotactic, such a local structure, which does not contain a mirror plane perpendicular to the chain, is not compensated by a glide-reflection operation: The resulting structure is therefore dissymmetric.

M and N are atoms or groups of atoms not necessarily dissymmetric. As typical examples of —M—N— successions, we can cite the following groups: —CH$_2$—O—, —CH$_2$—NH—, —CO—NH—, —CO—O—, —CH$_2$-(CH=CH)- (both *cis* and *trans*), etc., to which the following dissymmetric isotactic polymers correspond: poly(propylene oxide) (**7**) and (**8**) (R = CH$_3$), poly(propylene imine)(**22**) (from now on only one enantiomer for every structure will be shown), polyalanine (**23**), polylactide (**24**), 1,4-polypentadiene (**25**), etc.

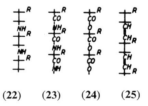

(**22**)   (**23**)   (**24**)   (**25**)

If, in its turn, M contains a tertiary carbon atom —CHR'—, which differs from the previous one, N can consist of only one atom or of a group symmetric in the two directions of the chain, e.g., —O—, —CH=CH— (*cis* or *trans*), —CH$_2$—CH$_2$—, etc. In this case both *erythro* and *threo* diisotactic structures are dissymmetric. We can mention here disubstituted polyethylene oxides (**26**) and (**27**) (R and R' are different from each other) and polysorbates (**28**) and (**29**) (R = CH$_3$, R' = COOR").

When the two tertiary carbon atoms are equal (R = R'), only the *threo* diisotactic structures are dissymmetric. For example, poly-2,3-epoxybutane (**30**), polymuconate and poly-2,4-hexadiene (**31**) (R is, respectively, COOR" and CH$_3$).

The above considerations on dissymmetric structures do not depend on the method by which they are obtained, i.e., by homopolymerization,

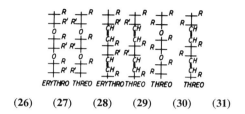

(26) (27) (28) (29) (30) (31)

copolymerization, polycondensation, or reaction on preformed polymers. Although the examples given so far refer to homopolymers, copolymers can also be included in the same scheme.

The possibility of obtaining intrinsically asymmetric copolymers was first observed by Frisch et al. (25); a systematic study was later published by Arcus (20).

The alternating isotactic copolymers (i.e., having identical substituents in the same position with respect to the chain), obtained from disubstituted olefins of the CHA=CHB type and ethylene, are dissymmetric, both in the *erythro* (32) and *threo* (33) forms. The different isomers of isotactic alternating copolymers of CHA=CHB monomers with vinyl monomers CH_2=CHR are also dissymmetric [schemes (34)–(37)].

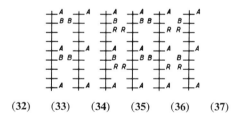

(32) (33) (34) (35) (36) (37)

If the disubstituted olefin is of the CHA=CHA type, structures similar to the previous ones (B=A) are also dissymmetric, except for the *erythro* (32) which is internally compensated. This case is formally identical to that of poly-2,3-epoxybutane or that of polymuconate.

The last class of intrinsically dissymmetric polymers we are going to consider are made up of cyclic monomer units. Due to the great number of possible structures, we will only consider the case of the homopolymers derived from cyclic monoolefins. As already observed by Arcus (19), *threo* diisotactic structures are dissymmetric both in the case of symmetrically (38) and of unsymmetrically substituted cycloolefins (39), while *erythro* diisotactic structures are dissymmetric only in the last case (40).

As possible examples for (38) we cite polycyclobutene, and for (39) and (40), polybenzofuran.

The diisotactic structures of cyclic polymers are dissymmetric, due to the presence of the ring that eliminates the mirror planes perpendicular to the chain, which are present in noncyclic structures (15) and (16). The tertiary atom of a cyclic homopolymer is nonsymmetrical with respect to

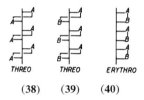

THREE   THREE   ERYTHRO

(38)   (39)   (40)

the two opposite directions of the chain: Therefore the presence of an atom or of a group of atoms between the subsequent rings is not necessary to guarantee dissymmetry in the structure.

Finally, we will briefly discuss the existence of asymmetric carbon atoms in the above structures. The particular model chosen by us (i.e., chains of infinite length) imposes the requirement that the tertiary chain atoms in structures (3)–(6), (9)–(12), and (15)–(17) are not asymmetric [see also Ref. (14)]. On the other hand, the tertiary carbon atoms of structures (7)–(8), (13)–(14), (18)–(20), and (22)–(40) are truly asymmetric. The particular symmetry properties of the atoms in structures (37)–(40) have been recently discussed by Natta and Farina (26).

An alternative model for the study of polymeric structures is based on chains of finite length with equal end groups (2,27,28). According to this model, the tertiary carbon atoms of isotactic vinyl polymers are also asymmetric, as they are bound to two chain portions of different lengths. The symmetry of the whole molecule is due to the presence, in the Fischer projection, of only one mirror plane perpendicular to the chain and placed at its middle point: The molecule therefore has a meso structure.

The two models lead to the same conclusions as to the prediction of the optical activity of high molecular weight polymeric structures.

We wish to emphasize that the considerations discussed so far are valid only for the examination of isolated polymeric structures and are not valid during the process of growth. In this phase, the growing chain end, where the new monomeric unit is inserted, is really asymmetric even in the case of vinyl monomers (3) and (9) or of the noncyclic monoolefins (15)–(17). As a consequence, when studying polymerization mechanisms, the growing macromolecule must be considered to be truly asymmetric.

IV. INTRINSICALLY DISSYMMETRIC POLYMERIC STRUCTURES

As previously seen, intrinsically dissymmetric polymeric structures can be obtained by various methods, the most important of which are reported below: polymerization of optically active monomers; selective polymerization of racemic monomers; asymmetric polymerization of non-dissymmetric monomers; copolymerization of vinyl monomers with 1,2 disubstituted olefins; and resolution of racemic mixtures of macromolecules.†

Some of the most important results in this field are described herein. Our discussion will particularly concern poly-addition polymers other than polypeptides, since the description of the synthesis and properties of the latter may be found in the texts and reviews dealing with natural polymers.

A. Polymers from Optically Active Monomers

Cyclic monomers that react by ring cleavage and give linear polymers have been widely studied. If we neglect *N*-carboxyanilides and other derivatives of α-amino acids, the largest amount of work has been carried out on propylene oxide and on compounds with an analogous structure. Noncyclic monomers of interest are, e.g., esters of sorbic acid with optically active alcohols or 1-alkyl butadienes with an asymmetric alkyl group. Some of these are at present under examination (*29*).

The preparation of optically pure propylene oxide and its polymerization since 1956 have been described by Price and Osgan (*30,31*). From the (+)monomer they obtained in the presence of KOH an optically active low molecular weight isotactic polymer. Under the same conditions, the racemic monomer yields a polymer lacking in steric order, which indicates the lack of selectivity of catalysis by KOH.

---

† The expressions *racemic mixture* and *resolution*, refer to systems consisting of true optical antipodes. For macromolecules, this case is merely ideal: it is very improbable that two real macromolecules have the same degree of polymerization and the same distribution of configurational irregularities so that they are exactly nonsuperimposable mirror images. That is why the correct expressions should be *optically inactive mixtures of macromolecules containing enantiomorphous monomeric units* and *fractionation of optically inactive mixtures of polymers into fractions showing optical activity of opposite sign* (*115*). However, this last operation differs completely from the usual polymer fractionations and is more like the procedures used for true resolutions into antipodes, since an asymmetric agent must be employed.

The polymerization mechanism proposed by Price and Osgan is characterized by the ring cleavage on the —O—CH$_2$— bond and consequent
retention of configuration of the asymmetric atom.

The polymerization of racemic and (+)propylene oxide in the presence
of FeCl$_3$, on the other hand, yields a higher molecular weight product,
consisting of a mixture of amorphous and crystalline polymers. The
(+)monomer yields an optically active polymer, the crystalline fraction of
which has values of the rotatory power which are close to those of the
polymer obtained with KOH. The amorphous fraction, instead, gives
considerably lower or zero values. With regard to the other physical
properties, the inactive crystalline polymer obtained from the racemic
monomer is quite similar to the crystalline fraction of the polymer obtained
from (+)monomer. These facts suggest that the inactive isotactic polymer
consists of a racemic mixture of polymeric molecules (see footnote,
page 193). The formation of isotactic polymer can be attributed to
heterogeneous asymmetric centers, probably insoluble complexes of D- or
L-propylene oxide with FeCl$_3$, which have a preferential reactivity for
propylenoxide with a given configuration. In subsequent research Price
and Spector (*31a*) established that the low-optical-activity amorphous
polymer obtained from the optically active monomer contains a high
amount of head-to-head monomeric units. The formation of such units
is due to the lack of selectivity of the ring opening which may occur on
the primary or on the secondary carbon atom. In the latter case, a
simultaneous inversion of configuration of the asymmetric carbon atom
takes place.

The conclusions on the structure of the inactive isotactic polymer were
confirmed by X-ray analysis (*32,32a*) and by resolution of the polymer
by asymmetric adsorption (*33,33a*).

Analogous research was carried out on propyleneimine (*34*), which was
polymerized by cationic catalysts, such as BF$_3$–Et$_2$O. D and L monomers
yielded polymers having high optical activity (with opposite sign of that
of the monomer) and melting points considerably higher than the polymer
obtained from the racemic monomer. Also in this case, a mechanism was
proposed with ring cleavage on the —CH$_2$—N— bond and retention of
configuration.

Another polymer of this series, (+)polyisobutylethyleneimine, was
employed by Tsuboyama for an interesting catalytic asymmetric synthesis.
In the presence of this polymer, the reaction between benzaldehyde and
HCN yields the corresponding cyanohydrin with optical purity ranging
from 10 to 20% (*35*).

Although they do not exactly fall into the scope of this chapter, we think it convenient to describe the investigations by Vandenberg on the polymerization of *cis*- and *trans*-2,3-epoxybutane, in view of the contribution they gave to the knowledge of the stereochemical aspects of these polymerizations (*36,37*).

Two isotactic and two syndiotactic polymers can in principle be obtained from *cis*- and *trans*-2,3-epoxybutane. They contain the sequences shown in structures (**41**)–(**44**).

d	*d*	*l*	*d*	*d*
l	*d*	*l*	*l*	*d*
O	O and O		O	O
d	*d*	*l*	*l*	*l*
l	*d*	*l*	*d*	*l*
erythro diisotactic meso	*threo* diisotactic D and L		*erythro* disyndiotactic meso	*threo* disyndiotactic meso
(**41**)	(**42**)		(**43**)	(**44**)

The polymerization of (+)*trans*-2,3-epoxybutane by *i*-Bu$_3$Al–0.5H$_2$O in heptane yields a highly crystalline inactive polymer. Structure (**41**) was attributed to it, by assuming a cationic mechanism with inversion of configuration of the ring-opening carbon atom. The physical properties of the polymer obtained from (+)2,3-epoxybutane are quite similar to those of the polymer from the corresponding racemic monomer; moreover, as revealed by IR spectra and by X-ray diffraction patterns, their structures are essentially similar. To obtain the same meso diisotactic polymer from the racemic monomer, the entering monomer at every propagation step must possess the same configuration.

The polymerization of meso-*cis*-2,3-epoxybutane, was, in its turn, carried out by an optically active catalyst obtained from AlEt$_3$, water, and acetylacetone in heptane–ether solution, with subsequent addition of (−)menthol (*37*). The polymer was optically active and possessed the diisotactic structure (**42**), resulting from the inversion of the configuration of the ring-opening carbon atom.

A further proof of the structure of the crystalline polymers from *cis*- and *trans*-2,3-epoxybutanes is obtained by examining the nature of mono- and dibutylene glycols obtained by polymer degradation. Meso-2,3-butanediol is obtained from poly-*trans*-2,3-epoxybutane, and racemic 2,3-butanediol from poly-*cis*-2,3-epoxybutane, according to scheme (**45**).

Finally, the relationships existing between two subsequent monomeric units were established from the nature of the isolated dibutylene glycol. This confirmed that, in both cases, the polymers were diisotactic.

An X-ray diffraction analysis has confirmed the structures proposed by Vandenberg (*37a*).

The mechanism with inversion of configuration at the ring-opening carbon atom proposed by Vandenberg was later also confirmed by Price

(45)

and Spector for the case of deuterated ethyleneoxides (*31a*). Finally (+)methyl 2,3-epoxybutyrate (or the methyl ester of β-methylglycidic acid) polymerized to optically active polymers in the presence of $Et_3Al–BF_3$ or $Et_3Al–SnCl_4$ (*37b*).

Other types of optically active monomers, the polymerization of which leads to the formation of intrinsically dissymmetric structures, belong to the class of lactams and of cyclic lactones.

In all cases observed, the physical properties—in particular, the melting points—of the polymers obtained from pure enantiomers are very different from those of the polymers obtained from either racemic mixtures or low optical purity monomers.

Polymers obtained from (−)lactide have melting points and crystallinities that increase with the rotatory power (*38*). Poly-L-lactide with the highest rotation melts at 176°C, while the corresponding inactive polymer has a softening point below 100°C.

Overberger and Jabloner (*39,40*) studied the polymerization of D(−)β-methyl-ε-caprolactam at 200–220°C in the presence of water as a catalyst. Also in this case, the melting point is higher by 90°C than that of the polyamide obtained from the racemic monomer.

Pure $(R)(+)$7-hydroxy-4-methylheptanoic acid gave a partially crystalline optically active polymer, whereas the incorporation of 10% of the enantiomeric monomer was sufficient to inhibit crystallization $(40a)$.

Finally, we mention the polymerization of a tertiary bicyclic amine, conidine, which, in the presence of BF_3–Et_2O, yields highly crystalline polymers from the pure antipodes, and a low-melting amorphous product from the racemic monomer (41).

B. Polymers from Racemic Monomers

Several investigations were also made on the polymerization of racemic propylene oxide by optically active catalysts. The resulting polymers possess monomeric units of a given configuration in excess over the opposite configuration, because of the preferential conversion of one of the two antipodes of the racemic monomer.

Several catalysts were specially examined by the Japanese school: Among them, the complexes $ZnEt_2$–optically active alcohols were studied systematically $(42–47)$. (See also Volume 2, Chapter 4.) Rigid alcohols, such as $(+)$borneol, $(-)$isoborneol, and $(-)$menthol appeared to be the most effective in asymmetric selection (48). Also, the catalysts $ZnEt_2$–optically active amino acid (49) as well as magnesium $(+)$tartrate (50) appeared to be stereoselective. In these cases, both polymer and residual monomer possessed detectable rotatory powers.

Furukawa and co-workers (51), on the other hand, produced an inactive polymer, using a catalyst obtained by partial hydrolysis of the $FeCl_3$–propylene oxide complex in the presence of d-bornyl ethyl ether. The residual monomer is optically active, thus indicating a preferential conversion of one of the two antipodes, followed by a racemizing step in polymerization. The same authors tried to interpret the experimental facts on the polymerization of propylene oxide, particularly the optical activity (or inactivity) of the polymer and of the residual monomer, on the basis of the different ways of coordination and of ring opening during the propagation.

To determine whether asymmetric polymerization of alkylene oxide occurs by a polymer chain-end controlled mechanism or by a catalyst controlled mechanism (see Sect. IVC), copolymerizations of ethylene oxide and propylene oxide were carried out in the presence of asymmetric catalysts $(51a)$. The results showed that the stereoselective propagation is catalyst controlled.

Catalyst systems of the type $ZnEt_2$–optically active alcohol are also effective in the selective asymmetric polymerization of epichlorohydrin (52) and styrene oxide (53).

C. Polymers from Nondissymmetric Monomers

The formation of optically active polymers from nondissymmetric monomers is a typical example of asymmetric synthesis. New centers of optical stereoisomerism (e.g., asymmetric carbon atoms) form in this process, the two enantiomeric forms being present in nonequivalent amounts.

The theoretical examination of the different ways of asymmetric induction was discussed in terms of copolymerization between D and L monomeric units (25,54). A very high (theoretically infinite) molecular weight polymer can be optically active only when the probability of DD succession is different from that of LL succession (process of asymmetric growth). If the DD probability is equal to LL, the effect of an asymmetric induction in the initiation stage (asymmetric initiation and symmetric propagation) decreases rapidly with the growth of the polymeric chain, with the exception of the case, which is probably only hypothetical, of a unity degree of stereospecificity (DD = LL = 1). Only if the macromolecular chain is relatively short (DP $\simeq$ 100 − 500) can a certain asymmetry be observed, when the stereospecificity is very high (55).

Therefore, the study of the relationship between rotatory power and degree of polymerization enables us to distinguish the two fundamental types of asymmetric induction. If [α] is substantially independent of [η], the polymerization occurs by an asymmetric growth, in which case the asymmetric agent (catalyst, monomer, solvent, circularly polarized light, etc.) determines the configuration of the entering monomeric unit in every stage. If [α] is inversely proportional to DP (when DP is sufficiently high), the process occurs by asymmetric initiation and symmetric growth.

To be precise, these relationships are valid for the optical purity (defined as (D − L)/(D + L) ratio, D and L being the number of D and L monomeric units) and not for the rotatory power: Deviations from the assumed linear relation between the two quantities might derive from differences in the distribution of configurational irregularities.

Asymmetric syntheses as defined above have been obtained so far with two classes of monomers: cyclic olefins and 1- or 1,4-substituted butadienes.

1. *Asymmetric Polymerization of Unsaturated Cyclic Monomers*

After the theoretical analysis done by Arcus (19), this problem was attacked by Schuerch (56,57). He tried to polymerize different monomers, such as indene, 1-methylcyclopentene, 4,5-dihydro-2-methylfuran, and α-angelica-lactone by asymmetric cationic catalysts. In no case, however, did the polymers obtained show a detectable optical activity.

The first asymmetric polymerization of cyclic monomers was achieved by Natta et al. in 1961 (*58,59*). Optically active polymers of benzofuran were obtained by cationic catalysts, consisting of complexes of Lewis acids with optically active Lewis bases. Benzofuran polymerizes by reaction on the double bond and not by ring cleavage, as shown by IR spectroscopy. The structure of these polymers could not be determined by X-ray diffraction since they are amorphous: however, a diisotactic structure was attributed to polybenzofuran on the basis of its optical activity. As shown in a previous section, no other simple structure can exist in enantiomeric forms. The two diisotactic structures of polybenzofuran are shown in (**46**) and (**47**).

ERYTHRO   THREO

(**46**)   (**47**)

The highest values of optical activity, $[\alpha]_D \simeq (+)$ or $(-) 75°$ were obtained with a catalyst having an approximate composition of two molecules of $AlCl_3$ and one molecule of optically active β-phenylalanine in toluene at $-75°C$. Other active catalysts were recently obtained from $AlCl_3$, Et_3SnCl, and $(-)$menthyl-$OSnEt_3$ (*60*).

The $AlCl_3$–phenylalanine polymerization occurs by an asymmetric growth process (DD $\neq$ LL), as revealed by the relationship between rotatory power and degree of polymerization. This is caused by the presence of the asymmetric counterion containing phenylalanine, which determines the configuration of each entering monomer unit (*55*). The polymer fractionation showed that the rotatory power is essentially constant on varying $[\eta]$, at least in low-conversion runs. For higher conversions, $[\alpha]$ increases with increasing $[\eta]$. This can be attributed to an alteration of the catalyst connected with termination reactions.

In the polymerization of benzofuran by $AlCl_3$–phenylalanine at low monomer concentrations, the highest values of optical activity are obtained when some polymer is initially present in the system (*61,62*). This autocatalytic behavior was explained by assuming that polybenzofuran can modify the composition or the structure of the counterion, thus increasing its asymmetric induction power.

Subsequent studies led to the conclusion that the complex $AlCl_3$–phenylalanine is not effective toward simpler cyclic ethers, such as dihydrofuran and its substitution products (*63*). However, using this catalyst, the synthesis of optically active poly-α-naphthofuran and poly-β-naphthofuran with specific rotatory powers close to (+) or (−) 150° was achieved. Unlike polybenzofuran, they were also obtained in crystalline form (*63*).

2. Asymmetric Polymerization of Dienic Monomers

The synthesis of optically active polysorbates by Natta et al. dates back to 1960 and is the first example of the asymmetric synthesis of homopolymers (*64*).

Alkyl esters of *trans-trans*-sorbic acid and its homologs had already been polymerized to crystalline macromolecules, by butyllithium in toluene, at low temperature (*65*). On the basis of the IR and X-ray data an *erythro*-diiso-*trans*-tactic structure was attributed to them [see structure (**48**)].

(**48**)

These polymers were obtained in the optically active form by using as catalysts (*R*)-2-methylbutyllithium (*64*), the complex butyllithium–(−)menthylethyl ether (*66*), or the reaction products of ethyllithium and optically active primary amines, such as pinacolilamine or α-phenylethylamine (*67*). The various catalysts act in homogeneous phase and yield polymers with substantially the same structure.

The presence of an asymmetric end group derived from the catalyst cannot be responsible for the optical activity observed, the polymer having a sufficiently high molecular weight.

A conclusive proof of the asymmetric induction was obtained by oxidative degradation of polysorbate and polystyrylacrylate to methyl- or phenylsuccinic acid, respectively (*68*). These acids are optically active with optical purities up to 6%; this value corresponds to the minimum optical purity of the polymer.

From the sign of rotation of the acids obtained, it is possible to determine the absolute configuration of the polymer (**49**).

$$
\begin{array}{cccc}
 & \overset{|}{CH} & & \\
 & \overset{||}{CH} & & COOH \\
 & | & & | \\
 & H{-}C{-}R & & H{-}C{-}R \\
 & | & & | \\
 & H{-}C{-}COOR' & \rightarrow & CH_2 \\
 & | & & | \\
 & CH & & COOH \\
 & \overset{||}{CH} & & (+)(R)\text{methylsuccinic acid} \\
 & | & & \\
\end{array}
$$

(+)poly(methylsorbate)

(**49**)

The asymmetric polymerization of a diene hydrocarbon (*trans*-1,3-pentadiene) was subsequently carried out by Natta et al. (*69*). A crystalline *cis*-1,4 polymer was obtained with two different catalysts: (+)tris(2-methylbutyl)aluminum and titanium tetrabutoxide, and triethylaluminum and (−)titanium tetramenthoxide. The high molecular weight polymers obtained with the former catalyst were inactive. However, the latter catalyst yielded high molecular weight polymers with considerable optical activity. Their degradation by ozonolysis gave optically active methyl-succinic acid, as a proof of the preferential configuration induced in the chain. The fractionation of this polymer led to fractions with different *cis*-1,4 unit contents. The highest rotatory powers were observed in the fractions with higher *cis*-1,4 unit content (in particular for a content of 78%, $[\alpha]_D = -22.8$). It is of interest that the asymmetric synthesis takes place only when the asymmetric groups are bound to titanium.

Trans-1,4 isotactic polymers of 1,3-pentadiene were also obtained by the heterogeneous system $(+)\text{Al}(i\text{-}C_5H_{11})_3\text{-}(C_2H_5)_2O\text{-}VCl_3$ (*70*). Optical activity is, in this case, rather low and decreases with increase in molecular weight; thus a mechanism of asymmetric initiation can be supposed.

Optically active poly-1-phenylbutadiene has recently been obtained in the presence of (*R*)-2-methylbutyllithium or of a complex between butyl-lithium and (−)menthylethyl ether (*71*). The study of the dependence of optical activity on the intrinsic viscosity suggested that in the former case the asymmetric induction was limited to the initiation step, while in the latter an asymmetric propagation took place (*71a*).

A new kind of asymmetric polymerization has been obtained by Farina et al. (72) by γ-irradiation of *trans*-1,3-pentadiene included in (−)perhydrotriphenylene (PHTP) (72a). Both racemic and optically active PHTP, a polycyclic saturated hydrocarbon, form crystalline channel-like inclusion compounds with low and high molecular weight substances of linear structure (72b). The solid-state polymerization of *trans*-1,3-pentadiene included in racemic PHTP gives rise to a *trans*-1,4 isotactic polymer (72c); when the polymerization is carried out on the dissymmetric inclusion compound, the resulting polymer shows a rotatory power opposite to that of the PHTP used.

D. Copolymers

The dissymmetric structures that can be obtained by copolymerization were discussed in a previous section: among these, only those obtained by alternate copolymerization of monomers of the CH_2=CHR or CH_2=CRR' and *cis*-CHA=CHA type have been the subject of experimental investigations. Beredijck and Schuerch copolymerized L-α-methylbenzylmethacrylate and maleic anhydride with azobisisobutyronitrile (73,74). The resulting (−)polymer was hydrolized and the asymmetric side group was eliminated. The product showed a detectable rotation of (+) sign. This was the first asymmetric synthesis in the field of macromolecular chemistry.

An analogous study was subsequently made by Schmitt and Schuerch on the radical copolymerization of maleic anhydride with L-α-methyl benzylvinyl ether (75). The copolymers have maleic anhydride/vinyl ether ratios ranging from 1.3:1 to 1.5:1 and present optical activity of the same sign as that of the active monomer. Complete debenzylation yields a polymer with opposite rotatory power having a rather small, although detectable, rotation.

In these two cases, asymmetric induction due to the presence of asymmetric side groups was proved to occur also in radical processes; however, the degree of such induction appears to be rather low.

V. NONINTRINSICALLY DISSYMMETRIC POLYMERIC STRUCTURES

A. Polymers from Optically Active Monomers

The study of the optical activity of these polymers allows us to draw very interesting conclusions on the conformation of the chains in solution.

Systematic studies were carried out on poly-α-olefins, but nonhydrocarbon polymers, in particular poly(vinyl ethers), polyaldehydes, and polymers of acrylic derivatives, were also investigated.

1. Poly-α-Olefins

The polymerization of optically active α-olefins of the type

$$\begin{array}{c} CH_3 \\ \diagdown \\ CH-(CH_2)_n-CH=CH_2 \\ \diagup \\ C_2H_5 \end{array} \qquad (50)$$

by Ziegler–Natta catalysts was investigated by several authors. In 1959, Natta et al. (76) obtained optically active polymers from various monomers of this type [(50), $n = 0$, 1, 2]. Subsequently, Bailey and Yates (77) polymerized (S)-3-methyl-(1)-pentene [(50) $n = 0$] and Murahashi and co-workers (78) studied poly(S)-3-methyl-1-pentene and poly(S)-4-methyl-1-hexene [(50) $n = 0$ and 1, respectively].

Pino and co-workers extensively studied polymers derived from (S)α-olefins [(50) $n = 0$, 1, 2, 3] and from (R)-3,7-dimethyl-1-octene (79–82). Their results led to important conclusions on polymer conformation both in solution and in the molten state. Their basic observations can be summarized as follows:

1. The most stereoregular fractions of poly-α-olefins show an increase in the molar rotation with respect to the low molecular weight paraffins having a structure similar to that of the monomeric unit (model compounds).

2. Such an increase reaches its maximum when the asymmetric carbon atom is in the β position with respect to the main chain and becomes very low when it is in the δ position.

3. When considerable differences exist in the molar rotation between polymer and model, the value of optical activity depends on the stereoregularity of the chain and increases with the increase of the latter.

4. In the same cases, the rotation decreases considerably with the increase in temperature. The values of $\Delta[M]/\Delta T$ are at least 10 times higher than those of model compounds.

These findings can be explained by assuming that the presence of asymmetric carbon atoms in the side chains influences the conformation of the main chain. This fact causes the predominance of conformations with a large contribution to the rotatory power, thus explaining the increase in optical activity with respect to model compounds. The values of the molar rotation of the polymers having asymmetric carbon atoms in α and β positions are of the same order of magnitude as those calculated for the highest-optical-activity conformation of the model compounds according to Brewster (*11*). The isotactic succession of monomer units with this conformation leads to a right- or left-handed helix (*83*). More precisely, if the absolute configuration of the monomer is (*S*) or (*R*), the experimental values of the optical activity agree with a left- or right-handed helix, respectively.

The optical activity of poly-α-olefins in the solid state in which they generally possess a helix-type structure, supplied further proof of the proposed scheme (*84*). On this basis it was suggested that in the molten state and in solution, the main chain of optically active isotactic poly-α-olefins possesses sections with helix-type conformation. One helix sense predominates, depending on the absolute configuration of the side asymmetric carbon atoms (*82*). The conformational equilibrium among portions with different helix sense is a function of temperature; consequently, the value of the temperature coefficient $\Delta[M]/\Delta T$ becomes of considerable importance as an index of mobility of the system.

This hypothesis was confirmed by Birshtein and Luisi (*85*) and Allegra et al. (*86*), who have discussed on a theoretical basis the possible conformations of isotactic poly-α-olefins with asymmetric carbon atoms in the side chain.

Substantially analogous conclusions, although with less emphasis on the helicity of the chain, were drawn by Goodman for poly(*R*)-3,7-dimethyl-1-octene (*87*).

Although they do not exactly belong to this class, we cite here the polymers obtained from (*S*)(+)4-methyl-hexyne-1 (*87a*). This polymer is of interest because the chromophoric system formed by the alternated double bonds of the chain might be dissymmetric. If it is not planar, but is distorted in a helix form, a strong circular dichroism would be observed. Unfortunately the strong absorption of the chromophore has not yet allowed a detailed examination of this phenomenon.

2. Nonhydrocarbon Polymers

Optically active vinyl ethers were polymerized by Schmitt and Schuerch (*75*), Basagni et al. (*88*), Lorenzi et al. (*89*), and Pino and Lorenzi (*90*). In this case also, differences were found between the rotatory powers of the polymers and of their model compounds, to an extent that depends on the distance of the asymmetric center from the main chain. The highest increase is observed for the β position: In this case the optical activity and its temperature coefficient depend on the stereoregularity of the polymer.

An interesting enhancement of the optical rotation was observed by Pino and Lorenzi (*90,91*) when poly[(*S*)-2-methylbutyl vinyl ether] was complexed with strong Lewis acids, such as Al(*i*-Bu)$_3$. This was attributed both to a modification of the chromophor and to conformational effects, due to the larger bulkiness of the side chain.

Conformational rigidity seems also to be responsible for the enhancement of optical activity of (−)poly(menthyl vinyl ether) and (+)poly(neomenthyl vinyl ether) with respect to the corresponding monomers (*91a*). Such an effect does not occur in (+)poly(isomenthyl vinyl ether) because of its higher mobility.

Optically active syndiotactic macromolecules were obtained for the first time by Goodman and Fan (*92*) from α-methylvinylalkyl ethers. No increase in the optical activity with respect to the model compounds was observed, although the stabilization of particular asymmetric conformations can also be theoretically predicted for syndiotactic structures.

Abe and Goodman (*93*) have polymerized optically active aldehydes to polyacetals. In this case also, remarkable increases in optical activity were observed depending on the distance of the asymmetric side atom from the main chain. A particular study was made of poly(*S*)-2-methylbutanal, poly(*R*)-citronellal, and poly(*R*)-6-methoxy-4-methylhexanal.

The polymerization of acrylic, methacrylic, and chloroacrylic esters of optically active alcohols (menthol, borneol, *sec*-butanol, 2-methylbutanol, 1,3-dimethylbutanol, 1-phenylethanol) by anionic and radical catalysts was studied by Schulz and other authors (*94–96*). Optical activity of the polymers is generally close to that of the model compounds.

In agreement with what was previously observed, an asymmetric center in the γ position does not involve any considerable increase in rotatory power, even for the most stereoregular fractions. It is also interesting that poly[(*S*)-5-methyl-1-heptene] shows a higher increase in molar rotation than poly[(*S*)-2-methylbutylvinyl ether] or poly[(*S*)-1,3-dimethylbutyl methacrylate] with respect to the corresponding model compounds. The different behavior can be explained by the presence, in these last two cases, of an oxygen atom between the asymmetric carbon atom and the main chain, resulting in a lower conformational rigidity.

B. Polymers from Racemic Monomers

The particular stereoselectivity of the catalysts from TiCl$_3$ and AlR$_3$ in the polymerization of racemic α-olefins was demonstrated by Pino et al. (*97*). These authors obtained by chromatographic methods the separation of polymers of racemic 4-methyl-1-hexene in fractions having opposite rotation. Some of these fractions showed a prevalence of monomeric units of a given sign up to about 40%. The asymmetric adsorbent for these fractionations was an insoluble fraction of poly(S)-3-methylpentene.

Another method used to investigate the mechanism of these stereoselective processes was the use of asymmetric catalysts. Pino and co-workers (*24,98,99*) polymerized racemic 3-methyl-1-pentene, 3,7-dimethyl-1-octene, and 4-methyl-1-hexene by tris(S)-2-methylbutylaluminum, bis(S)-2-methylbutylzinc, or (R)-2-methylbutyllithium, and TiCl$_3$ or TiCl$_4$. In the polymerization of the first and of the second olefin listed by bis(S)-2-methylbutylzinc/TiCl$_4$, both polymer and residual monomer proved to be optically active. On the contrary, poly-4-methyl-1-hexene obtained by the same catalyst showed a very low optical purity (*24*). Positive results were obtained only with vinyl monomers having the asymmetric carbon atom in the α position with respect to the double bond. Moreover, the examination of the rotatory power of the polymer and of the residual monomer demonstrated that the polymerization preferentially occurs on the antipode having the same configuration as the asymmetric group of the catalyst.

An interesting method for the synthesis of optically active polymers was recently demonstrated by copolymerizing a racemic monomer with an optically active monomer of similar structure (*100*). The latter copolymerizes preferentially with the antipode that possesses the same absolute configuration, while the other antipode gives a homopolymer. The two products can be separated, owing to their different solubilities. It is thus possible to obtain homopolymers with high optical purity, using only small amounts of a different optically active monomer.

VI. SIGNIFICANCE AND MAIN TRENDS OF RESEARCH ON OPTICALLY ACTIVE POLYMERS

To conclude this survey of the main types of optically active polymers, their properties, and methods of preparation, we wish to point out the leading reasons that have prompted such research and to outline the trends of its progress.

Optically active polymers were obtained only after investigating the symmetry properties of polymeric structures: In turn, the results achieved spurred further research in this field, as described in detail in a previous section. Research on these polymers has also made a considerable contribution to the conformational analysis of macromolecular systems. The study of the relationships between physical properties in solution and the conformation of macromolecules is becoming more and more a topic of interest. Unfortunately, the experimental data presently available derive from the properties of the whole molecule and are rather indirectly related to the conformational parameters, e.g., the mean square distance and its temperature coefficient. The use of a new parameter, the rotatory power, which is more directly connected with the presence of particular local conformations, seems to be one of the most fruitful methods in this field, particularly when the new techniques, optical rotatory dispersion and circular dichroism, are employed. The experimental investigations by Pino et al. (79–83) and the methods of conformational analysis formulated by Birshtein and Luisi (85) and Allegra et al. (86) are stimulating examples.

In this area of research, the isolation of polymer chains with only conformational dissymmetry would be of considerable interest.

A second reason for interest in optically active polymers concerns the contribution they have made to the study of polymerization mechanisms. The stereochemical examination of polymerization processes was made possible only by the polymerization of olefins containing an internal double bond (CHA=CHB), for example, deuteropropylene (101), alkenyl ethers (102), β-chlorovinylethers (103), cycloolefins (104), and deuteroacrylates (105–108). It was thus possible to determine the steric relationships between the monomer and polymer structures, in terms of the type of addition to the double bond and the mode of presentation of the monomer (19,103). The asymmetric polymerization of nondissymmetric monomers and the selective polymerization of racemic monomers is able to provide further important information. It can, for example, indicate the relationship between the steric structure of the catalyst and the type of asymmetric induction, the influence of different asymmetric groups in the monomers, and the type of transmission of the asymmetric induction, i.e., whether it is exclusively present in the initiation step or in every step of growth. Analogous information can be obtained, at least in part, by studying the stereospecific polymerization of racemic monomers, followed by fractionation of the antipodes (33,97).

However, a careful criticism is necessary when, on the basis of such data, one wishes to interpret the mechanism of stereospecific polymerization of simple olefins such as propylene. From a logical point of view, the data obtained in the case of dissymmetric monomers and catalysts (even if racemic) cannot be applied to the case of nondissymmetric monomers or catalysts. In the former case, the diastereoisomeric arrangements with different energy, both in the stable and in the transition states, generally differ from those of the latter, and the process can follow a path that does not necessarily occur in the latter. In particular, this remark is essential when one wants to deduce, from the type of asymmetric induction, the type of distribution of the configurational defects in stereoregular polymers.

Optically active synthetic polymers are also of interest because they can be studied as models for the most complex biological macromolecular systems. Helpful information can be obtained for the interpretation of the structures, the mechanisms of formation, and the reactions of natural polymers. The conformational stability of several proteins, the helix-random coil transition, the phenomenon of hypochromism, and the consistency of ORD curves to the Moffitt equation have been extensively studied using model compounds, which are very close to the natural compounds. The substantially unitary behavior of high molecular weight materials is becoming increasingly evident. Thus the methods of conformational analysis, at first applied to simple cases, such as vinyl and vinylidene polymers (*109–111*) allow the prediction of the most stable forms of protein chains (*112,113*).

Both asymmetric and selective polymerizations of simple monomers, although occurring with low optical yield, are formally based on the same principles that allow the highly specific syntheses of natural compounds. The influence exerted by macromolecular systems on the stereospecificity of some reactions has already been observed in some cases (*35,61,62*). Knowledge of the steric factors required to increase the optical yield of these processes can, in turn, contribute to the interpretation of the reactivity factors in biological processes.

Finally, optically active polymers can find important practical applications. For two reasons they can be particularly useful: The first arises from the possible different properties of the optically active compound compared to the racemic one. For crystalline polymers, the intermolecular packing may be different in the two cases and this may result in different melting points and different mechanical properties in the solid state. Differences in properties of this type can be expected also in the amorphous and molten states or in concentrated solutions when intermolecular interactions are still strong.

A second characteristic of optically active polymers concerns the noncompensation between enantiomeric structures and the resulting possibility that they might be employed for the production of other physical or chemical dissymmetries. Positive results have already been attained using optically active compounds as adsorbents for chromatographic resolutions (*97*) and as asymmetric catalysts (*35*). The ever increasing importance of the industrial production of optically active compounds for drugs and food requires the study of such nonclassical procedures of resolution, which can be based on the use of natural or synthetic macromolecules of suitable structure.

REFERENCES

1. R. C. Schulz and E. Kaiser, *Advan. Polymer Sci.*, **4**, 236 (1965).
2. P. Pino, *Advan. Polymer Sci.*, **4**, 393 (1965).
3. M. Goodman, A. Abe, and Y. L. Fan, *Macromol. Rev.*, **1**, 1 (1966).
4. C. L. Arcus, in *Progress in Stereochemistry* (P.B.D. de la Mare and W. Klyne, eds.), Vol. 3, Butterworth, London, 1962.
5. W. Kuhn, in *Stereochemie* (K. Freundenberg, ed.), Deuticke, Leipzig, 1932.
6. R. L. Shriner, R. Adams, and C. S. Marvel, in *Organic Chemistry: An Advanced Treatise* (H. Gilman, ed.), Vol. 1. 2nd ed., Wiley, New York, 1949.
7. G. W. Wheland, *Advanced Organic Chemistry*, 3rd ed., Wiley, New York, 1960, Chap. 6.
8. I. Tinoco, Jr., *Adv. Chem. Phys.*, **4**, 113 (1962).
9. H. H. Jaffé and M. Orchin, *Symmetry in Chemistry*, Wiley, New York, 1965, Chaps. 2 and 3.
10. K. Mislow, *Introduction to Stereochemistry*, Benjamin, New York, 1965.
11. J. H. Brewster, *J. Am. Chem. Soc.*, **81**, 5475 (1959).
12. R. E. Marker, *J. Am. Chem. Soc.*, **58**, 976 (1936).
13. P. Corradini, *Rend. Accad. Nazl. Lincei*, **28**(8), 632 (1960).
14. M. Farina, M. Peraldo, and G. Natta, *Angew. Chem.*, **77**, 149 (1965); *Intern. Ed.*, **4**, 107 (1965).
15. G. W. Wheland, see Ref. *7*, p. 279.
16. H. H. Jaffé and M. Orchin, see Ref. *9*, p. 26.
17. K. Mislow, see Ref. *10*, p. 93.
18. G. Natta, M. Peraldo, and M. Farina, *J. Polymer Sci.*, **43**, 289 (1960).
19. C. L. Arcus, *J. Chem. Soc.*, **(1955)**, 2801.
20. C. L. Arcus, *J. Chem. Soc.*, **(1957)**, 1189.
21. S. Murahashi, S. Nozakura, and S. Takeuchi, *Bull. Chem. Soc. Japan*, **33**, 658 (1960).
22. G. I. Frey and R. Robinson, *Tetrahedron*, **18**, 261 (1962).
23. D. Braun, H. Hintz, and W. Kern, *Makromol. Chem.*, **68**, 48 (1963).
24. P. Pino, F. Ciardelli, and G. P. Lorenzi, *J. Polymer Sci.*, **C4**, 21 (1964).
25. H. L. Frisch, C. Schuerch, and M. Szwarc, *J. Polymer Sci.*, **11**, 559 (1953).
26. G. Natta and M. Farina, *Tetrahedron Letters*, **(1963)**, 703.
27. G. Natta, P. Pino, and G. Mazzanti, *Gazz. Chim. Ital.*, **87**, 528 (1957).
28. M. L. Huggins, G. Natta, V. Desreux, and H. Mark, *J. Polymer Sci.*, **56**, 153 (1961).
29. M. Farina, to be published.
30. C. C. Price, M. Osgan, R. E. Hughes, and C. Shambelan, *J. Am. Chem. Soc.*, **78**, 690 (1956).
31. C. C. Price and M. Osgan, *J. Am. Chem. Soc.*, **78**, 4787 (1956).
31a. C. C. Price and R. Spector, *J. Am. Chem. Soc.*, **87**, 2069 (1965).
32. G. Natta, P. Corradini, and G. Dall'Asta, *Rend. Accad. Nazl. Lincei*, **20**(8), 408 (1956).
32a. M. Cesari, G. Perego, and W. Marconi, *Makromol. Chem.*, **94**, 194 (1966).

33. T. Tsuruta, S. Inoue, and J. Tsukuma, *Makromol. Chem.*, **84**, 298 (1965).

33a. J. Furukawa, S. Akutsu, and T. Saegusa, *Makromol. Chem.*, **94**, 68 (1966).

34. Y. Minoura, M. Takebayashi, and C. C. Price, *J. Am. Chem. Soc.*, **81**, 4689 (1959).

35. S. Tsuboyama, *Bull. Chem. Soc. Japan*, **35**, 1004 (1962).

36. E. J. Vandenberg, *J. Am. Chem. Soc.*, **83**, 3538 (1961).

37. E. J. Vandenberg, *J. Polymer Sci.*, **B2**, 1085 (1964).

37a. M. Barlow, *J. Polymer Sci.*, **A2**(4), 121 (1966).

37b. H. Shimasaki, *J. Chem. Soc. Japan*, **87**, 462 (1966); *CA*, **65**, 15299h (1966).

38. J. Kleine and H. H. Kleine, *Makromol. Chem.*, **30**, 23 (1959).

39. C. G. Overberger and H. Jabloner, *J. Polymer Sci.*, **55**, S32 (1961).

40. C. G. Overberger and H. Jabloner, *J. Am. Chem. Soc.*, **85**, 3431 (1963).

40a. C. G. Overberger, S. Ozaki, and D. M. Braunstein, *Makromol. Chem.*, **93**, 13 (1966).

41. M. S. Toy and C. C. Price, *J. Am. Chem. Soc.*, **82**, 2613 (1960).

42. S. Inoue, T. Tsuruta, and J. Furukawa, *Makromol. Chem.*, **53**, 215 (1962).

43. J. Furukawa and T. Saegusa, *Polymerization of Aldehydes and Oxides*, Wiley (Interscience), New York, 1963, p. 426.

44. T. Tsuruta, S. Inoue, M. Ishimori, and N. Yoshida, *J. Polymer Sci.*, **C4**, 267 (1963).

45. S. Inoue, T. Tsuruta, and N. Yoshida, *Makromol. Chem.*, **79**, 34 (1964).

46. T. Tsuruta, S. Inoue, N. Yoshida, and Y. Yokota, *Makromol. Chem.*, **81**, 191 (1965).

47. K. Matsuura, T. Tsuruta, Y. Terada, and S. Inoue, *Makromol. Chem.*, **81**, 258 (1965).

48. S. Inoue, Y. Yokota, N. Yoshida, and T. Tsuruta, *Makromol. Chem.*, **90**, 131 (1966).

49. J. Furukawa, T. Saegusa, S. Yasui, and S. Akutsu, *Makromol. Chem.*, **94**, 74 (1966).

50. O. V. Krylov and V. S. Livshits, *Tetrahedron Letters*, **(1965)**, 1181.

51. J. Furukawa, S. Akutsu, and T. Saegusa, *Makromol. Chem.*, **81**, 100 (1965).

51a. Y. Kumata, J. Furukawa, and T. Saegusa, *Makromol. Chem.*, **105**, 138 (1967).

52. M. Ishimori and T. Tsuruta; Communication presented at the *16th Annual Meeting of Chemical Society of Japan, Tokyo, March 1963*, see Ref. *5* in Ref. *48.*

53. M. Ishimori and T. Tsuruta; Communication presented at the *12th Annual Meeting of Society of Polymer Science of Japan, Tokyo, May 1963*, see Ref. *6* in Ref. *48.*

54. T. Fueno and J. Furukawa, *J. Polymer Sci.*, **A2**, 3681 (1964).

55. M. Farina and G. Bressan, *Makromol. Chem.*, **61**, 79 (1963).

56. C. Schuerch, *J. Polymer Sci.*, **40**, 533 (1959).

57. G. J. Schmitt and C. Schuerch, *J. Polymer Sci.*, **49**, 287 (1961).

58. G. Natta, M. Farina, M. Peraldo, and G. Bressan, *Chim. Ind.* (*Milan*), **43**, 161 (1961).

59. G. Natta, M. Farina, M. Peraldo, and G. Bressan, *Makromol. Chem.*, **43**, 68 (1961).

60. Y. Takeda, Y. Hayakawa, T. Fueno, and J. Furukawa, *Makromol. Chem.*, **83**, 234 (1965).

61. G. Natta, G. Bressan, and M. Farina, *Rend. Accad. Nazl. Lincei*, **34**(8), 475 (1963).

62. M. Farina, G. Natta, and G. Bressan, *J. Polymer Sci.*, **C4**, 141(1963).

63. G. Bressan, M. Farina, and G. Natta, *Makromol. Chem.*, **93**, 283 (1966).

64. G. Natta, M. Farina, M. Donati, and M. Peraldo, *Chim. Ind.* (*Milan*), **42**, 1363 (1960).

65. G. Natta, M. Farina, P. Corradini, M. Peraldo, M. Donati, and P. Ganis, *Chim. Ind.* (*Milan*), **42**, 1361 (1960).

66. G. Natta, M. Farina, and M. Donati, *Makromol. Chem.*, **43**, 251 (1961).
67. M. Farina and D. Fabbro, to be published.
68. M. Farina, M. Modena, and W. Ghizzoni, *Rend. Accad. Nazl. Lincei*, **32**(8), 91 (1962).
69. G. Natta, L. Porri, and S. Valenti, *Makromol. Chem.*, **67**, 225 (1963).
70. G. Natta, L. Porri, A. Carbonaro, and G. Lugli, *Chim. Ind.* (*Milan*), **43**, 529 (1961).
71. A. D. Aliev, B. A. Krentsel, and T. N. Fedotova, *Vysokomolekul. Soedin.*, **7**, 1442 (1965).
71a. A. D. Aliev and B. A. Krentsel, *Vysokomolekul. Soedin.*, **9**, 1464 (1967).
72. M. Farina, G. Audisio, and G. Natta, *J. Am. Chem. Soc.*, **89**, 5071 (1967).
72a. M. Farina and G. Audisio, *Tetrahedron Letters*, **1967**, 1285.
72b. M. Farina, G. Allegra, and G. Natta, *J. Am. Chem. Soc.*, **86**, 516 (1964).
72c. M. Farina, G. Natta, G. Allegra, and M. Löffelholz, *J. Polymer Sci.*, **C16**, 2517 (1967).
73. N. Beredjick and C. Schuerch, *J. Am. Chem. Soc.*, **78**, 2646 (1956).
74. N. Beredjick and C. Schuerch, *J. Am. Chem. Soc.*, **80**, 1933 (1958).
75. G. J. Schmitt and C. Schuerch, *J. Polymer Sci.*, **45**, 313 (1960).
76. G. Natta, P. Pino, and G. P. Lorenzi, Ital. Pat. 605,786, January, 1959.
77. W. J. Bailey and E. T. Yates, *J. Org. Chem.*, **25**, 1800 (1960).
78. S. Nozakura, S. Takeuchi, H. Yuki, and S. Murahashi, *Bull. Chem. Soc. Japan*, **34**, 1673 (1961).
79. P. Pino, G. P. Lorenzi, and L. Lardicci, *Chim. Ind.* (*Milan*), **42**, 712 (1960).
80. P. Pino and G. P. Lorenzi, *J. Am. Chem. Soc.*, **82**, 4745 (1960).
81. P. Pino, G. P. Lorenzi, and L. Lardicci, *J. Polymer Sci.*, **53**, 340 (1961).
82. P. Pino, F. Ciardelli, G. P. Lorenzi, and G. Montagnoli, *Makromol. Chem.*, **61**, 207 (1963).
83. P. Pino, in *Chimica delle Macromolecole*, Consiglio Nazionale delle Ricerche, Rome, 1963, p. 121.
84. P. Pino and G. P. Lorenzi, see (2) Ref. *112*.
85. T. M. Birshtein and P. L. Luisi, *Vysokomolekul. Soedin.*, **6**, 1238 (1964).
86. G. Allegra, P. Corradini, and P. Ganis, *Makromol. Chem.*, **90**, 60 (1966).
87. M. Goodman, K. J. Clark, M. A. Stake, and A. Abe, *Makromol. Chem.*, **72**, 131 (1964).
87a. F. Ciardelli, E. Benedetti, and O. Pieroni, *Makromol. Chem.*, **103**, 1 (1967).
88. D. Basagni, A. M. Liquori, and B. Pispisa, *J. Polymer Sci.*, **B2**, 241 (1964).
89. G. P. Lorenzi, E. Benedetti, and E. Chiellini, *Chim. Ind.* (*Milan*), **46**, 1474 (1964).
90. P. Pino and G. P. Lorenzi, *Makromol. Chem.*, **47**, 242 (1961).
91. P. Pino, G. P. Lorenzi, and E. Chiellini, paper presented at the International Symposium on Macromolecular Chemistry, preprint 455, Prague, 1965.
91a. A. M. Liquori and B. Pispisa, *J. Polymer Sci.*, **B5**, 375 (1967).
92. Y. L. Fan, see (3) Ref. *78*.
93. A. Abe and M. Goodman, *J. Polymer Sci.*, **A1**, 2193 (1963).
94. R. C. Schulz, *Z. Naturforsch.*, **19b**, 387 (1964).
95. R. C. Schulz and H. Hilpert, *Makromol. Chem.*, **55**, 132 (1962).
96. H. Sobue, K. Matsuzaki, and S. Nakano, *J. Polymer Sci.*, **A2**, 3339 (1964).
97. P. Pino, F. Ciardelli, G. P. Lorenzi, and G. Natta, *J. Am. Chem. Soc.*, **84**, 1487 (1962).
98. P. Pino, F. Ciardelli, and G. P. Lorenzi, *J. Am. Chem. Soc.*, **85**, 3888 (1963).

99. P. Pino, F. Ciardelli, and G. P. Lorenzi, *Makromol. Chem.*, **70**, 182 (1964).
100. F. Ciardelli, E. Benedetti, G. Montagnoli, L. Lucarini, and P. Pino, *Chem. Commun.*, **(1965)**, 285.
101. G. Natta, M. Farina, and M. Peraldo, *Rend. Accad. Nazl. Lincei*, **25**(8), 424 (1958).
102. G. Natta, M. Farina, M. Peraldo, P. Corradini, G. Bressan, and P. Ganis, *Rend. Accad. Nazl. Lincei*, **28**(8), 442 (1960).
103. G. Natta, M. Peraldo, M. Farina, and G. Bressan, *Makromol. Chem.*, **55**, 139 (1962).
104. G. Dall'Asta and G. Mazzanti, *Makromol. Chem.*, **61**, 178 (1963).
105. C. Schuerch, W. Fowells, A. Yamada, F. A. Bovey, F. P. Hood, and E. W. Anderson, *J. Am. Chem. Soc.*, **86**, 4481 (1964).
106. T. Yoshino, J. Komiyama, and M. Shinomiya, *J. Am. Chem. Soc.*, **86**, 4482 (1964).
107. T. Yoshino, M. Shinomiya, and J. Komiyama, *J. Am. Chem. Soc.*, **87**, 387 (1965).
108. T. Yoshino and K. Kuno, *J. Am. Chem. Soc.*, **87**, 4404 (1965).
109. G. Natta, P. Corradini, and P. Ganis, *Makromol. Chem.*, **39**, 238 (1960).
110. P. De Santis, E. Giglio, A. M. Liquori, and A. Ripamonti, *J. Polymer Sci.*, **A1**, 1383 (1963).
111. P. J. Flory, J. E. Mark, and A. Abe, *J. Am. Chem. Soc.*, **88**, 639 (1966).
112. P. De Santis, E. Giglio, A. M. Liquori, and A. Ripamonti, *Nature*, **206**, 456 (1965).
113. G. Némethy and H. A. Scheraga, *Biopolymers*, **3**, 155 (1965).
114. R. Ullman, *J. Polymer Sci.*, **C12**, 317 (1966).
115. P. Pino, G. Montagnoli, F. Ciardelli, and E. Benedetti, *Makromol. Chem.*, **93**, 158 (1966).

CHAPTER 5

Physical Properties of Stereoregular Polymers in the Solid State

Julian F. Johnson
CHEVRON RESEARCH COMPANY
RICHMOND, CALIFORNIA

Roger S. Porter
UNIVERSITY OF MASSACHUSETTS
AMHERST, MASSACHUSETTS

I. INTRODUCTION

The influence of stereoregularity on the physical properties of polymers in the solid state is pronounced in many cases. Indeed, the improved mechanical properties of stereoregular polymers are the primary reasons for their widespread use. However, experimental studies are rare where a given property of a solid polymer has been extensively studied as a function of stereoregularity. Yet more difficult is the problem of isolating sufficient amounts of physically homogeneous atactic, syndiotactic, and isotactic polymer on which to carry out physical testing.

213

This chapter reviews the limited available literature on solid state properties of polymers which have been studied as a function of stereoregularity. The limited literature is the result of the relatively recent development of the field. A very early example (1948) of variations in polymer properties with differences in chain structure was revealed by syntheses for poly(vinyl isobutyl ethers) (*1*). The polymer obtained by fast reaction, using boron fluoride catalyst, was tacky and amorphous and had a brittle point of −22°C. The polymer obtained by slow reaction, using a boron fluoride ether complex as a catalyst, gave a distinctly different polymer which was nontacky, gave X-ray fiber diagrams, and had a brittle point of −18°C. The differences between these two polymers were attributed correctly, even at that time (1948), to be due to differences in chain structure (*1*). All subsequent studies to be cited here will include the investigation of physical properties of at least two different levels of stereoregularity for each polymer. The effects of crystallinity and tacticity are frequently difficult to divorce.

Many papers of a qualitative nature are not cited. Many of these involve changes in polymer properties with extraction history. Extraction at various temperatures with different solvents can provide samples which vary regularly in tacticity. However, this method of itself does not provide an absolute tacticity scale. Also, the results on such a series can be clouded by effects other than tacticity, such as variations in molecular weight and chain branching.

Certain of the properties have been measured as a function of tacticity on polymer of only a single chemical type, e.g., dielectric properties of poly(vinyl alcohol) and vapor sorption on polystyrenes. In many other cases, the data are scant. It is the hope that this compilation will aid investigators in the promising and obviously little explored field of properties of solid polymers as a function of stereoregularity.

II. MELTING POINT

An important fundamental property of solid polymer that is markedly dependent on stereoregularity is the melting point. Coleman has suggested a method of estimating isotacticity from melting points (*1a*). In general, the packing density is greater for syndiotactic polymers than for the corresponding isotactic conformation and this leads to a higher melting point (*2*). Table 1 lists melting points as a function of tacticity for a number of polymers (*3–12*). Less well-defined measurements have also been reported for comparison of melting points for atactic and isotactic

TABLE 1

Melting Points of Some Stereoregular Polymers

Polymer	Melting point, °C		Ref.
	Syndiotactic	Isotactic	
Poly(tert-butyl methacrylate)	150–160 (165)	100 (104)	3
cis-1,4-poly(1,3-pentadiene)	52–53	44	4,5
1,2-Poly(1,3-butadiene)	154	120, 125	6,7
Poly(methyl methacrylate)	≥ 200	160	8,9,10
Poly(isopropyl acrylate)	115	162	11,12

polymers [see Table 2 (13)]. A widely different value from one in Table 2 has been reported. The softening point of atactic polypropylene has been given at 121–125°C vs. that of isotactic polymer at 170–176°C (14). In rare cases melting points have been determined for mixtures of tactic species of the same polymer. Figure 1 shows the melting temperatures of mixtures of isotactic and atactic polypropylene and of stereoblock poly-propylenes of different crystallinity (15). Melting points of polypropylenes as a function of tacticity have also been developed elsewhere (16).

Considerable interest has been expressed in polypropylenes, both syndio-tactic and isotactic, because of their potential ultimate properties such as melting point. Natta and co-workers have reported melting points ranging to 165°C for partially crystalline samples of syndiotactic polypropylene that were chromatographically isolated from predominantly isotactic polymer (17). Modification of the synthesis systems used by Natta et al. has provided a family of polymers having moderate to high syndiotactic regularity. From data on these samples, it has been concluded that

TABLE 2

Melting Points of Atactic and Isotactic Polymers (13)

Polymer	Melting points, °C	
	Atactic[a]	Isotactic
Polypropylene	−35	160–170
Poly-1-butene	−42	120–130
Polystyrene	85	230

[a] These values, referred to in Ref. (13) as "melting points," presum-ably are softening temperatures.

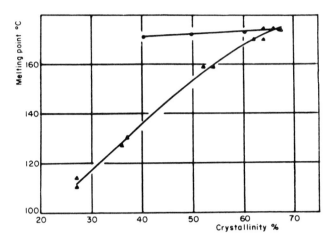

Fig. 1. Melting temperature of mixtures of isotactic and atactic polypropylenes, (circles) and of stereoblock polypropylenes (triangles) having different crystallinity (*15*).

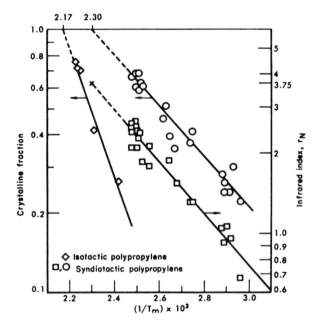

Fig. 2. Ultimate melting points (*18*).

syndiotactic polypropylene melts significantly below isotactic polypropylene (*18*). Application of simple melting point depression theory, log crystalline fraction vs. reciprocal of absolute melting point, with extrapolation to 100 % crystallinity (see Fig. 2), gave 161°C as the ultimate melting point. An infrared index is also given (*18*). This same method of data treatment using Newman's data (*19*) gave 188°C as the ultimate melting point of isotactic polypropylene. This value is somewhat below the value of 200°C projected by Farrow (*20*) from his annealing experiments. It has been considered that a melting point of 131°C for the best syndiotactic samples of Boor and Youngman is close to the maximum reliable value under practical molding conditions and that this is the value which should be compared with 165°C, the melting point frequently associated with highly isotactic polypropylene (*18*).

In one case the melting points of polymer gels have been measured as a function of tacticity (*21*). A comparison of gel melting points and NMR results has led to the conclusion that gel melting point measures some relative weighted average sequence length of syndiotactic placements in poly(methyl methacrylate). It was found that the gel formed when isotactic and syndiotactic poly(methyl methacrylate) are mixed together, in all except very good solvents for the polymer, can be melted over a narrow temperature range. It was suggested that the melting point was probably a true first-order transition with the melting points correlating with known syndiotactic placement (*21*). Table 3 illustrates the effect of total polymer

TABLE 3

Gel Melting Points (°C) as a Function of Total Polymer Concentration (*21*)
[Poly(methyl methacrylates) in dimethylformamide]

	Syndiotactic polymer	Equal wt. blends with an isotactic polymer; total polymer concn., wt. %				
No.	$M_v \times 10^{-5}$	1.0	3.0	5.0	7.0	9.0
7	31.50	60.9	62.0	[a]	[a]	[a]
6	25.10	55.6	61.4	60.1	[a]	[a]
5	16.10	50.5	61.0	60.6	[a]	[a]
4	2.18	[b]	57.4	60.3	61.9	[a]
3	0.42	[b]	46.7–55.5	60.8	61.7	62.5
2	0.17	[b]	42.0–52.6	58.5	61.3	62.5
1	0.10	[b]	41.4–43.6	57.0	59.6	58.6

[a] Gel too viscous for accurate measurement.
[b] Gel too loose for accurate measurement.

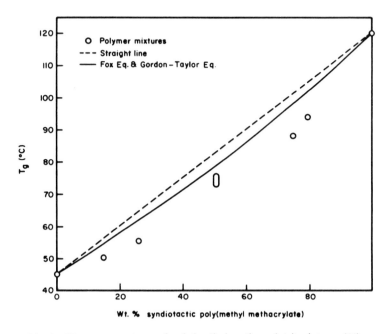

Fig. 3. Glass temperatures of poly(methyl methacrylate) mixtures (*22*).

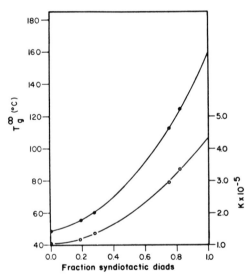

Fig. 4. T_g^∞, filled circles, and K, open circles, vs. fraction of syndiotactic diads for poly(methyl methacrylate), where $T_g = T_g^\infty - K(1/Mn)$ (*26*).

concentration on the melting point of gels prepared in dimethylformamide from equal weights of syndiotactic polymers of varying molecular weight and a standard isotactic polymer.

III. GLASS-TRANSITION TEMPERATURE

The effect of tacticity on the glass-transition temperature of poly(methyl methacrylate) has been widely studied. In an early study by Krause and Roman (22), mixtures of isotactic and syndiotactic poly(methyl methacrylate)were measured. Tacticity assignments were made both from X-ray diffraction and infrared measurements. Glass-transition temperatures were determined dilatometrically. In Fig. 3, which shows these results, the dashed line is simply the straight line between the values for the homopolymers, whereas the solid line represents the Gordon–Taylor equation for glass transitions of copolymers (23) and for the Fox equation derived for both copolymers and mixtures of polymers with placticizers (24). The experimental points are not in good agreement with equations. The values for the glass-transition temperature of 100% syndiotactic and 100% isotactic poly(methyl methacrylate) are the same as those reported earlier by Fox et al. (8), 45 and 115°C, respectively. Similar values have been measured by other techniques (10,25).

Thompson reported on the dependence of the glass-transition temperature of poly(methyl methacrylate) on both tacticity and molecular weight (26). Tacticity was measured by NMR spectroscopy and glass-transition temperatures were determined by differential thermal analysis. Figure 4 shows glass-transition temperatures plotted as a function of the fraction of syndiotactic diads (26). The glass-transition temperature increases markedly as the syndiotacticity increases. This use of the diad fraction may, in some cases, be misleading because it is possible to have two polymers with the same diad analysis that are in reality quite different because of heterotacticity. Nevertheless, the influence of tacticity on glass-transition temperature is real and pronounced.

In earlier work, no large differences were found between conventional and stereoregular forms of the same polymer. Thus, Natta et al. and others (25), using dilatometric methods, found a glass-transition temperature of 90°C for both isotactic and atactic polystyrene. Similarly, the same workers concluded for a series of poly-α-olefins that the glass-transition temperature was almost independent of stereoregularity. Using heat distortion measurements, Newman and Cox (27) found only small effects on the glass temperatures for polypropylene and polystyrene in the

TABLE 4

Glass-Transition Temperatures, °C

Polymer	Atactic	Ref.	Isotactic	Ref.	Syndio-tactic	Ref.
Poly(methyl methacrylate)	104	*10*	43–50	*10*	115–122	*10*
	103	*31*	42	*31*		
			45	*22*	120	*22*
			45	*29*	105, 120	*29*
Poly(1-butene)	−45	*31a*	−25, 42	*31a, b*		
Poly(α-methylstyrene)	170	*32*	117	*33*		
Poly(styrene)	89	*28*	87	*28*		
	80–100	*33a*	85	*33a*		
Polypropylene	−24	*34*	−13	*34*		
	−14	*35*	−7	*35*		
	−35	*31a*	−35	*31a*		
Conventional [a]						
Poly(ethyl methacrylate)	66	*10*	8–12	*10*		
Poly(isopropyl methacrylate)	81	*10*	27	*10*	85	*10*
Poly(butyl methacrylate)	19	*10*	−24	*10*		
Poly(isobutyl methacrylate)	53	*10*	8	*10*		
Poly(cyclohexyl methacrylate)	66	*10*	51	*10*		
Poly(isobornyl methacrylate)			110	*10*	111	*10*
Poly(methyl acrylate)	8	*10*	10	*10*		
Poly(ethyl acrylate)	−24	*10*	−24	*10*	−25	*10*
Poly(isopropyl acrylate)	−3 to −6	*10*	−11	*10*	−2–11	*10*
Poly(*sec*-butyl acrylate)	−22	*10*	−23	*10*	−20	*10*
Poly(*tert*-butyl acrylate)	43	*10*	40	*10*	40	*10*
Poly(cyclohexyl acrylate)	19	*10*	12	*10*	16	*10*
Poly(isobornyl acrylate)	94	*10*	90	*10*	96	*10*

[a] Refers to free-radical polymerization at ambient temperature to produce "conventional" polymer. May be essentially syndiotactic.

unannealed, unstretched state. These differences can be partially reconciled from two viewpoints. First, the variations in glass transition with stereoregularity depend markedly on polymer type. For example, the precise calorimetric measurements of Karasz et al. (*28*) gave values of 89 and 87°C for atactic and isotactic polystyrene; these are close to the earlier values of 90°C obtained for both forms (*30*), although higher values near 100°C have been cited (*29*). Additionally, the well-documented presence of considerable amounts of syndiotactic polymer in the atactic type of some polymers can make experimental determinations of glass transitions diffi-cult. Also, individual polymers may exhibit multiple glass-transition temperatures which may be difficult to distinguish and correlate as a function of tacticity. For example, atactic polystyrene exhibits, in the melt, a unique transition at about 160°C distinct from the T_g near 100°C (30).

The evidence on the majority of documented polymers does show that stereoregularity may significantly affect glass-transition temperatures. Table 4 tabulates a number of glass-transition temperatures reported in the literature.

In a study of changes in glass-transition temperatures for a series of methacrylate and acrylate polymers with stereoregularity, Shetter (10) obtained the values given in the latter part of Table 4. Figure 5 shows a plot of ΔT_g, the difference between T_g of the conventionally prepared polymer (probably essentially syndiotactic) minus T_g of the isotactic polymer, as a function of the number of carbons in the alkyl ester group. A reasonable degree of correlation is shown considering the $\pm 2°C$ error in measurement of T_g and the possibility that varying lengths of syndio-tactic and isotactic sequences may be present in the samples (10).

IV. INTERNAL FRICTION

The internal friction of poly(methyl methacrylate) has been measured by Gall and McCrum (36,37). Figure 6 shows results for the internal friction as a function of temperature for conventional, isotactic and syndiotactic polymers. Significant differences are apparent. The authors concluded, in agreement with others, that the "conventional" poly(methyl methacrylate) was not truly atactic but had considerable syndiotactic character (36,37).

V. MECHANICAL MODULI

The dynamic shear modulus will similarly be affected by tacticity. Figure 7 shows a typical curve where the dynamic shear modulus was measured at a temperature just above the glass-transition temperature (38). Figure 7 was developed using polyethylene as a model polymer for maxi-mum crystallinity as a function of isotacticity. Polyethylene may be used as a model polymer as it is a degenerate case of an isotactic material in which branch points or comonomer units act like atactic links to break up the polymer chain into stereoblocks. For nylon, where the whole chain can be considered to act as a single long block, it is found that the shear

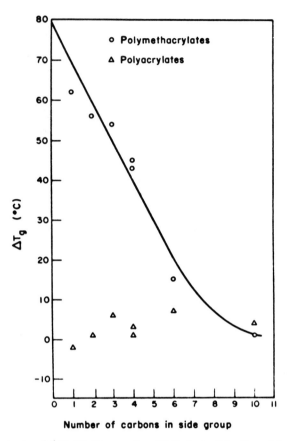

Fig. 5. Dependence of ΔT_g (T_g "conventional"–T_g isotactic) of acrylate and metha-crylate polymers on the number of carbon numbers in the alkyl side group (*10*).

modulus is essentially temperature independent. For polymers with a broad distribution in the length of the blocks, for example, an ethylene–vinyl acetate copolymer, the modulus is strongly temperature dependent. Other polymers may fall between these extremes. The effect, therefore, of tacticity on dynamic shear modulus must also be considered as a tempera-ture-dependent property. This is illustrated in Fig. 8, where the torsion modulus of conventional, isotactic, and syndiotactic methyl methacrylate polymers is shown as a function of temperature (*36*). The effect of stereo-regularity on the main-chain relaxation is illustrated by comparing the temperatures at which the torsion moduli attained an arbitrary value of

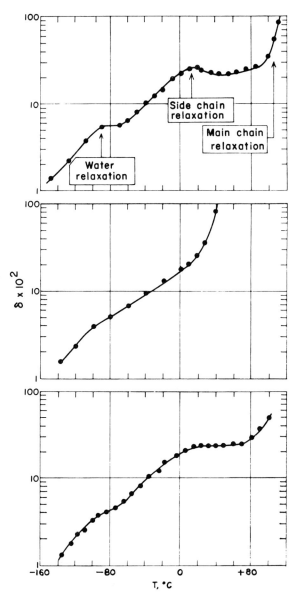

Fig. 6. Internal friction of conventional (upper graph), isotactic (intermediate graph), and syndiotactic (lower graph) poly(methyl methacrylates) (36).

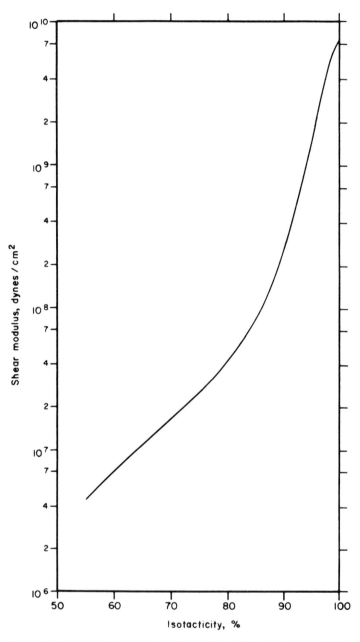

Fig. 7. Dynamic shear modulus as a function of isotacticity using polyethylene as a model polymer (*38*).

224

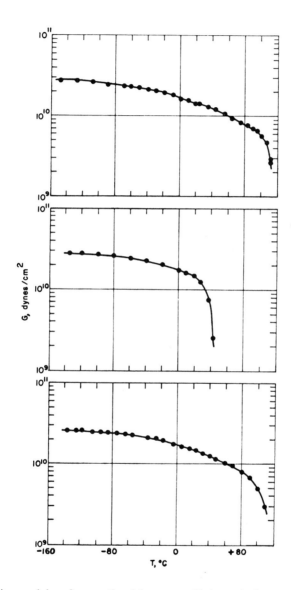

Fig. 8. Torsion modulus of conventional (upper graph), isotactic (intermediate graph), and syndiotactic (lower graph) poly(methyl methacrylate) (*36*).

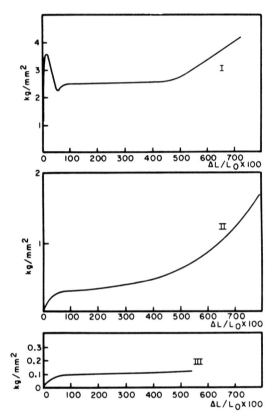

Fig. 9. Stress–strain curves for highly isotactic (I), stereoblock (II), and atactic (III) polypropylenes (15,39).

4×10^9 dynes/cm². These temperatures were $108°C$ for conventional, $42°C$ for isotactic, and $105°C$ for syndiotactic poly(methyl methacrylates), respectively.

Garbunglio et al. (36a) found a linear correlation for the tangential elasticity modulus of poly(vinyl chloride) measured at $120°C$ with stereoregularity determined by infrared measurements.

A number of mechanical studies have been made on polypropylene samples with varying tacticity. Stress–strain curves and tensile and storage moduli have been developed for a series of polypropylene fractions (16). The purpose was to study the efficiency of fractionation and the effect of stereoregularity on the orientation mechanism and mechanical properties of polypropylene. Natta has given measurements (*15*), which have subsequently been republished (*39*), which show distinct differences in mechanical properties among isotactic, stereoblock, and atactic polypropylenes (see Fig. 9). The stereoblock polypropylene is seen to have properties intermediate between the corresponding isotactic and atactic polymers. The shorter the length of stereoblock sequences, the lower is the apparent melting point and percent crystallinity. The initial moduli for atactic and stereoblock polypropylenes are low compared to isotactic polypropylene. Stereoblocks are apparently elastic when oriented. Indeed, Natta has suggested that certain oriented stereoblock polypropylenes may be considered true elastomers (*15*).

Stress–strain curves for isotactic, atactic, and stereoblock polypropylenes have also been determined by Raspopov and co-workers (*40*). They found that the yield point of isotactic polypropylene was independent of molecular weight from at least 20,000 to 160,000. With increasing atactic and stereoblock content, the yield value and tensile strength were found to decrease rapidly and almost proportionally to concentration for both oriented and isotropic samples of polypropylene (*40*). Dynamic mechanical properties of atactic and isotactic forms of polypropylene (*40a*) and polystyrene (*40b*) have been extensively studied by Sauer and Woodward with co-workers. Their measurements from 80°K up through the melting point ranges for these polymers indicated that the significant differences observed could be attributed principally to variations in crystallinity.

Mechanical properties have been reported for polystyrenes with a range of tactic structures (*41*). The study included (a) atactic, (b) isotactic, (c) pure graft copolymer containing 85% by weight of atactic polymer, in branches of molecular weight 200,000, on 15% by weight of isotactic main-chain segments of molecular weight 80,000, and (d) mixtures of (c) with (a). The temperature dependence of elastic moduli for these polystyrenes was intercompared. Crystallinity was found to be absent in (a) and (c). Isothermal curves of stretching at 50°C for films obtained from benzene solution indicated that the grafting of isotactic and atactic polystyrene caused plasticization, an increase of break elongation up to 350%, and a decrease of modulus of elasticity. At 50°C the tensile strengths of (a), (b), (c), and (d) were 58, 160, 40, and 112 kg/cm^2; elongations were 130, 30, 350, and 90% and moduli of elasticity were 68, 500, 33, and 60 kg/cm^2, respectively (*41*).

Fragmentary mechanical and viscoelastic measurements have been reported on additional polymers, such as poly(vinyl alcohols), with differences in stereoregularity (*42*).

VI. SORPTION ISOTHERMS

Sorption and desorption isotherms of polystyrene at 20°C have been measured on a tacticity set of polystyrenes prepared and evaluated by Shibaev and co-workers (*41*). The results suggested that atactic polystyrene was the "most loosely packed" and isotactic polystyrene the most dense among the set studied.

VII. AUTOHESION

Autohesion of polystyrene was measured by Shtarkman and co-workers (*43*). It was found that isotactic samples in the amorphous state were less capable of autohesion than the corresponding atactic ones because of the higher order of their structure within the amorphous state due to the higher degree of regularity of the chains.

VIII. SPECIFIC HEAT

A considerable body of information on the specific heat and related thermodynamic properties of polypropylene and polystyrene has been developed as a function of tacticity. Dainton et al. (*34*), Passaglia and Kevorkian (*35*), and Wilkinson and Dole (*44*) have studied polypropylene. Figure 10 compares the specific heats of atactic and isotactic polypropylenes over a temperature range of 90–475°K (*35*). At temperatures up to

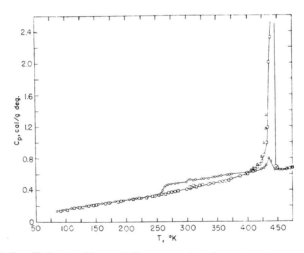

Fig. 10. Specific heats of isotactic (lower curve) and atactic polypropylene (*35*).

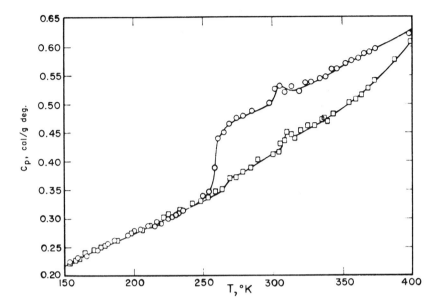

Fig. 11. Specific heats of isotactic and atactic polypropylene around the glass transition (*35*).

about 260°K, the values are very similar. From 260 to about 400°K, the atactic polymer has a significantly higher specific heat. The heat capacity of the isotactic polymer rises sharply in the neighborhood of 443°K, i.e., near the melting point. Above the melting point of isotactic polypropylene, the specific heat of the atactic material is approximately the same as that of the isotactic material. Wilkinson and Dole have concluded that the specific heat of the atactic was slightly higher than that of the corresponding isotactic melt (*44*); Passaglia and Kevorkian (*35*) found the difference to be in the opposite direction but of such a magnitude that it was within experimental error. Figure 11 shows the behavior of isotactic and atactic polypropylenes in the glass-transition region. A small transition at 310°K is observed for both polymers. The cause of this transition is not known. The computed enthalpies as a function of temperature are plotted in Fig. 12. The atactic enthalpy exceeds that of the isotactic from about 100 to 440°K; above this temperature the reverse holds true. Similarly, the difference between the entropy of the isotactic and atactic polypropylene (see Fig. 13) changes sign at about 440°K (*35*). The small difference below 260°K is probably due to the existence of a slightly higher specific heat of the atactic polymer below the glass-transition temperature.

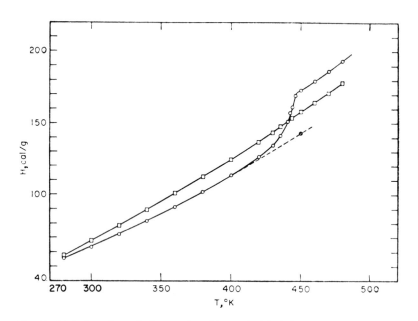

Fig. 12. Enthalpy of atactic (squares) and isotactic (circles) polypropylenes (*35*).

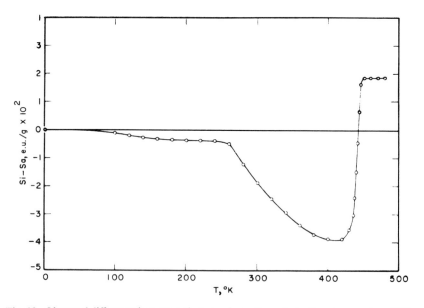

Fig. 13. Observed difference in entropy between isotactic and atactic polypropylene (*35*).

Studies on the thermal properties of atactic and isotactic polystyrene have also been carried out by Abu-Isa and Dole (*45*) and Karasz et al. (*28*). Differences in heat capacity due to tacticity for polystyrene are much smaller than those for polypropylene. Figure 14 gives heat-capacity curves for atactic (untreated), atactic (annealed), isotactic amorphous, and isotactic crystalline polystyrene. Crystallinity produces larger differences than those attributable to tacticity.

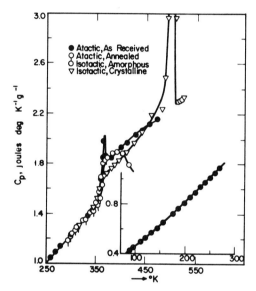

Fig. 14. Heat capacity of atactic and isotactic polystyrene (*28*).

Karasz et al. (*46*), using a precision adiabatic calorimeter, measured the heat capacity of syndiotactic and atactic poly(methyl methacrylate) from 80 to 450°K and O'Reilly et al. (*31*), using the same equipment and conditions, studied amorphous and crystalline isotactic poly(methyl methacrylate). The thermal behavior of atactic and syndiotactic polymers was very similar, probably because the atactic polymer contains a significant amount of syndiotactic placements. The heat capacity at low temperatures was almost identical for the atactic and syndiotactic polymers. A smooth function of temperature was obtained from 80 to 350°K. For atactic poly(methyl methacrylate) a sharp upward curvature in the heat capacity occurred 10–15° below the glass-transition temperature. A similar but smaller effect was observed for the syndiotactic poly(methyl methacrylate).

IX. DIELECTRIC PROPERTIES

The differences between isotactic and syndiotactic poly(vinyl alcohols) have been investigated by the dielectric method (*47,48,48a*). The dielectric primary relaxation and local mode relaxation have been reported for atactic, syndiotactic, and isotactic samples. The relaxation strength of local mode relaxation is higher for atactic and syndiotactic samples than

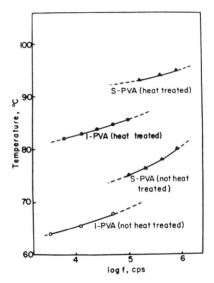

Fig. 15. Transition map of α_a-absorption for isotactic and syndiotactic poly(vinyl alcohols) (*47*).

for isotactic samples when compared at zero crystallinity. This behavior is reasonably explained in terms of interchain hydrogen bonds in the former and intrachain hydrogen bonds in the latter.

Takayanagi and co-workers compared the primary relaxations of syndiotactic and isotactic samples and explained the difference, assuming the nature of hydrogen bonds to be essentially similar in the amorphous phase and the crystalline phase. A high-temperature absorption and a low-temperature absorption can be observed. The height of the high-temperature peak in dielectric measurements ε''_{max} decreases by heat treatment in both the isotactic and syndiotactic polymers. The apparent activation energy calculated from the results in Fig. 15 is about 100–200 kcal/mole. This high-temperature absorption is attributed to segmental diffusional motion in the amorphous region. The authors call it an α_a-absorption where the subscript a means amorphous. Two absorptions are observed in the low-temperature range which represent fine structure of the low-temperature absorption shown in Fig. 16. The low-temperature absorption can be divided into two components because the dielectric behavior is measured as frequency dependent instead of as temperature dependent. The high-temperature absorption was not measured in terms of frequency

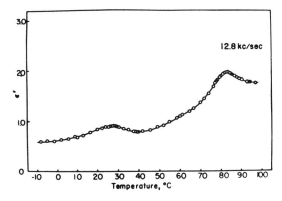

Fig. 16. ε'' vs. temperature for isotactic poly(vinyl alcohol) (*47*).

dependence but in terms of temperature dependence, since the frequency dependence is hidden by large ionic conduction (*47,48*).

The low-temperature absorption is attributable to the disordered region. The apparent activation energy calculated from the temperature dependence of this ε''_{max} frequency is about 10 kcal/mole, and these absorptions can be observed in the glassy state of the polymer. It is therefore concluded that these absorptions are caused by local twisting motion of main chains in the disordered region.

X. FILM PRESSURE

Pressure–area isotherms for isotactic, syndiotactic, and stereoblock poly(methyl methacrylates) have been measured and intercompared. The measurement technique has been separately described (*49,50*). Monolayers were spread from benzene solution and studied at 25°C. Figure 17 shows that at low pressures the isotherm for stereoblock polymer is intermediate between those for the isotactic and syndiotactic forms. At higher pressures the stereoblock polymer is at the smallest area of the three. Both stereoblock and isotactic poly(methyl methacrylates) yield a well-defined film structure at large areas and both reveal a possible inflection point near 8 dynes/cm. However, the stereoblock polymer definitely packs more closely and has the highest collapse pressure of the three. The film of the stereoblock polymer thus has the stronger cohesive and adhesive forces (*49–51*).

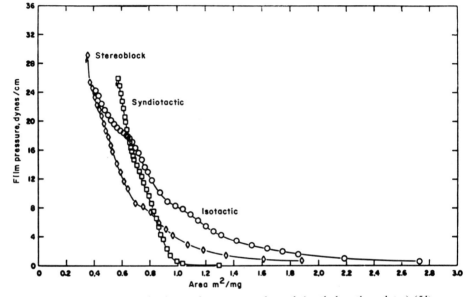

Fig. 17. Pressure–area isotherms for stereoregular poly(methyl methacrylates) (*51*).

The effect of pressure on an isotherm for an equal-weight mixture of isotactic and syndiotactic polymers was also compared with the isotherms for the individual components. The behavior of the physical mixture is similar to that of the stereoblock polymer. The similarity is strikingly evident in Fig. 18, the difference being principally at high pressures (*51*).

XI. WATER RESISTANCE

It has been known for over 10 years that the degree of swelling in water of poly(vinyl alcohol), PVA, depends on the polymerization temperature of the original poly(vinyl acetate) (*52*). It has also been shown that, if the swelling test is carried out in hot water, the effect of stereoregularity on the water resistance of PVA is still large even after crystallization (*52a,53*).

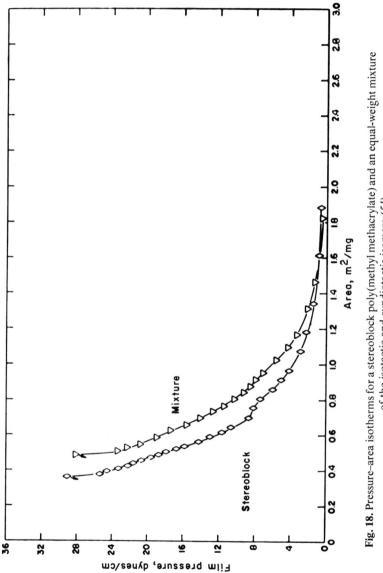

Fig. 18. Pressure–area isotherms for a stereoblock poly(methyl methacrylate) and an equal-weight mixture of the isotactic and syndiotactic isomers (51).

Rosen et al. have supposed that the higher water resistance is related to the stereoregular structure in the amorphous regions (54). Fujii et al. (53) suggest that the water resistance of the crystalline portions must also be considered for a proper understanding of the water resistance of PVA. The unique water solubility of highly stereoregular PVA is illustrated in Table 5 (55). The tactic concentrations given in the table were determined by high-resolution nuclear magnetic resonance.

TABLE 5

Solubilities of Poly(vinyl alcohols) in Water (55)

Sample no.	Isotactic, % in diads	Solubility in water
1	91	Insoluble in cold; soluble at 100°C
2	87.5	Soluble in cold
4 (commercial)	55	Insoluble in cold; soluble at 100°C
6	48.5	Insoluble in cold; soluble at 100°C
10	26	Insoluble at 150°C; soluble at 160°C

It is of interest to emphasize that the side chain OH in PVA is so small in size that it can be interchangeable with the hydrogen atom in the crystalline lattice. The arrangement of hydrogen bonding in PVA should be different, however, depending on tactic placement (53). In a planar zig-zag chain, isotactic configuration favors intramolecular hydrogen bonding, whereas syndiotactic configuration favors interchain hydrogen bonding. Thus, the interchain force in the crystalline part may vary with the tactic structure of the PVA. The cohesion of the crystalline portion of PVA may also depend on tactic placement (53).

XII. LOW-RESOLUTION NUCLEAR MAGNETIC RESONANCE

Proton spin–lattice relaxation time, T_1, has been measured as a function of temperature for three samples of poly(methyl methacrylate) of different tacticities. The measurements were made by Powles and Strange at a resonance frequency of 21.5 Mc/sec by the 180-degree, 90-degree pulse method. Dynamic mechanical losses were also measured in the frequency region of about 200 c/sec by a vibrating reed method (56). The T_1 results for the poly(methyl methacrylates) are given in Fig. 19. The minimum at the highest temperature for T_1 for the commercial sample and the main peak in tan δ are associated with the softening or α process presumed to be

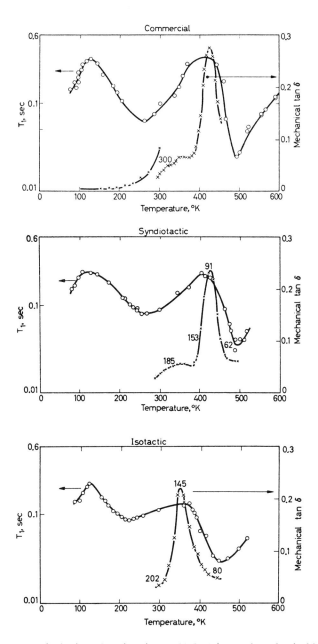

Fig. 19. Proton spin–lattice relaxation time at 21.5 Mc/sec and mechanical loss tan δ at the frequencies indicated as a function of absolute temperature for a sample of commercial poly(methyl methacrylate). The mechanical loss curve including the principal loss maximum is for commercial material diluted with 66% Tufuit. The lower temperature curve is for the undiluted commercial polymer. The intermediate curve is for isotactic polymer (56).

237

connected with macromotions of the main chain. The second minimum in T_1 at about 260°K has been associated with reorientation of the α-CH$_3$ group. No sign of a peak down to 77°K at 460 c/sec was observed. Both minima of T_1 can be satisfactorily correlated with line narrowing in the broad-line proton magnetic resonance spectra which fits the temperatures at which a molecular motion is at about 10^4 c/sec. Below 90°K, a third minimum in T_1 has been postulated for the reorientation of the side-chain methyl group.

The syndiotactic sample reported in Fig. 19 was found by high-resolution nuclear magnetic resonance to possess over 90% syndiotactic placement. Both mechanical and magnetic resonance measurements on this sample are hardly distinguishable from those on the commercial polymer. This is in agreement with an NMR tacticity analysis which indicated that the commercial material is quite (60%) syndiotactic.

The isotactic poly(methyl methacrylate) also described in Fig. 19 was found by NMR-calibrated infrared analysis to contain less than 24% atactic material. This polymer shows a marked change in both T_1 and tan δ as compared to the syndiotactic polymer. The upper minimum in T_1 is shifted down 40°C, and the mechanical loss peak has also been shifted down by 75°C. It can be concluded that not only are the motions slower at a given temperature in the syndiotactic polymer but that the motions change more rapidly with temperature. These two effects have been ascribed to a greater hindrance to main-chain reorientation in the syndiotactic form as compared to the isotactic poly(methyl methacrylate) (56).

Low-resolution proton magnetic resonance investigations have been made on a series of polypropylenes (57–59). Data have been reported on isotactic, atactic, and isotactic polypropylene with the CH$_3$ group in the latter changed to a CD$_3$ group but with protons in the chain remaining intact. Figure 20 shows resonance line widths plotted as a function of temperature as given by Slichter and Mandell (58,59). For isotactic and atactic polypropylenes, the line widths drop in the beginning of the temperature range followed by a region of approximately constant line width up to about 250°K. In the case of the deuterated isotactic polypropylene, there was no change or transition at the beginning of the temperature range (57). It has therefore been concluded that this low-temperature transition near liquid nitrogen temperature is due to CH$_3$ group rotation. All the polymers exhibit a transition at above 250°K (see Fig. 20). The isotactic and atactic polypropylenes exhibit the transition at about 285 and 270°K, respectively. Similar conclusions are obtained from the second moment of resonance vs. temperature plots, except that the latter indicate slightly higher transition temperatures than line width studies. The second, high-temperature transition, 250–300°K, is due to chain segment motion in all polypropylenes studied.

In isotactic polypropylene, the magnetic resonance consists jointly of narrow and broad components over a wide temperature interval (see Fig. 20). The resonance narrows at somewhat lower temperatures in atactic

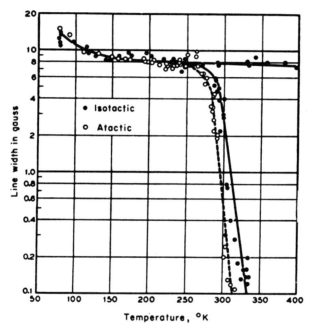

Fig. 20. Temperature variation of proton magnetic resonance line width in isotactic and atactic polypropylene (58,59).

polypropylene than in the amorphous regions of the isotactic polymer. This difference probably reflects constraints on the segmental motions in the amorphous regions imposed by the crystal structure in the isotactic polypropylene. The resonances observed tend, even at room temperature, toward small widths typical of liquids. This liquidlike behavior in the motion of amorphous segments is consistent with the rubbery nature of atactic polypropylene. The relatively constant broad resonance in isotactic polymer shows that there is little motion in the crystalline regions (see Fig. 20) (58,59).

XIII. BULK DENSITY

In general, stereoregularity may be expected to have a measurable influence on the density or molar volume of undiluted and concentrated systems of linear polymers. That is, the closeness of packing of amorphous chains should be, a priori, affected by microtacticity. The data available, however, have lead to the conclusion that density as well as other thermodynamic properties are virtually independent of tacticity. Limited examples included published molar volumes of atactic and isotactic polypropylene (60) and atactic and isotactic polystyrene (25). In these cases, molar volume differences attributable to tactic variation are small to negligible. Indeed, the calculation of percent crystallinity from density is usually based on the assumption that molar volume is independent of stereoregularity. To the contrary, there is at least one well-documented polymer for which stereoregularity has a marked effect on bulk density and molar volume. For poly(methyl methacrylate) at 25°C, specific volumes of the amorphous isotactic, syndiotactic, and atactic derivatives are 0.820, 0.841, and 0.845 ml/g, respectively (61,62).

ACKNOWLEDGMENTS

The authors are pleased to acknowledge the courtesy of Interscience Publishers, a division of John Wiley and Sons, Inc., for permitting reproduction of Figs. 1–6, 8, 9, and 15–18 and Table 5 from the *Journal of Polymer Science* and Fig. 7 from the *Journal of Applied Polymer Science;* to the American Institute of Physics for Figs. 10–12 from the *Journal of Applied Physics;* to the American Chemical Society for Fig. 14 and Table 3 from the *Journal of Physical Chemistry;* and to Butterworth for Fig. 19 from *Polymer*.

REFERENCES

1. C. E. Schildknecht, S. T. Gross, H. R. Davidson, I. M. Lambert, and A. D. Zoss, *Ind. Eng. Chem.*, **40**, 2104 (1948).
1a. B. D. Coleman, *J. Polymer Sci.*, **31**, 155 (1958).
2. V. D. Gupta and R. B. Beevers, *Chem. Rev.*, **62**, 665 (1962).
3. K. Matsuzaki, T. Okamoto, A. Ishida, and H. Sobue, *J. Polymer Sci.*, **A2**, 1105 (1964).
4. G. Natta, L. Porri, G. Stoppa, G. Allegra, and F. Ciampelli, *J. Polymer Sci.*, **B1**, 67 (1963).
5. G. Natta, L. Porri, A. Carbonaro, F. Ciampelli, and G. Allegra, *Makromol. Chem.*, **51**, 229 (1962).

6. G. Natta and P. Corradini, *J. Polymer Sci.*, **20**, 251 (1956).
7. G. Natta, *Chem. Ind. (London)*, **(1957)**, 1520.
8. T. G. Fox, B. S. Garrett, W. E. Goode, S. Gratch, J. F. Kincaid, A. Spell, and J. D. Stroupe, *J. Am. Chem. Soc.*, **80**, 1768 (1958).
9. B. S. Garrett, W. E. Goode, S. Gratch, J. F. Kincaid, C. L. Levesque, A. Spell, J. D. Stroupe, and W. H. Watanabe, *J. Am. Chem. Soc.*, **81**, 1007 (1958).
10. J. A. Shetter, *J. Polymer Sci.*, **B1**, 209 (1963).
11. C. F. Ryan and J. J. Gormley, *Macromol. Syn.*, **1**, 30 (1963).
12. W. E. Goode, R. P. Fellman, and F. H. Owens, *Macromol. Syn.*, **1**, 25 (1963).
13. A. Ledwith, *Ind. Chemist*, **37**, 71 (1961).
14. K.-S. Chia and U.-P. Wang, *Hua Hsueh Hsueh Pao*, **11**(3), 150 (1964).
15. G. Natta, *J. Polymer Sci.*, **34**, 531 (1959).
16. H. Takahara and H. Kawai, *Seni-i Gakkaishi*, **21**, 565 (1965).
17. G. Natta, I. Pasquon, P. Corradini, M. Peraldo, M. Pegoraro, and A. Zambelli, *Atti Accad. Nazl. Lincei, Rend., Classe Sci. Fis. Mat. Nat.*, **28**, 539 (1960).
18. J. Boor, Jr., and E. A. Youngman, *J. Polymer Sci.*, **B3**, 577 (1965).
19. S. Newman, *J. Polymer Sci.*, **47**, 111 (1960).
20. G. Farrow, *Polymer*, **4**, 191 (1963).
21. C. F. Ryan and P. C. Fleischer, Jr., *J. Phys. Chem.*, **69**, 3384 (1965).
22. S. Krause and N. Roman, *J. Polymer Sci.*, **A3**, 1631 (1965).
23. M. Gordon and J. S. Taylor, *J. Appl. Chem.*, **2**, 493 (1952).
24. T. G. Fox, *Bull. Am. Phys. Soc.*, **1**, 123 (1956).
25. G. P. Mikhaelov and T. I. Borisvva, *Vysokomolekul. Soedin.*, **2**, 619 (1960); G. Natta, F. Danusso, and G. Moraglia, *Makromol. Chem.*, **28**, 166 (1958); G. Natta, F. Danusso, and G. Moraglia, *Atti Accad. Nazl. Lincei, Rend., Classe Sci. Fis. Mat. Nat.*, **24**, 254 (1958).
26. E. V. Thompson, *J. Polymer Sci.*, **(A-2)4**, 199 (1966).
27. S. Newman and W. P. Cox, *J. Polymer Sci.*, **46**, 29 (1960).
28. F. E. Karasz, H. E. Bair, and J. M. O'Reilly, *J. Phys. Chem.*, **69**, 2657 (1965).
29. L. E. Nielsen, *Mechanical Properties of Polymers*, Reinhold, New York, 1962, pp. 23, 24.
30. R. F. Boyer, *Polymer Preprints*, **6**, 721 (1965).
31. J. M. O'Reilly, F. E. Karasz, and H. E. Bair, *Bull. Am. Phys. Soc.*, **9**, 285 (1964).
31a. G. Natta, *Angew. Chem.*, **68**, 393 (1956).
31b. F. P. Reding, *J. Polymer Sci.*, **21**, 547 (1956).
32. R. F. Boyer, *Rubber Chem. Technol.*, **36**, 1303 (1963).
33. Y. Sakurada, K. Imai, and M. Matsumoto, *Kobunshi Kagaku*, **20**, 429 (1963).
33a. G. Natta, *Makromol. Chem.*, **16**, 213 (1955).
34. F. S. Dainton, D. M. Evans, F. E. Hoare, and T. P. Melia, *Polymer*, **3**, 286 (1962).
35. E. Passaglia and H. K. Kevorkian, *J. Appl. Phys.*, **34**, 90 (1963).
36. W. G. Gall and N. G. McCrum, *J. Polymer Sci.*, **50**, 489 (1961).
36a. C. Garbunglio, A. Rodella, G. C. Borsini, and E. Gallinella, *Chim. Ind. (Milan)*, **46**(2), 166 (1964).
37. N. G. McCrum, *J. Polymer Sci.*, **34**, 355 (1959).
38. L. E. Nielsen, *J. Appl. Polymer Sci.*, **2**, 351 (1959).
39. J. L. Koenig, *Offic. Dig. Federation Sov. Paint Technol.*, **36**, 502 (1964).
40. L. N. Raspopov, O. N. Pirogov, N. M. Chirkov, and D. M. Lisitsyn, *Vysokomolekul. Soedin*, **5**(12), 1761 (1963).

40a. J. A. Sauer, R. A. Wall, N. Fuschillo, and A. E. Woodward, *J. Appl. Phys.*, **29**, 1385 (1959).

40b. R. A. Wall, J. A. Sauer, and A. E. Woodward, *J. Polymer Sci.*, **35**, 281 (1959).

41. V. P. Shibaev, N. A. Plate, H. Trang, and V. A. Kargin, *Vysokomolekul. Soedin.*, **6**(1), 107 (1964).

42. M. Takayanagi and A. Nagai, *Rept. Progr. Polymer Phys. Japan*, **6**, 249 (1964).

43. B. P. Shtarkman, S. S. Voyuitskii, and V. A. Kargin, *Vysokomolekul. Soedin.*, **7**(1), 141 (1965).

44. R. W. Wilkinson and M. Dole, *J. Polymer Sci.*, **58**, 1089 (1962).

45. I. Abu-Isa and M. Dole, *J. Phys. Chem.*, **69**, 2668 (1965).

46. F. E. Karasz, J. M. O'Reilly, and H. E. Bair, *Bull. Am. Phys. Soc.*, **9**, 285 (1964).

47. T. Kajiyama, S. Togami, Y. Ishida, and M. Takayanagi, *J. Polymer Sci.*, **B3**, 103 (1965).

48. Y. Ishida, M. Yoshino, M. Takayanagi, and F. Irie, *J. Appl. Polymer Sci.*, **1**, 229 (1959).

48a. K. Shida and Y. Wada, *J. Appl. Polymer Sci.*, **10**, 1483 (1966).

49. H. E. Ries, Jr., and H. D. Cook, *J. Colloid Sci.*, **9**, 535 (1954).

50. H. E. Ries, Jr., and D. C. Walker, *J. Colloid Sci.*, **16**, 361 (1961).

51. N. Beredjick and H. E. Ries, Jr., *J. Polymer Sci.*, **62**, S64 (1962).

52. J. Ukida, R. Naito, and T. Kominami, *J. Chem. Soc. Japan, Ind. Chem. Sect.*, **58**, 128, 717 (1955).

52a. K. Fujii, S. Imoto, J. Ukida, and M. Matsumoto, preprint for the *Symposium on Polymer Chemistry, Kyoto, November 1960.*

53. K. Fujii, T. Mochizuki, J. Ukida, and M. Matusmoto, *J. Polymer Sci.*, **B1**, 696 (1963).

54. I. Rosen, G. H. McCain, A. L. Endrey, and C. L. Sturm, *J. Polymer Sci.*, **A1**, 951 (1963).

55. S. Murahashi, S. Nozakura, M. Sumi, and K. Matsumura, *J. Polymer Sci.*, **B4**, 59 (1966).

56. J. G. Powles, J. H. Strange, and D. J. H. Sandiford, *Polymer*, **4**, 401 (1963).

57. R. P. Gupta, *Kolloid-Z.*, **174**, 73 (1961).

58. W. P. Slichter and E. R. Mandell, *J. Chem. Phys.*, **29**, 232 (1958).

59. W. P. Slichter and E. R. Mandell, *J. Appl. Phys.*, **29**, 1438 (1958).

60. S. Newman, *J. Polymer Sci.*, **47**, 111 (1960).

61. W. E. Goode, F. H. Owens, R. P. Fellmann, W. H. Snyder, snd J. E. Moore, *J. Polymer Sci.*, **46**, 317 (1960).

62. A. J. Kovacs and J. Wittman, paper presented at the *International Symposium on Macromolecular Chemistry, Prague, 1965.*

CHAPTER 6

Properties of Synthetic Linear Stereoregular Polymers in Solution

V. Crescenzi

ISTITUTO CHIMICO
UNIVERSITÀ DI NAPOLI
NAPLES, ITALY

I. INTRODUCTION

Stereoregular synthetic macromolecules are often capable of assuming highly ordered regular conformations in the solid state. The conformation assumed by a polymer in the crystalline state is, in general, a very close approximation of the form corresponding to the lowest energy of the isolated chain, being affected only to a minor extent by intermolecular forces (*1*). In view of this, it is clear that when such chain molecules are transferred from a perfect crystal to a dilute solution, the conformational restraints imposed by nonbonded atom interactions along each chain will still markedly influence polymer conformations. This is clearly opposed to the dissolution process of crystals of a low molecular weight compound, in consequence of which the molecules of the latter are, statistically, homogeneously dispersed in the solvent, the features of the crystalline state being completely lost in the final mixture.

It appears, therefore, that evaluation of factors leading to the existence of a most stable ordered conformation of a polymer chain should precede consideration of the configuration of an ensemble of such chains when necessarily in a more disordered state, i.e., dispersed in an excess of low molecular weight solvent.

Next, and only for the purpose of convenience, the problem of the elucidation of physicochemical properties of stereoregular polymers in dilute solution should be formally divided in two parts. In the first part experimental evaluation and theoretical prediction of average chain dimensions in the so-called "unperturbed state" are considered. In this state the macromolecules may assume domains in space which are amenable to treatments based on the knowledge of configurational and conformational features of the isolated chains only.

In the second part attention is focused on the physicochemical behavior of stereoregular polymers in good solvents, where perturbations in the shapes of the macromolecules which are brought about by their spatial requirements and by energetic interactions which depend on the nature of the solvent have to be accounted for.

In what follows, the presentation scheme outlined above will be tentatively followed. We hope that, despite these artificial divisions, a unified viewpoint will stem as a logical consequence of this treatment.

II. ORDERED CONFORMATIONS OF LINEAR MACROMOLECULES IN THE SOLID STATE

As clearly indicated by Liquori et al. (1,2), the ordered conformations that a given linear macromolecule may assume in the solid state form a special class which can be selected by utilizing the same basic concepts applicable to small molecules (ethane, propane, etc.) to each repeating unit along the chain, and by imposing, furthermore, the very restrictive condition of the "conformational equivalence" of each unit with respect to the next in the chain (3).

Consider, for example, a vinylidene polymer which may be represented as:

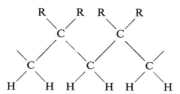

Any ordered conformation of the chain is defined by the angles of rotation ψ_1 and ψ_2 about the two skeletal bonds. Two types of ordered conformations may be expected when the sequence of rotations is such that ψ_1 and ψ_2 are identical in pairs, i.e.,

$$\cdots \psi_1\psi_2\psi_1\psi_2\psi_1\psi_2 \cdots$$

A helix is obtained, implying a conformational equivalence between consecutive monomeric units. When the bond rotations sequence is

$$\cdots \psi_1\psi_2 \quad \psi_1 \quad \psi_2\psi_1\psi_2 \quad \psi_1 \quad \psi_2 \cdots$$

a regular conformation having a glide symmetry is generated. Both forms are possible for a polyvinylidene chain since each monomer unit contains a dyad axis.

On the other hand, in the case of isotactic vinyl polymers such as poly-α-olefins, which may be represented as:

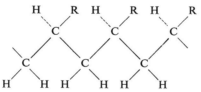

the only types of ordered conformations are helical and in order for the condition of conformational equivalence to be applicable there must be a configurational equivalence between consecutive monomer units. Both these restrictions are related to the absence of a dyad axis in the monomer units.

Consider now a syndiotactic vinyl chain possessing monomer units with alternating "opposite configurations":

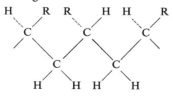

The symmetry of the ordered conformations can be characterized either by a glide plane relating the monomer units or by a helix. In the latter case the repeating units are made of two consecutive monomer units containing a dyad axis and the conformational sequence is:

$$\cdots \psi_1\psi_2\psi_2\psi_1 \quad \psi_1\psi_2\psi_2\psi_1 \quad \psi_1\psi_2\psi_2\psi_1 \cdots$$

With regard to the problem of establishing which pair of values of the angles of rotation ψ_1 and ψ_2 lead to the more stable conformation of a chain in each case, it must be immediately pointed out that the solution cannot be found by applying simple staggering rules to each of the skeletal bonds of the monomer units *separately*. This is mainly due to the high degree of cooperation in the interactions between monomer units in a linear chain.

Liquori et al. (*1–3*) have recently carried out a systematic analysis of the stability of helical chain conformations based on the assumption that the most stable helix of a given infinite linear macromolecule may be predicted by locating the deepest minimum in the potential energy, calculated as a function of the angles of rotation around the nonequivalent bonds of a monomer unit with fixed bond angles and bond lengths. The changes of the potential energy with the angle of rotation may be calculated from the corresponding changes of the interaction potentials between atoms not chemically bonded in the chain as a function of distance. Such calculations obviously require the appropriate choice of:

a. Bond length and bond angles

b. Functions correlating the distances between nonbonded atoms to the angles of rotation about the bonds

c. Potential functions describing pairwise interactions between non-bonded atoms as a function of distance

Points (a) and (b) are easily fulfilled by using structural data obtainable from X-ray studies on simple molecules and by extending the known matrix transformation methods.

On the other hand, the choice of potential functions describing inter-actions between nonbonded atoms clearly constitutes the main approxima-tion underlying the analysis. The present knowledge of the factors hindering rotation about chemical bonds is, in fact, still so poor that exact calculations are not possible even for very simple molecules like ethane.

It is not within the scope of this brief discussion to enter into details about this particular problem, nor to illustrate the associated mathe-matical complexities. A few results of the systematic work carried out by Liquori et al. will simply be reported here.

In Fig. 1 the conformational potential energy of a polytetrafluoroethylene helix is shown as a function of the angles of rotation about the C—C bond (*1*). The deepest minimum is found at 165°, which corresponds to an helix with 2.17 monomers per turn, in excellent agreement with the helix having 13/6 monomers per turn found at room temperature for this polymer by Bunn and Howells (*4*). The symmetrical minima correspond to the enantiomorphous helices, which are isoenergetic since there are no asymmetric atoms.

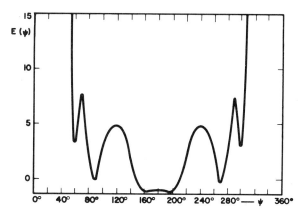

Fig. 1. Conformational potential energy of a polytetrafluoroethylene helix as a function of the angle of rotation about the C—C skeleton bonds (*1*).

In Fig. 2 the conformational potential energy of a polyisobutylene helix is plotted as a function of the angles of rotations about the two skeleton bonds of a monomer unit (*1*). The diagonal $\psi_1 = \psi_2$ in this diagram corresponds to a symmetry operation which interchanges the substituents R. The diagonal $\psi_1 = 2\pi - \psi_2$ separates isoenergetic enantiomorphous helices. The deepest minima are at $\psi_1 = \psi_2 = 85°$ and at $\psi_1 = 155°$, $\psi_2 = 45°$, the first corresponding to a conformation very similar to the helix with 8/5 monomers per turn found for this polymer when it crystallizes on stretching (*5*).

In Fig. 3 the potential energy diagram of an isotactic polypropylene helix (*1*) is shown; the deepest minimum in the diagram corresponds very closely to the threefold helix found in the crystalline polymer by X-ray diffraction (*6*). The deepest minimum is at $\psi_1 = 180°$ (or T) and $\psi_2 = 60°$ (or G) and corresponds to a helix which is only twofold degenerate. In fact, an equivalent minimum is obtained by operation of the diagonal

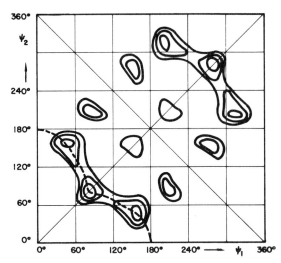

Fig. 2. Two-dimensional plot of the conformational potential energy of a polyisobutylene helix as a function of the angles of rotation Ψ'_1 and Ψ'_2 around the skeleton bonds of the monomer unit (*1*).

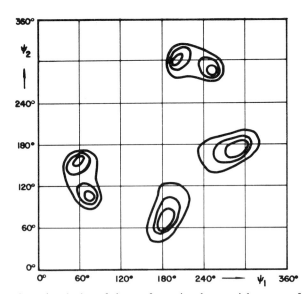

Fig. 3. Two-dimensional plot of the conformational potential energy of an isotactic polypropylene helix as a function of the angles of rotation Ψ'_1 and Ψ'_2 around the skeleton bonds of the monomer unit (*1*).

$\psi_1 = \psi_2$, which corresponds to a helix with opposite screw sense of the same energy.

In poly(methyl methacrylate), the isotactic chain forms a helix with five monomers per turn (according to the sequence of rotation angles $\psi_1 = 180°$ and $\psi_2 = 108°$), while for the syndiotactic chain an extended form with the conformational sequence $(TG_+TG_-)_n$ has been proposed (2c).†

Other interesting instances of agreement between theoretical predictions and X-ray crystal structure data for crystalline polymers might be discussed. This general agreement indicates that in spite of the drastic approximations implied in the choice of the potential functions it has been successfully demonstrated that intramolecular nonbonded van der Waals' interactions are the main factors responsible for the stability of ordered conformations of polyvinyl and polyhydrocarbon polymers.

The point to be emphasized here is that the tendency to perpetuate bond rotation angles which minimize the internal energy of a macromolecule is great in vinyl stereoregular polymers, the passage to other sets of angles involving a destruction of the crystal lattice and an increase in energy of several kilocalories per bond. Particularly severe restrictions are found in the case of vinyl polymers bearing bulky substituents. This is quite naturally expected to be reflected in some of the properties exhibited by such polymers in solution, particularly in the "unperturbed" state.

III. LINEAR STEREOREGULAR CHAINS IN SOLUTION

A. General Considerations

As outlined in the preceding section, the regularity of the crystalline state of a polymer requires the same sign and value of rotation for each equivalent bond along the stereoregular chains; sign and value of rotation being the result of cooperative interactions. A regular array of helices, in each of which the same direction is maintained throughout, meets these requirements and minimizes the internal energy of the crystal. In the amorphous state or in solution, however, the sign of bond rotation may in principle change at successive bonds and this is necessary to keep the free energy of the solution at a minimum.

† Throughout this chapter the symbols T, G, and G* are used for the *trans, gauche,* and *gauche** states of the bonds. This symbolism is commonly used by our laboratory and is equivalent to t, g, and g⁻ used by some other workers for the angles of rotation ψ_1 and ψ_2. It is obvious, however, that they must not be intended to exactly define, in general, angles of rotation of 180° (or 0°) and of ±60° (or ±120°) around skeletal bonds, but angles of rotations lying within some ±10° of these values.

Steric interferences do, however, still markedly influence chain conformation at the local level. In syndiotactic polymers, for example, in which the configurations of successive asymmetric carbon atoms alternate regularly, a given pair of bonds must be either both *trans* or both *gauche*, in the first approximation. Each *gauche* pair must be of the type G_+G_+ or G_-G_-, depending on the configuration of the preceding asymmetric carbon atom in the chain. Furthermore, minimum interference between neighboring chain substituents requires a GG pair to be flanked by units with a TT conformation. Therefore, the conformation of syndiotactic chains in solution should be described as:

$$(TT)(TT)(GG)(TT)(TT) \ldots (TT)(GG)(TT) \ldots$$

In the case of isotactic polymer chains the situation appears more uncertain, since all deviations from a regular alternation of *trans* and *gauche* bond rotations produce large steric stresses. Birshtein (7) and Nagai (8) have proposed conformations of the type:

$$(TG_+)(TG_+)(TG_+) \ldots (G_-T)(G_-T)(TG_+)(TG_+) \ldots$$

Such conformations, however, contain G_+G_- junctions which are energetically highly unfavorable.

Allegra et al. (9) have suggested that the strain is largely relieved by substituting for G_+G_- the sequences EG_- or E^*G_+, where E and E^* represent eclipsed conformations with the same sense of rotation as G_+ and G_-, respectively. Steric repulsions in the model of these authors is estimated to involve an energy of 2.7 kcal/mole in the case of polypropylene.

The case of vinyl polymers which are optically active deserves special mention. Let us consider a perfect isotactic vinyl chain (isolated) bearing asymmetric substituents. It is easily recognized that the probability of occurrence of TG or GT bond conformations for each repeating unit is now not the same. In fact, owing to the asymmetry of the side group, the set of rotational states and the associated energies of the side group when the chain conformation is TG may be both different from the corresponding set compatible with a main GT conformation. This situation leads to the conclusion that one screw sense will prevail along the chain, and will also be preferentially populated in solution.

An effect of a cooperative type is thus displayed between side-chain and main-chain conformations, leading to a possible explanation of the very high values of optical activity found by Pino et al. in the case of some highly stereoregular vinyl polymers (10). The problem of average chain dimensions of perfectly isotactic vinyl polymers with an asymmetric side chain has been treated theoretically by Birshtein and Luisi (*11*). These authors have shown, in the case of a poly-α-olefin with asymmetric side groups, that a small difference in the conformational free energies of the repeating units, when part of a right-handed or left-handed helical section, is sufficient to account for a considerable prevalence of one sense of spiralization.

Furthermore, according to the calculations of these authors, the average dimensions of a chain with asymmetric side groups are only slightly greater than those of a reference optically inactive isotactic chain, for reasonable values of the excess of one sense spiralization. The same conclusions have recently and independently been reached by Allegra et al. (*12*) by applying the Gibbs and Di Marzio method of calculation.

No experimental data are available in the literature on unperturbed dimensions of isotactic vinyl polymers which are optically active. This point, however, together with the study of temperature coefficients of both optical rotatory dispersion and average dimensions of such polymers, deserves particular attention. Whatever the model and the case, it is important to point out that, taking the regular conformational characteristics of the crystalline state as reference, permissible alternative rotational (or configurational?) states introduce sharp kinks in the chain in solution. In general, these kinks are sufficient to allow polymer chains, stereoregular or not, to display the usual properties of random coils in dilute solution.

In solution, furthermore, there is no longer a need for well-defined values of rotation angles but, instead, these may vary within a range, increasing the flexibility of the macromolecular conformation. Chain flexibility is here considered in terms of the accessibility of different shapes (equilibrium) and not from the kinetic point of view. The latter would involve a detailed knowledge of barrier heights and shapes. This knowledge is actually in a rather unsatisfactory state.

Theoretical treatments of average coil conformations assumed by stereoregular chains in dilute solution attack the problem by taking advantage of the results obtained in the elucidation of stable conformations of crystalline chain structures. The final results are expressed in terms of the so-called unperturbed mean-square end-to-end dimensions. Correctness of a theoretical approach is judged by its success in predicting values of the latter quantity which are in agreement with experimental values.

The results of experimental investigations on average size of a coiled chain in solution are, in fact, generally expressed in terms of its mean-square end-to-end distance $\langle r^2 \rangle$, or by the mean square of its radius of gyration $\langle s^2 \rangle$. The latter quantity is normally one-sixth of $\langle r^2 \rangle$ for linear chains, hence it need not be treated separately. We confine our attention to $\langle r^2 \rangle$, as a very convenient index of the domain in space of a macromolecular chain.

B. "Characteristic Ratio"

The extension of the domain of a macromolecule in solution is strongly influenced by interactions between chain elements, which we may briefly refer to as "short range" interactions and "long range" interactions. The former are of main relevance to our discussion since they are those between atoms or groups separated only by a small number of valence bonds and dictate the conformation of the isolated macromolecules. Long range interactions, i.e., those between nonbonded groups which are separated in the basic chain structure by many valence bonds, give rise to the so-called "excluded volume effect" which can be visualized as an osmotic swelling of the randomly coiled polymer chain promoted by the excess solvent–polymer interactions.

For a macromolecule dissolved in a good solvent, as a result of the superposition of both type of interactions, the average dimension, i.e., the value of $\langle r^2 \rangle$, will depend upon n, the number of bonds in the chain, in a complicated fashion. It is well established, however, that the excluded volume effect vanishes under a special condition of temperature (or solvent) known as the Flory "theta" temperature (or solvent) (13). At this stage the chain without long range interactions is called the "unperturbed" chain and the ratio $\langle r^2 \rangle_0/nl^2$ (where l is the length of chain bonds) acquires the significance of a characteristic ratio (13), whose value is solely determined by structural features of the chain skeleton and temperature, independent of n (for large n) and independent of solvent (as a first approximation). It is important to recall that the theta point is thus defined in complete analogy with the Boyle point for a real gas.

Theoretical evaluation of $\langle r^2 \rangle_0/nl^2$ is a difficult task. As already pointed out, a valuable estimate of the characteristic ratios of stereoregular vinyl chains must necessarily take into account the interdependence of the angles of rotation for adjacent bonds. This, of course, is common to all treatments proposed today.

The success of the theoretical approach in predicting characteristic ratios for linear macromolecules in solution is well documented in a number of instances. In these cases, evaluation of the temperature coefficient of polymer unperturbed dimensions has also been made. This temperature coefficient is an even more significant quantity than the characteristic ratio $\langle r^2 \rangle_0 / nl^2$ from the standpoint of establishing the connection between chain structure and conformation. The ability to predict the correct value, in value and sign, for the quantity $(d\ln\langle r^2 \rangle_0 / dT)$ is actually a most severe test for a theory of linear chain conformation. Information gained in studying the most stable conformations of these chains in the crystalline state has proved invaluable for elucidating the rules to be applied in the amorphous (liquid or solution) state.

An attempt to summarize the theoretical framework underlying calculations of $\langle r^2 \rangle_0 / nl^2$ for stereoregular vinyl chains, isotactic or syndiotactic, encounters serious obstacles because of the inevitable mathematical complexities of the different treatments. On the other hand, treatments of simple hypothetical cases, such as the freely jointed chain or similar unrealistic items, are redundant in review literature. We prefer to directly approach the problem in terms of the results, which may be of interest to all polymer chemists, presenting a list of experimental values and then considering how good the agreement is between theory and experiment.

It may be anticipated that theoretical treatments based on the assumption of perfect stereoregularity for isotactic chains invariably appear to lead to $\langle r^2 \rangle_0 / nl^2$ values which are too high, and, furthermore, to a marked negative temperature coefficient of chain dimensions.

Before passing on to review experimental $\langle r^2 \rangle_0 / nl^2$ values, let us digress and briefly consider some experimental means by which these values may be obtained.

C. Experimental Evaluation of $\langle r^2 \rangle_0 / nl^2$

Methods for determining $\langle r^2 \rangle_0$ values in dilute solutions of macromolecules are generally based on measurements of the angular dissymetry of scattered visible light or on one of several hydrodynamic measurements: viscosity, sedimentation velocity, or diffusion.

It is not within the scope of this brief review to discuss these various techniques. The reader is referred to the comprehensive recent book of Morawetz (14) in which both theoretical concepts of high polymer solutions and fundamental aspects of the various experimental techniques used in the study of these solutions are covered in a masterly way from a viewpoint which is very up to date. It is sufficient here to give a brief outline of simple methods which appear to offer, in actual practice, a straightforward and successful way to evaluate unperturbed dimensions of linear chains in dilute solutions. These methods, furthermore, avoid working under Θ conditions, a procedure which is often difficult to apply.

In fact, polymers which are prone to crystallize, as are many of those on which we focus attention here, do not, in general, dissolve in theta solvents unless temperatures which may impair the stability of the polymer are used.

One method makes use of the well-known relationship between intrinsic viscosity $[\eta]$ and average coil dimensions (13):

$$[\eta] = \phi \frac{\langle r^2 \rangle^{3/2}}{M} \tag{1}$$

where ϕ is a universal constant whose theoretical value (15) is $\phi = 2.8 \times 10^{21}$, with $[\eta]$ in deciliters per gram, r in centimeters, and M in grams per mole. The molecular weight M should be the viscosity average, M_v. However, unless the polydispersity of the sample is very large, the weight average M_w, obtained, for example, by the light scattering method, may be used.

The value of $\langle r^2 \rangle$ derived in this manner depends on the solvent medium and consequently is not, in general, useful for comparison with the results of theoretical calculations. It is therefore necessary to estimate the value of the expansion factor α, defined by:

$$\alpha^2 = \langle r^2 \rangle / \langle r^2 \rangle_0 \tag{2}$$

and thus to calculate unperturbed average dimensions from perturbed ones.

According to Flory and Fox (16), Eq. (1) may be written:

$$[\eta] = \phi [\langle r^2 \rangle_0 / M]^{3/2} M^{1/2} \alpha^3 \tag{3}$$

Under Θ conditions, therefore:

$$[\eta]_\Theta = k_\Theta M^{1/2} \tag{3a}$$

as is abundantly confirmed by a host of experimental evidence, and

$$\alpha^3 = [\eta] / [\eta]_\Theta \tag{4}$$

The theory in Ref. (16) furthermore predicts that:

$$\alpha^5 - \alpha^3 = 27(2\pi)^{-3/2}(v^2/N_A V_1)[\langle r^2 \rangle_0 / M]^{-3/2} M^{1/2} \psi_1 \left(1 - \frac{\Theta}{T}\right) \tag{5}$$

where v is the specific volume of the polymer, V_1 the molar volume of the solvent, N_A Avogadro's number, ψ_1 the entropy of mixing parameters, and Θ the Θ temperature, which is proportional, according to definition (13), to the ratio of the enthalpy K_1 and entropy ψ_1 of dilution parameters, $\Theta = (K_1/\psi_1)T$.

The expansion factor α is thus dependent on the magnitude of the polymer–solvent interactions. This interaction, of course, is included among the factors which determine the second virial coefficient A_2 of the polymeric solute. A theoretical expression for A_2 must therefore contain the parameter α, and its importance in our context resides in the practical possibility of determining, through its application, the unperturbed dimensions of a chain by using experimental data in good solvents.

The method of Orofino and Flory (*17*) is particularly useful in this connection. The approximate relationship is:

$$\ln\left[1 + \sqrt{\pi}/2(\alpha^2 - 1)\right] = (27\phi/2^{5/2}\pi N_A)\left(\frac{A_2 M}{[\eta]}\right) \qquad (6)$$

Thus having determined the intrinsic viscosity, the molecular weight, and the second virial coefficient of a single polymer fraction, combined use of Eq. (3), (4), and (6) readily gives the "characteristic ratio" value of the polymer:

$$\langle r^2\rangle_0/nl^2 = (M_b/l^2\phi^{2/3})([\eta]_\Theta/M^{1/2})^{2/3} \qquad (7)$$

where $M_b = M/n$ is the molecular weight per bond.

From the experimental standpoint, $[\eta]$ values are easily obtained using good solvents and A_2 values are easily within the reach of many investigators with the development of reliable, fast response osmometers.

Application of a method like that described above appears necessary, for example, in the case of polypeptides, the unperturbed dimensions $\langle r^2\rangle_0$ of which are unattainable directly owing to the preference of the macromolecules for highly ordered conformations in Θ solvents (*18*).

If a sufficient number of polymer fractions of known average molecular weight are available, determination of intrinsic viscosity in a given good solvent for the polymer and elaboration of the results, without direct knowledge of A_2 values, may also yield $\langle r^2\rangle_0/nl^2$ values. The principle of the method consists of considering Eq. (3) and (5), from which it can be seen that a linear extrapolation of a plot of $[\eta]^{3/2}M^{-1/2}$ values against $M/[\eta]$ to the ordinate intercept yields $\{\phi^{2/3}\langle r^2\rangle_0/M\}$.

Some authors state that a better analysis of the data obtained in good solvents is provided by the Stockmayer and Fixman (*19*) expression:

$$[\eta]/M^{1/2} = \phi_0 K_\Theta^{3/2} + BM^{1/2} \qquad (8)$$

where B is a parameter taking into account polymer solvent interactions. This method has been supported by the observation that extrapolation of $[\eta]M^{-1/2}$ vs. $M^{1/2}$ plots for a given polymer in a variety of solvents leads to a common intercept, i.e., to the same value for the characteristic ratio.

The applicability of the method to a wide range of molecular weights has recently been discussed by Baumann (20). More recently, however, results have been reported in the literature which indicate that in the case of a polar polymer the $\langle r^2 \rangle_0/nl^2$ values determined in this way depend on the solvent. A specific solvent effect on the unperturbed dimensions of the polymer appears to be the most reasonable cause of this effect. This will be discussed later.

In some instances, Θ conditions are easily attainable with stereoregular polymer solutions. In this case, direct evaluation of $\langle r^2 \rangle_0/nl^2$ values is feasible by light scattering measurements or by viscosity measurements and the aid of Eq. (3a).

Let us now review some recent experimental data on unperturbed dimensions of linear stereoregular chains. Comparison with theoretical predictions will be the purpose of the final discussion.

D. Experimental Results

A number of values of the characteristic ratio $\langle r^2 \rangle_0/nl^2$, which recently appeared in the literature, for a variety of linear and stereoregular polymers, are reported in Table 1. Comparison between dimensions of stereoregular chains with their atactic counterparts is made as often as possible.

According to a variety of experimental evidence, however, atactic chains in the full sense of the word probably do not exist, preference for isotactic or syndiotactic sequences being more or less pronounced in the different cases depending upon the nature of monomer and mode of growth of the chain. If by atactic polymer is meant, as usual, a polymer sample prepared without employing specific stereoregulating catalytic systems, then the term "conventional" (instead of atactic) appears a more reasonable one, and will be adopted in the following pages.

E. Comparison with Theoretical Predictions

1. Linear Polymers

Experimental average unperturbed dimensions of linear polymers have been successfully correlated with chain structures and associated hindrances to bond rotations. Mathematical methods applicable to these cases are based on the well-known theory originally developed for a linear array of interacting magnetic dipoles (39,40).

Adaptations to the treatment of the unperturbed dimensions and dipole moments of linear polymers have been made by Birshtein and Ptitsyn (41), Lifson (42), Nagai (43), and Hoeve (44). These methods have been applied

TABLE 1

Characteristic Ratio, $\langle r^2 \rangle_0 / nl^2$, Values for a Number of Linear, Stereo-regular, and Related Conventional Synthetic Polymers

Polymer	$\langle r^2 \rangle_0 / nl^2$	Ref.
Polymethylene	6.8	(21)
Polymethylene	6.9	(22)
Poly(methylene oxide)	$\geqslant 4$	(23,23)
Poly(ethylene oxide)	4.1	(24,25)
Poly(dimethylsiloxane)	6.3; 7.7	(26)
Polypropylene, isotactic	5.2	(27)
Polypropylene, isotactic	7.4	(28)
Polypropylene, conventional	7.0	(29)
Poly(butene-1), isotactic	9.4	(30,31)
Poly(butene-1), conventional	7.2	(32)
Poly(pentene-1) isotactic	9.2	(31)
Poly(pentene-1) isotactic	9.5	(33)
Polystyrene, isotactic	10.6	(27)
Polystyrene, conventional	10.0	(20)
Poly(isopropyl acrylate), isotactic	9.7	(34)
Poly(isopropyl acrylate), conventional	7.1	(34)
Poly(isopropyl acrylate), syndiotactic	7.2	(34)
Poly(isopropyl acrylate), isotactic	15.2	(35)
Poly(isopropyl acrylate), conventional	14.8	(35)
Poly(methyl methacrylate), isotactic	9.6	(36)
Poly(methyl methacrylate,) isotactic	9.6	(37)
Poly(methyl methacrylate), syndiotactic	7.4	(36)
Poly(methyl methacrylate), conventional	7.5	(20)
Poly(methyl methacrylate), conventional	11.5	(37)

to the case of polyethylene (45), poly(dimethyl siloxane) (46), polyoxy-methylene (23a), and polyoxyethylene (25).

A satisfactory description of the average spatial conformations in all these cases in terms of structural considerations appears to have been achieved, as shown by the coincidence between predicted and experimental values of $\langle r^2 \rangle_0 / nl^2$ and of its temperature coefficient.

2. Stereoregular Polymers

Correlation of experimental data with theory has, on the contrary, encountered difficulties in the case of stereoregular vinyl chains. A very important feature which results from comparing the values of $\langle r^2 \rangle_0 / nl^2$ for the different stereoregular vinyl polymers listed in Table 1 is the fact that, notwithstanding a scatter of the values, the characteristic ratio is only a little greater than the value of the ratio for conventional chains. The expectation, on the other hand, was that the severe steric restrictions in the case of isotactic polymers would lead to much higher values of the characteristic ratio because of the tendency to perpetuate relatively long helical sequences along these chains. Examination of potential energy maps, such as that reported in Fig. 3, immediately emphasizes the fact that incidence of conformations other than the preferred one entails a considerably greater energy for the chain. Furthermore, this leads one to predict a pronounced negative temperature coefficient for $\langle r^2 \rangle_0$, contrary to the experimental evidence. This crucial point appears to have been successfully attacked by Flory et al. (47), whose theoretical approach is, with a minimum of very reasonable assumptions, capable of yielding results in satisfactory agreement with experiments.

For details about the exact development of the treatment and for a full justification of assumptions, the reader is referred to the recent papers of Flory et al. (47). Briefly, according to Flory et al., trying to account for experimentally determined values of both the unperturbed dimensions and their temperature coefficients for so-called perfectly isotactic chains in solution in terms of any realistic model for these polymers (9,48) would be impossible.

This situation has led to consideration of the possible effects of absence of a perfect regularity in the steric configurations of successive units along isotactic vinyl chains. Configurational defects probably consist of syndio-tactic units or occasional head-to-head junctions. The former possibility, at least, appears to be an extremely likely one.

To evaluate the effect of stereoirregularity, Flory et al. have studied the dependence of $\langle r^2 \rangle_0/nl^2$ on the incidence of a few syndiotactic units randomly interdispersed among units in the isotactic asymmetric form. For a correct calculation of the characteristic ratio for a copolymer of this type, it is of course necessary to choose a definite succession of D and L units. For specified values of the probability of the next unit of the chain having its —CHR— group in the same configuration as its predecessor, Monte Carlo chains of 10^2 units may be generated. The results obtained by Flory, according to this method and taking into account also possible deviations, $\Delta\phi$, of the angles of internal rotation from that of a 3/1 helix (for which $\Delta\psi = 0$), clearly indicate that the presence of a few syndiotactic units distributed at random along an otherwise isotactic chain has a striking effect on the value of the characteristic ratio and is sufficient to produce agreement between theory and experiment. This is shown in Fig. 4.

In conclusion, if it is assumed that typical isotactic vinyl polymers possess a small fraction of atactic units, then the small differences in unperturbed chain dimensions between these polymers and the related conventional ones are readily completely explained by Flory's theoretical calculations. Discussion arises at this point about the compatibility between the number of atypical units in a given stereoregular chain, which

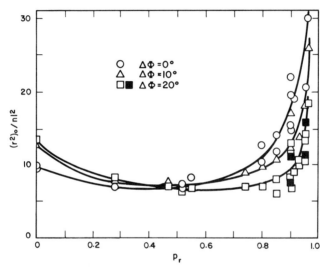

Fig. 4. Variation of the characteristic ratio with the replication probability p_r, calculated for a chain sequence of 100 monomer units using the three-state scheme with $w = 0$ [w denotes the relative statistical weight associated with a steric overlap G^+G^- (or G^-G^+)]. Results obtained for 200 monomer units are also included and shown by open squares (*47*).

is found according to Flory to yield the $\langle r^2 \rangle_0 / nl^2$ value closest to the experimental value, and the high crystallinity exhibited by these chains in the solid state. Maximum tolerance to incorporation of stereoregular units by a crystalline structure must, however, be decided in each particular case, i.e., for each macromolecule and relative mode of chain packing.

The presence of 5–10% stereoirregular units, i.e., of an appreciable fraction of syndiotactic units (dyads) in isotactic polymers like polypropylene and poly(isopropyl acrylate) does appear to be at variance with their NMR spectra (*48a*). However, as pointed out by Flory and Baldeschwieler (*48b*), the time-averaged conformation for an isolated syndiotactic dyad will differ markedly from that of such a dyad within a predominantly syndiotactic chain. Consequently, the NMR peaks for the dyad should occur at different locations in the two distinct cases. The shifted peak for the isolated syndiotactic dyad is thus possibly buried within regions of the spectrum where strong characteristic absorption of isotactic sequences occurs and, as a result, the NMR method may be incapable of detecting minor percentages of syndiotactic units.

Another point of particular importance, in the author's opinion, is that regarding the comparison of results on average unperturbed chain dimension obtained in various laboratories, using different samples of possible different steric purity. Putting aside questions on the accuracy of experimental data and fractionation procedures, the possibility remains that different isotactic samples may yield different values of $\langle r^2 \rangle_0/nl^2$ in the hands of different workers because of only slightly different syndiotactic content, in the neighborhood of a few percent, in light of Flory's findings. It appears, therefore, necessary, in principle, that data on $\langle r^2 \rangle_0/nl^2$ of synthetic stereoregular polymers be correlated with other data obtained by independent measurements on the steric purity of the samples used. Application of nuclear magnetic resonance appears to be a suitable procedure. Extreme care should be exercised in obtaining both types of data, however, since possible discrepancies are not beyond the accuracy of the experimental methods employed.

Let us finally and briefly discuss the temperature coefficients of unperturbed chain dimensions of polymers.

Values for $dln\langle r^2 \rangle_0/dt$ are generally deduced by two quite independent methods, one involving measurements on linear polymer molecules in dilute solution and the other the stress of a cross-linked network.

For the evaluation of temperature coefficients by solution methods, the intrinsic viscosity $[\eta]$ is determined, at different Θ temperatures or, using good solvents in a range of temperatures, naturally above Θ conditions.

In the case of a most nonpolar polymer, polyethylene, this kind of procedure has proved to give excellent results. According to recent data reported by Chiang (48c), the temperature coefficient, $dln\langle r^2 \rangle_0/dT$ of the unperturbed dimensions of polyethylene calculated from intrinsic viscosities in biphenyl and diphenylmethane is $-(1.18 \pm 0.5) \times 10^{-3}$ and $-(1.19 \pm 0.2) \times 10^{-3}$ from intrinsic viscosities in 1-octanol, 1-decanol, and 1-dodecanol (always under Θ conditions, in the range of temperature 127.5–180.1°C). Chiang's data are in essential agreement with data obtained by stress–temperature measurements and by intrinsic viscosity measurements in athermal solvents (48d). It should be recalled, however, that the use of different Θ solvents may impair to some extent the validity of the results obtained with more polar polymers because of specific solvent (Θ) effects, as will be discussed in a following paragraph.

The second method appears preferable from many aspects, particularly when a solvent–polymer system is studied such that the Θ temperature may, with a good approximation, be made equal to $0°K$ (athermal mixture).

Differentiation (31) of Eqs. (3) and (5) with respect to temperature yields in this case:

$$\frac{dln\langle r^2\rangle_0}{dT} = \frac{5}{3}\frac{dln[\eta]}{dT} - \frac{dln(v^2/V_1)}{dT} - \frac{1}{\alpha^2}\left[\frac{dln[\eta]}{dT} - \frac{dln(v^2/V_1)}{dT}\right]$$

The value of $dln(v^2/V_1)/dT$ may be obtained by knowledge of specific volume and thermal expansion coefficients of the polymer and the solvent.

There are many instances of agreement between the values obtained by the solution method and by the stress–temperature method, i.e., polyethylene, poly(dimethyl siloxane), atactic polystyrene, and isotactic poly(pentene-1). The over-all picture gained by examination of the various, although often conflicting data, which have now accumulated in the literature is that small positive temperature coefficients for $\langle r^2\rangle_0$ appear to be the rule among vinyl polymers. It is not our task to enter into any detail on the possible sources of discrepancies in the values reported by different authors. The important fact is that, contrary to common expectation, isotactic vinyl chains also exhibit $dln\langle r^2\rangle_0/dt$ values close to zero.

IV. DILUTE SOLUTION PROPERTIES OF SYNTHETIC STEREOREGULAR POLYMERS IN THERMODYNAMICALLY GOOD SOLVENTS

A. Second Virial Coefficient

The study of solution properties of synthetic stereoregular polymers in thermodynamically good solvents has provided a number of interesting results.

Danusso and Moraglio were the first workers to perform a detailed study of dilute solution properties of a highly stereoregular sample of a vinyl polymer, polystyrene (*49,50*). Two indications of their comparative study of the physicochemical behavior of isotactic and conventional polystyrene are particularly noteworthy: (a) the same intrinsic viscosity–molecular weight relation is obeyed by both the isotactic and conventional samples, in common good solvents; (b) the second virial coefficient, A_2, of the isotactic sample is smaller than that of the conventional sample, the difference vanishing, however, for molecular weights exceeding 10^6. A similar behavior had been reported earlier by Muthana and Mark, who compared crystalline and amorphous poly(vinyl isobutyl ether) (51).

These early results of Danusso and Moraglio have been quoted first not only for historical reasons but also because they have been confirmed in a number of instances and actually appear to be accepted almost as "rules" in the realm of vinyl polymer solutions.

A rather complete and up-to-date list of the values of the parameters K and a of the Mark–Houwink equation $[\eta] = KM^a$, for the isotactic and conventional forms of polypropylene, polystyrene, and polybutene-1 in different good solvents, may be found in the review of Trementozzi and Newman (52). The data show that there is little observable difference between the atactic and stereoregular forms of the same polymer, particularly convincing evidence being afforded in the case of polystyrene. Also, in the case of isotactic, syndiotactic, and conventional poly(methyl methacrylate) in benzene solution, the same $[\eta]–M$ relation, namely, $[\eta] = 0.55 \times 10^{-4} \times M^{0.76}$, has been found to hold by Schulz et al. (36). Qualitatively similar results have been reported by Tsvetkov et al. (53), for the system poly(methyl methacrylate)–benzene (at an unspecified temperature), polymer samples of different degree and type of stereoregularity having been examined. In the case of isotactic and conventional polyisopropylacrylate, the same $[\eta]–M$ relation in bromobenzene at 60°C and in benzene at 25°C has been found by Mark et al. (34). In all these instances, therefore, average coil dimensions of isotactic chains and of their atactic counterparts have been found to be practically the same.

Similar conclusions have now been reached for unperturbed dimensions. In view of this similarity of dimension it is difficult to understand the differences reported in second virial coefficients between stereoisomeric chains. In this connection let us, however, briefly review a few of the more interesting experimental results.

Polystyrene has been treated by a number of authors, and their results strengthen the belief in a smaller A_2 value for the isotactic polymer. Highly stereoregular polystyrene fractions, obtained by stepwise separation of crystalline solid precipitate from isotactic polystyrene–monochlorobenzene–cyclohexanol at 80°, have recently been studied by Utiyama (54). On each fraction, characterized in terms of its ease and degree of crystallization by means of an infrared spectroscopic method, light scattering and viscosity measurements were carried out at 25°C using monochlorobenzene as solvent and 2,4,6-trimethylphenol as antioxidant. The fraction of supposedly highest steric purity showed a negative initial slope and a minimum in the plot of the reciprocal scattered intensity function vs. $\sin^2 \Theta/2$ (see Fig. 5). Utiyama concludes that this anomaly is due to a large optical anisotropy of the isotactic polystyrene chains (40 times as large as that for atactic polystyrene). The second virial coefficient, corrected for the effect of optical anisotropy, was found to be exceptionally small.

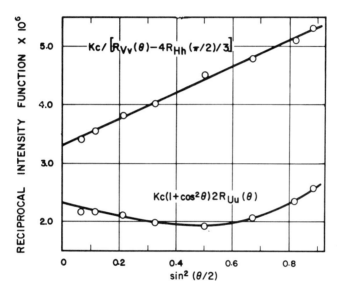

Fig. 5. Reciprocal reduced intensity plots for a highly stereoregular isotactic polystyrene fraction, $M_w = 3.41 \times 10^5$, in monochlorobenzene at 25.3°, $c = 0.107$ g/dl. The lower plotted points are the conventional reciprocal light scattering intensity function and the upper points show the function corrected for the effect of optical anisotropy (54).

For the same polystyrene fraction Utiyama's results further indicate that the unperturbed dimensions of the highly stereoregular fraction are decidedly greater than those of conventional polystyrene, although the results do not allow a definite estimation of the characteristic ratio for the isotactic sample to be made. Smaller second virial coefficients for isotactic polymer have been also found by Kinsinger and Hughes, who studied isomeric polypropylenes in α-chloronaphtalene at 125°C by means of light scattering (55).

Osmotic pressure determinations carried out by Krigbaum et al. (30) for isotactic and atactic fraction of poly(butene-1) in toluene at 45°C also indicate that the isotactic form exhibits a lower second virial coefficient for a given molecular weight up to 1 million.

An important exception has been provided by the results of Schulz et al. (36). These authors have shown that in the case of poly(methyl methacrylate) (PMMA) the isotactic form had a higher second virial coefficient than the conventional form and the syndiotactic form (Fig. 6).

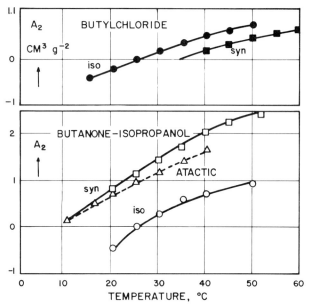

Fig. 6. Poly(methyl methacrylate) second virial coefficient vs. the temperature (36). ●, Isotactic in butyl chloride: ○, isotactic in a solvent mixture (butanone–isopropanol 55:45 vol.%); ■, syndiotactic in butyl chloride; □, syndiotactic in the solvent mixture; △, conventional in the solvent mixture.

Their light scattering results indicated that this was true in a whole range of temperatures, down to the respective Θ points of the two forms of PMMA.

Very recently, interesting results have been reported by Allen et al. (56) on dilute solution properties of poly(propylene oxide). Thermodynamic parameters for the stereoregular polymer have been determined in n-hexane at 46°C and in isooctane in the temperature range 46 to 89°. In summary, the results of Allen et al. indicate that stereoregular poly(propylene oxide) fractions in hexane exhibit [η] values which are essentially independent of temperature in the range 40 to 60°C (an indirect indication that hexane is a good solvent for the polymer) but also very small A_2 values at 46°C, and dimensions much larger than those found in isooctane at 50°C (Θ temperature). These conflicting data have been interpreted by assuming that hexane is actually a good solvent for stereoregular poly(propylene oxide) and that the reason the A_2 values were so small was because of some form of interchain association which precluded polymer precipitation. Furthermore, no difference in Θ temperature and in the value of the entropy of mixing parameter ψ_1 could be detected for the different stereoisomers ($\Theta = 50 \pm 1°$; $\psi_1 = 0.47$) in isooctane. This is the first case in which there has been cognizance of the possible influence of polymer aggregation on the low values for the second virial coefficient of stereoregular chains in solution.

Discussion of the difference in A_2 between stereoisomeric chains (with the assumption that these differences are not, in general, to be charged to experimental inaccuracy, either in the measurements themselves or in the heterogeneity of the samples) would naturally entail examination of the possible contribution to the observed effects of other thermodynamic parameters characteristic of high polymer solutions. This is a very difficult problem, which furthermore does not appear to lend itself to any convincing generalization based on the experimental results accumulated at present. Nevertheless, even a simple review of experimental findings on differences in solution thermodynamic parameters between stereoisomeric chains appears to be very interesting. It will also introduce the examination of another important point, namely, that of specific solvent effects on the properties of macromolecules in solution.

B. Thermodynamic Parameters

Thermodynamic parameters of well-known importance in high polymer solution theory are: Θ temperature, K_1, the enthalpy of mixing, and ψ_1, the entropy of mixing. According to definition:

$$\Theta = \frac{K_1}{\psi_1} T$$

Given a polymer–solvent system, at the Θ temperature the second virial coefficient of the polymer is zero and the solubility of the latter becomes zero in the limit of infinite molecular weight. Accordingly, one method of evaluating Θ temperatures is based on the determination by light scattering or osmotic measurements of the temperature at which a given polymer fraction in the chosen solvent has a null second virial coefficient, and the other is based on the determination of critical-miscibility temperatures T_c for a number of polymer fractions. In the latter procedure, extrapolation of the T_c values for $M \rightarrow \infty$ is necessary to evaluate the Θ temperature. The relevant equation in this case is, (13):

$$1/T_c = 1/\Theta \left[1 + \frac{1}{\psi_1} \left(\frac{1}{x^{1/2}} + \frac{1}{2x} \right) \right] \tag{9}$$

where T_c is the critical-miscibility temperature and x the ratio of molar volumes of polymer and solvent.

The parameter ψ_1 is obtainable by investigation of the temperature dependence of A_2 in the neighborhood of the Θ point and the application of the approximate equation:

$$A_2 = \left(\frac{v^2}{V_1} \right) \psi_1 \left(1 - \frac{\Theta}{T} \right) \tag{10}$$

or by precipitation temperature studies and interpolation of the data according to Eq. (9). The corresponding value of the enthalpic term K_1 may be evaluated at each given temperature T. In general, however, agreement between the results of the two approaches has not proved to be good.

Direct comparison between experimental values of thermodynamic parameters of stereoisomeric chains is limited to a few cases (see Table 2). However, all data reported in the literature indicate that $\psi_{iso} > \psi_{conv}$. An analogous regular pattern is not found when the Θ temperatures are compared.

The results of Kinsinger and Wessling (57) indicate that atactic polypropylene has a higher Θ temperature in diphenyl ether than the isotactic form. Their data suggest, rather surprisingly, that for polypropylene the isotactic polymer should be less soluble only for low molecular weights, while for sufficiently long chains the atactic form is less soluble. A study of the poly(butene-1)–anisole system made by Krigbaum et al. (30) yielded the opposite result, namely, that the isotactic modification has the higher Θ point and lower solubility for all molecular weights. Analogously, Krigbaum and Woods have found that $\Theta_{iso} > \Theta_{conv}$ for poly(pentene-1) in phenetole (59).

The case of poly(methyl methacrylate) appears even more intricate according to some recent results. Sakurada et al. (58) have determined Θ temperature and ψ_1 values by precipitation temperature measurements for isotactic and conventional poly(methyl methacrylate) fractions in methylethylketone–isopropanol (1:1 mixture), n-propanol, 3-heptanone, and

TABLE 2

Polymer	Stereoregularity	Solvent	Θ, °K	ψ_1
Polypropylene	Isotactic (57)	Diphenyl ether	419.4	1.414
	Conventional (28)	Diphenyl ether	426.5	0.986
Poly(butene-1)	Isotactic (30)	Anisole	362.3	0.956
	Conventional (30)	Anisole	359.4	0.740
Poly(pentene-1)	Isotactic (31)	2-Pentanol	335.5	—
	Conventional (31)	2-Pentanol		
	Isotactic (33)	Isoamyl acetate	305.0	—
Poly(methyl methacrylate)	Isotactic (58)	Butanone–isopropanol (1:1)	303.5	1.32
	Conventional (58)	Butanone–isopropanol (1:1)	298.2	—
	Isotactic (58)	3-Heptanone	313.2	0.83
	Conventional (58)	3-Heptanone	306.9	0.56
	Isotactic (58)	n-Propanol	349.1	2.32
	Conventional (58)	n-Propanol	357.6	1.94
	Isotactic (58)	p-Cymene	425.3	0.88
	Conventional (58)	p-Cymene	432.9	0.86
	Isotactic (36)	Butyl chloride	299.5	0.59
	Syndiotactic (36)	Butyl chloride	308	0.51
	Isotactic (36)	Butanone–isopropanol (55:45 vol. %)	298	1.31
	Syndiotactic (36)	Butanone–isopropanol (55:45 vol. %)	281	1.06
Poly(isopropyl acrylate)	Isotactic (35)	n-Decane	451	1.02
	Conventional (35)	n-Decane	439.6	0.97
	Syndiotactic (35)	n-Decane	441.3	0.97
	Isotactic (35)	1,2-butanediol–1,3-butanediol (68.4:31.6 wt. %)	396.5	1.26
	Conventional (35)	1,2-butanediol–1,3-butanediol (68.4:31.6 wt. %)	394.1	1.05

p-cymene, respectively. The ψ values show that $\psi_{\text{iso}} > \psi_{\text{conv}}$ in all the solvents studied. However, $\Theta_{\text{iso}} > \Theta_{\text{conv}}$ in the mixed solvent and in 3-heptanone but the reverse is true in the other two solvents. Furthermore, intrinsic viscosities of the isotactic and syndiotactic polymer under Θ conditions in the solvents quoted above would suggest a negative trend of the isotactic unperturbed dimensions with temperature.

Recently, Schulz et al. (*36*) have found that Θ temperatures of isotactic and syndiotactic poly(methyl methacrylate) are different, with the relative positions of the two theta points depending on the solvent. Using butyl chlorides as solvent, the results of light scattering measurements indicate that $A_2^{iso} > A_2^{syn}$ and $\Theta_{iso} < \Theta_{syn}$, while in the mixed butanone–isopropanol (1:2:1) solvent the contrary holds true.

A peculiar dependence of unperturbed PMMA dimension upon temperature would appear to exist if the data of Schulz et al. and those of Sakurada et al. are compared. This conclusion, however, appears questionable once it is remembered that the nature of the Θ solvent may influence to some degree the value of the characteristic ratio of a polymeric chain. This is an interesting aspect which will be briefly discussed in the following section.

C. Specific Solvent Effects

A strong effect of this kind was first reported by Ivin et al. (*60*), who studied solution properties of hexene–1-polysulfone in a number of theta solvents, including mixed solvents. These authors have found that average unperturbed dimensions of the polysulfone chains were nearly 30% larger in n-hexyl chloride ($\Theta = 13°C$) than in butanone–isopropanol (0.71:1) at $\Theta = 23.5°C$ (or 0.59:1, and $\Theta = 4°C$). In the less polar Θ solvent more extended conformations of the polysulfone chains would thus be preferred, leading to a greater partial cancellation of the dipoles of adjacent sulfone groups. Similar effects were found by Crescenzi and Flory (*26*) with poly(dimethyl siloxane), which was considerably less expanded in a Θ solvent that was more polar than the polymer than in a highly nonpolar medium.

Recently, the results of a study carried out by Elias and Etter (*61*) have shown that in the case of polystyrene there is also a marked dependence of unperturbed dimensions upon the Θ solvent, at a fixed temperature (25°C). They found very large variations in chain extension, e.g., $\langle s^2 \rangle$ values over 30% larger in a benzene–methanol Θ mixture than in a benzene–cyclohexanol Θ system.

A study of the behavior of polystyrene in a single solvent at the Θ temperature carried out by Orofino and Mickey (*62*) revealed a much smaller but significant variation in the unperturbed chain dimensions with the nature of the solvent medium. Even nonpolar polymer coil dimensions appear, therefore, to be more susceptible to variation in Θ solvent, at a given temperature, than it was once assumed (*63*).

Concerning the influence of solvent nature on polymer physicochemical behavior, the results recently reported by Hamori et al. (*37*) are worth a

particular mention. These authors have studied the viscosity–molecular
weight relationship for conventional and isotactic poly(methyl methacrylate) in 2,2,3,3-tetrafluoropropanol at 25°C. The fluorinated alcohol
appears to be the thermodynamically best solvent for PMMA, among
those for which systematic $[\eta]$–M relationship determinations have been
carried out. Hamori et al., using their $[\eta]$ experimental data for a number
of PMMA isotactic and conventional sample fractions (of known M_v,

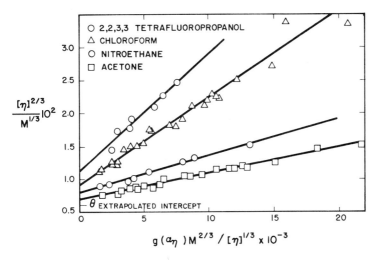

Fig. 7. Kurata–Stockmayer–Roig analysis of atactic poly(methyl methacrylate) viscosity
data in various solvents at 25° (*37*). Data for chloroform, nitroethane, and acetone are
from Ref. (*27*). Extrapolated intercept for Θ solvents is from Ref. (*38*).

under the assumption that the equation $[\eta] = 0.57 \times 10^{-4} \times M^{0.76}$ holds
for both isotactic and conventional PMMA in benzene at 25°C), obtained
values of the parameters of the Mark–Houwink equation significantly
different for the two PMMA samples.

By an elaboration of the intrinsic viscosity data in terms of the Kurata–
Stockmayer–Roig method, by an interactive procedure, or according to
the simplified method of Stockmayer and Fixman, Hamori et al. obtained
for the significant quantity $(\langle r^2 \rangle_0/M)^{1/2}$ the following values: $(740 \pm 60) \times$
10^{-11} for conventional PMMA and $(673 \pm 50) \times 10^{-11}$ for isotactic
PMMA (corresponding $\langle r^2 \rangle_0/nl^2$ approximate values are 11.5 and 9.6,
which are also listed in Table 1). Results obtained by these authors for
conventional PMMA are reported in Fig. 7.

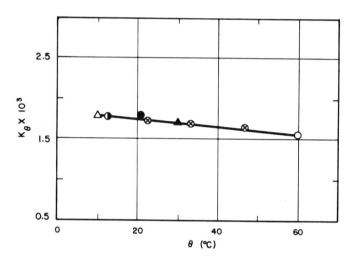

Fig. 8. Temperature dependence of K_Θ for *cis*-1,4-polybutadiene *(64)*. ○, Methyl-*n*-propyl ketone (MNPK); ◑, methylisoamyl ketone (MIAK); △, diethyl ketone (DEK); ⊗, MNPK + MIAK (vol.%, 1:3; 1:1; 3:1); ▲, MNPK + DEK (vol.%, 2:3); ●, isobutyl acetate [Ref. *(65)*].

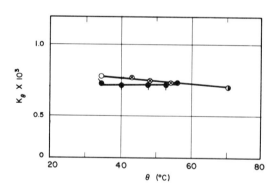

Fig. 9. Temperature dependence of K_Θ for polystyrene *(64)*; ○, Cyclohexane (CH); ◑, methylcyclohexane (MCH); ⊗, CH + MCH (vol.%, 2:1; 1:1; 1:2); ◗, diethylmalonate (DEMT); ●, diethyloxalate (DEOT); ◆, DEMT + DEOT (vol.%, 4:1; 1:1; 1:4).

According to these results, therefore, both perturbed and unperturbed average dimensions of isotactic and conventional PMMA chains would be different in the strongly interacting fluorinated solvent. Furthermore, conventional PMMA would exhibit the larger unperturbed dimensions. This observation is noteworthy because it is the reverse of that found for the same polymers in poorer solvents such as acetone and under Θ conditions.

Hamori et al. have shown also in the case of poly(isopropyl acrylate) that markedly larger $\langle r^2 \rangle_0 / nl^2$ values are obtained using the fluorinated solvent (35).

Use of mixed solvents is frequently made in the study of solution properties of high polymers, but the meaning of the results appears not to have been clearly discerned. In this connection, the first systematic study of the influence of varying Θ solvent composition upon polymeric solute properties appears to have been made by Abe and Fujita (64). These authors have described the phase equilibrium and viscosity behavior of cis-1,4-polybutadiene and conventional polystyrene in a number of solvents prepared by mixing in pairs pure solvents which resemble one another both chemically and physically. Furthermore, each starting solvent was a Θ solvent for one or the other of the polymers studied.

The results of phase separation determinations indicated that for polybutadiene the value of $\psi_1 \Theta$ in the pure and in the mixed Θ solvents was essentially constant and, consequently, that the K_1 parameter was the same in all cases (at a given absolute temperature T). Θ temperatures were found to vary nearly linearly with the volume fraction of solvent components (Fig. 8).

The results for polystyrene indicated a different trend (Fig. 9). Values of K_1 parameters were found to vary with Θ solvent in agreement with the results of Orofino and Mickey (62).

Intrinsic viscosity measurements of polybutadiene and polystyrene in the various solvents have yielded interesting results. Abe and Fujita show that the values of K_Θ in the equation $[\eta]_\Theta = K_\Theta M^{1/2}$ for polybutadiene fall on a single straight line having a small negative slope, and conclude that, at least in the range of temperatures studied, the factor K_Θ for cis-1,4-polybutadiene depends essentially on temperature only. The K_Θ value obtained by Danusso et al. (65) with isobutyl acetate as Θ solvent comes close to the linear K_Θ–Θ relationship found by Abe and Fujita. According to these authors, the correlation of K_Θ values found for polybutadiene occur since the K_1 values for the various solvents (pure and mixed) are nearly the same. In the case of polystyrene, the slope of the K_Θ against Θ

plots was found to be different for different Θ mixtures, corresponding to differences in the relative K_1 values. Abe and Fujita conclude that in a series of solvents which are characterized by similar energetic interactions with a given polymer, the parameter K_Θ will change with Θ in a more or less regular fashion, the slope of the correlation line depending in value and sign on the parameter K_1.

In conclusion, it appears, in the author's opinion, that although a dependence of thermodynamic parameters upon chain stereoregularity is strongly suggested by some of the results presented above, the correlation is still uncertain. In particular, the results obtainable using mixed solvents appear to deserve more systematic investigation. This uncertainty is reflected in the still ambiguous interpretation of alleged differences in second virial coefficients of stereoisomeric forms of the same polymer.

It is also relevant to point out that instead of comparing properties of isotactic chains with those of atactic ones, of often unknown degree and type of stereoregularity, a more sound comparison could be made using the syndiotactic counterparts as reference materials.

D. Complex Formation between Stereoisomeric Chains in Dilute Solutions

In closing this section, it is interesting to recall another peculiar phenomenon which has been observed in the case of vinyl stereoregular polymers in good solvents, namely, the formation of an association complex between stereoisomeric chains.

Watanabe et al. (66) found that the mixing of dilute solutions of isotactic and syndiotactic poly(methyl methacrylate) resulted in instantaneous gelation. The gels had a rather well-defined melting point, which depended on the steric purity of the PMMA samples and was quite insensitive to the ratio in which the two polymeric components were mixed. The data suggested that a stoichiometric complex was formed from the two stereoisomeric polymers. More recently, Ryan and Fleischer (67) have demonstrated that gel melting points can be closely correlated with reaction variables in the preparation of the syndiotactic polymer and thereby with the tacticity of syndiotactic polymer.

Liquori et al. (68,69) have carried out a detailed investigation of this phenomenon and their results disclose some further interesting features of the dilute solution properties of stereoregular PMMA.

It has been observed that the UV spectrum of syndiotactic PMMA, in acetonitrile and in dioxane, consists of a very broad structureless band with a maximum at about 213 mμ, showing a remarkable constancy with increasing temperature (from 16.5 to 65°C). On the other hand, in the same solvents and at room temperature, the isotactic polymer spectrum contains several characteristic features and exhibits a much larger over-all absorption than that of the syndiotactic polymer in both solvents studied.

With increasing temperature the isotactic PMMA spectra undergo marked changes and a discontinuous decrease in absorption at around 43°C. A plausible explanation of these effects has been advanced in terms

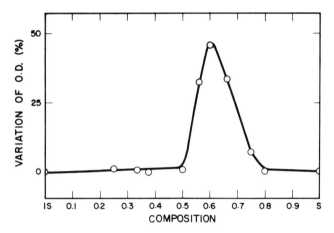

Fig. 10. Percentage change of optical density at 212.5 mμ as a function of composition for mixtures of isotactic and syndiotactic poly(methyl methacrylate) in acetonitrile at a concentration of 0.045 g/dl (69).

of a temperature-controlled equilibrium between two different conformations in which the chain chromophores of PMMA would be correlated to a different extent and modality. A similar phenomenon has been observed in the case of isotactic polystyrene in dilute decalin solutions (70a).

When relatively dilute solutions of isotactic and of syndiotactic PMMA in dimethylformamide are mixed together, the turbidity of the resultant solutions exhibits a maximum at around a 2:1 ratio of concentration of the two stereoisomers. A similar behavior is observed in acetonitrile solutions. In this solvent the optical density of very dilute solutions of isotactic and syndiotactic PMMA was measured at 212.5 mμ for various compositions. The trend of optical density with the composition revealed a marked discontinuity at about the same composition as that at which the maximum in the turbidity occurred (Fig. 10). These results suggest that aggregates between isotactic and syndiotactic PMMA chains form in polar solvents.

Above a certain critical concentration and molecular weight, their stability is largely independent of concentration. Heating causes them to melt.

Liquori et al. (*69*) have also studied in detail the properties of the stiff, sharply melting gels which are formed upon mixing concentrated isotactic and syndiotactic PMMA (at a 1:1 ratio) solutions. This gelation is reminiscent of that exhibited by gelatine or nucleohistones. X-ray diffraction photographs of oriented fibers drawn from the 2:1 complex in dimethylformamide have been interpreted in terms of a structure of the

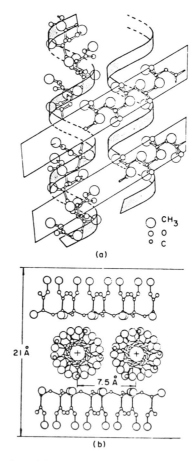

Fig. 11. Schematic drawing of the structure of PMMA stereo complex showing (a) the arrangement of isotactic and syndiotactic chains and (b) a projection of the chains on the plane normal to the fibre axis (*69*).

complex whose stability is due to the interlocking of syndiotactic molecules in channels formed by joining the helical grooves of adjacent helices: Neighboring helices are translated relative to each other by half a turn along the fiber axis (Fig. 11). Methyl groups of isotactic and syndiotactic PMMA would thus be brought into mutual van der Waals' contacts, and this explains why such a stereo complex is formed in polar solvents which enhance the stability of hydrophobic bonds. Correlation between configurational and conformational features of stereoregular chains and their behavior in solution is beautifully demonstrated in this case. Stereocomplex formation is naturally by no means limited to PMMA, but might be common, as suggested by Liquori et al. (*69*), to vinyl polymers having a certain amphyphyllic character.

These results are very important since they show that complex formation based on complementary stereochemical properties, which is characteristic of the specific interactions of proteins, is not a special feature of the macromolecules produced in living organisms.

V. OTHER SOLUTION PROPERTIES

A number of different experimental approaches have been employed to study solution properties of high polymers with the purpose of discriminating between properties of synthetic stereoregular polymers and those of atactic counterparts. These techniques include measurements of X-ray scattering, fluorescence spectra, NMR spectra, infrared spectra, dipole moments, and optical rotatory power. The results of most of these measurements will be reported and discussed in other chapters of this book. Only a few of the more recent results obtained employing X-ray scattering and fluorescence technique will be briefly reviewed here. These results appear to be of particular interest in relation to possible differences in conformations, at the local level, between stereoisomeric vinyl chains in solution.

A study of the X-ray scattering patterns of isotactic and syndiotactic poly(methyl methacrylate) in benzene carried out by Kirste and Wunderlich (*71*) revealed striking differences. This fact was correlated with the dependence of preferred conformations in solutions on the stereoisomerism of the polymer chain.

More recently, the same authors (*72*) have discussed the possibility of determining the thermodynamic parameters of solutions of polymer coils from X-ray small-angle measurements. They succeeded in obtaining data for a complete Zimm plot for a conventional poly(methyl methacrylate) fraction, of ebulliometric molecular weight $M_n = 1450$, in acetone. From this plot, values for M_w, A_2, and the Z-average radius of gyration of the polymer were obtained in good enough agreement with expectations based on light scattering and osmotic pressure measurements on high molecular weight fractions.

In the case of poly(p-iodostyrene), Brady and Salovey (73) found no difference in X-ray scattering curves of the isotactic and syndiotactic forms. This may be interpreted by considering that the heavy iodine atoms, which give the greatest contribution to the scattering, are far from the chain backbone. Furthermore, the conformation of the latter is not sufficiently sharply defined to permit observation of a preferred distance between nearest-neighbor iodine atoms.

Application of X-ray scattering techniques to the case of polyamino acids and polypeptides, including examination of nonisotropic solutions, may lead to interesting results in assessing preferred chain conformations (74, 76).

It appears, therefore, that although detailed interpretation of X-ray scattering data is quite a difficult task (75), this technique may be a powerful one for the study of the conformation of macromolecules in solution and its use will certainly be expanded in the near future.

The low-angle X-ray technique, furthermore, has been extended to the direct measurement of molecular dimensions in bulk polymers by Krigbaum and Godwin (77). These authors have examined a homogeneous polystyrene sample obtained by the Szwarc et al. (78) type of anionic polymerization. The polymer was terminated with CO_2 and converted to a disilver carboxylate salt. Samples were examined in the form of thin strips. Elaboration of the X-ray scattering data yielded: $(\langle r^2 \rangle_0)^{1/2} = 269$ Å for the average unperturbed displacement length of polystyrene of $Mn = 87,000$. This would lead to a value of the characteristic ratio of polystyrene that is too high compared to that observed for this polymer in the unperturbed state in solution. It should be noted, however, that, according to the results of Bueche et al. (79) obtained by a completely different approach for five bulk polymers, the displacement lengths exceed the unperturbed dimensions by about 30%. These results deserve special consideration since they cast some doubt upon the assumption of Flory that molecular dimensions in bulk polymers should be just the same as those of the unperturbed chains in solution.

Vala et al. (80) have recently reported the results of a careful experimental investigation of luminescence and energy trapping on atactic and isoatactic polystyrene and atactic poly(vinyl naphthalene). They conclude that the anomalous emission bands observed at 335 mμ in the polystyrenes and at 410 mμ in atactic poly(vinyl naphthalene) (1,2-dichloroethane as solvent) are due to transition from an excimer state resulting from the interaction of nearby chromophores on the same polymer chain. Investigations of the role played by the charge-transfer state to the splitting of rigidly helical isotactic polystyrene led Vala et al. to conclude that the conformations of the atactic and isotactic polymers are very similar in good solvents and slightly different in poor solvents. The isotactic polystyrene chain in solution is considered to possess short helical sections, comprising a few units.

The close similarity in the fluorescence spectra of isotactic and conventional polystyrene reported by Vala et al. is in contradiction with the results of Yanari et al. (*81*). However, according to the results of Basile (*82*), it appears very likely that the difference in fluorescence spectra recorded by Yanari et al. for isotactic and conventional polystyrene was due to the presence of residual styrene monomer in the latter sample.

VI. STEREOREGULAR VINYL POLYELECTROLYTES

Detailed comparison of solution properties of stereoregular and conventional vinyl polyelectrolytes is limited to only two cases; poly(acrylic acid) and poly(methacrylic acid). The scarcity of data should not, however, be interpreted as an indication that there is little interest in synthetic stereoregular polyelectrolytes. On the contrary, there are good grounds to believe that the study of the physicochemical properties of these macromolecules in solution may be of great value for a better understanding of the properties of important natural polyelectrolyte and biopolymers.

Most research on stereoregular polyelectrolytes in solution has dealt with properties of synthetic compounds, like the polyamino acids, which are somewhat similar to natural ones. A variety of polyamino acids having well-controlled chain size, polydispersity, and steric purity are, furthermore, at present more easily synthesized than stereoregular vinyl polyelectrolytes.

Copolyamino acids with a given amino acid composition and sequence clearly represent even better models for investigators interested in the field of biopolymer solutions. The phenomenon of helix → coil conformational transition, for example, characteristic of these macromolecules has been extensively examined from the experimental as well as from the theoretical standpoint. These aspects need not to be treated here. It is, however, relevant to point out that the importance of structural features of the solvent water, as well as the structural features of the solute chains, on the conformational stability of this class of macromolecules has been amply proved (*83*).

On the other hand, in the case of synthetic vinyl-type polyelectrolytes solutions, physicochemical properties are generally accounted for by a much more approximate picture where the dominant concept is the electrostatic interaction between ionized groups. Many of the observed properties are usually explained in terms of chain dimension variations which are controlled by the variation of electrostatic potential energy with the distances between fixed charges on the macroions. These ions, furthermore, are generally assumed to be immersed in a continuous structureless medium of high dielectric constant (*84*). Although this picture has provided useful models to interpret typical phenomena such as counterion binding (*85*) and many transport properties, it should be considered as a rather drastic oversimplification.

It must be emphasized, in fact, that in the case of solution properties of globular proteins the structure of water surrounding the macroion has been recognized as a factor of paramount importance, controlling the conformational stability of the molecule. Protein denaturation is now visualized as a cooperative process consisting of the rather sudden dissolution of the nonpolar chains in water with an opening up of the native protein structure so as to favor extensive solvation. The ordering of water molecules into a cagelike structure, as required for the solvation of portions of the denatured protein molecule, is considered to be compensated by the conformational disorder of the polypeptide chain and by the exothermal character of the hydration. A comparison between these two pictures, synthetic polyelectrolytes and globular proteins in water, reveals a large gap which cannot be entirely justified by their different chemical structure.

It is the author's opinion that the behavior of poly(methacrylic acid), PMA, in aqueous solution may be considered an example that emphasizes the desirability of a reconciliation between these discrepant views. PMA, furthermore, is the first example in which the influence of chemical constitution and stereoregularity on the properties of vinyl polyelectrolytes in aqueous solution has been considered in some detail.

Among results recently obtained on the influence of chain stereoregularity upon the properties of this polyelectrolyte in dilute water solutions, the potentiometric plots (*86*) reported in Fig. 12 appear particularly interesting. At least two features of the potentiometric plots deserve comment. The isotactic polyacid is seen to behave as a weaker acid, in

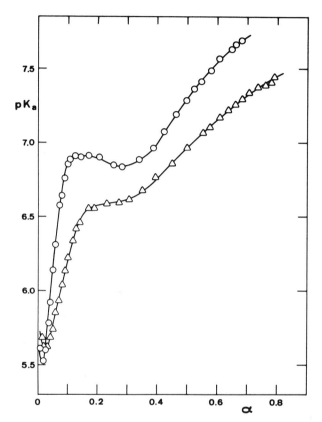

Fig. 12. Potentiometric plots for poly(methacrylic acid), PMA, (*86*). $pK_a = pH + 10 g(1 - \alpha)/\alpha$; α = degree of neutralization (with 0.1 N NaOH at 25°). $\bigcirc$, 8.55 × 10^{-3} N isotactic PMA; $\triangle$, 8.55 × 10^{-3} N syndiotactic PMA.

the whole range of degrees of neutralization, α, in comparison to the syndiotactic form. Similar results have also been obtained by Nagasawa et al. (*87*), and an indication of this fact was earlier given by Loebl and O'Neill (*88*). In all cases, however, the potentiometric plots reveal an anomaly at around $\alpha = 0.15$ [totally absent in the titration curve of poly-(acrylic acid) or of other vinyl polyelectrolytes thus far studied (*89*)].

Anomalous behavior of conventional PMA has also been found, in the same range of degree of neutralization, using a number of different experimental techniques. The anomalies have been attributed (*90*) to a conformational transition of the PMA chains taking place, with a distinctly cooperative character, in a narrow range of α values. Furthermore, the phenomenon is largely independent of polymer molecular weight and concentration. Further investigations have disclosed that this transition of PMA may be visualized as an unwinding of the tightly coiled chains,

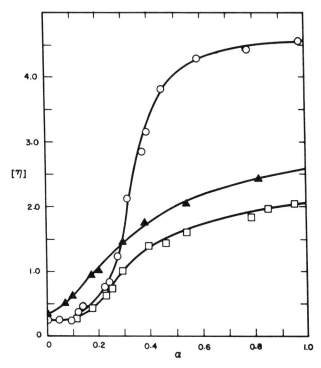

Fig. 13. Dependence of the intrinsic viscosity $[\eta]$ on the degree of neutralization α, in NaCl 0.1 N, for: ○, conventional poly(methacrylic acid); □, isotactic poly(methacrylic acid); ▲, conventional poly(acrylic acid). [From Ref. (*92*).]

which are stable at low degrees of neutralization, in favor of open highly solvated conformations.

Hydrophobic interactions would play a major role on the stability of the tightly coiled globule-shaped PMA chains at low pHs, as has been emphasized by Liquori et al. (*86*), whose views are essentially consistent with those of Birshtein et al. (*91*). For a more detailed discussion of the numerous results and of their interpretation, the original papers should be consulted.

The plots of Fig. 12 suggest that the conformational transition would occur in the case of isotactic and of conventional and syndiotactic PMA within a similar range of α values. A study of the viscometric behavior of the same polyelectrolytes has led to analogous conclusions (*92*) (Fig. 13). Intrinsic viscosity values increase discontinuously with increasing degree of neutralization, in 0.1 N NaCl, at around $\alpha = 0.15$ for both isotactic and conventional PMA. It is interesting to point out that the two PMA samples had nearly the same $[\eta]$ value, at $\alpha = 1$, in 2 N NaNO$_3$, while it is seen from the plot of Fig. 13 that the intrinsic viscosity of the conventional sample is more than twice that of the isotactic sample, in 0.1 N NaCl and $\alpha = 1$.

A different sensitivity to added salt concentration between isotactic and syndiotactic PMA has also been found studying their potentiometric behavior in NaCl at various ionic strengths (*93*). Important differences have also been revealed by the application of other experimental approaches.

Differences in the electrophoretic mobility of isotactic and syndiotactic PMA have been reported (*94*), indicating that the isotactic form is the slower moving one. A discontinuous dependence of macroion mobility on the degree of neutralization was observed, and again the effect has been consistently ascribed to the conformational transition of the polyelectrolyte (Fig. 14).

O'Neill et al. (*95*) have studied the dependence of the association of PMA with divalent cations on the stereoregularity of the polymer. Their results show that isotactic PMA has a higher affinity for Cu^{2+} ions, while Mg^{2+} ions are more strongly bound to the syndiotactic PMA, the difference becoming more pronounced at full neutralization of PMA.

For a consistent interpretation of the differences in the potentiometric and viscometric behavior, as well in the other solution properties, of PMA in terms of the influence of stereoregularity, more experimental data are necessary.

The observation that isotactic PMA is a weaker acid than conventional PMA is not in agreement with the theoretical predictions of Ptitsyn (*96*), according to which the isotactic polyelectrolyte should be more completely ionized and more highly expanded. In the case of poly(acrylic acid), on the other hand, no differences have been observed in the potentiometric behavior of isotactic and conventional samples (*97*).

It appears reasonable to qualitatively interpret the results obtained with PMA by assuming that the chemical constitution of the polyelectrolyte chains is responsible for the occurrence of the conformational transition in dilute water solution. Stereoregularity quite obviously produces the observed, superimposed differences in physicochemical behavior of isotactic and syndiotactic PMA, probably acting only at a local conformational level in short sections of the chains.

It is to be expected that a more detailed description of the physicochemical properties of stereoregular vinyl polyelectrolytes in aqueous

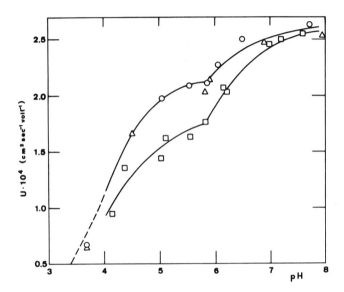

Fig. 14. Dependence of electrophoretic mobility upon the pH, for: ○, △, conventional poly(methacrylic acid); □, isotactic poly(methacrylic acid). [From Ref. (*94*).]

solution will develop when accompanied by a better evaluation of the chemical and structural features of the macroions as well as of the very unique solvent, water. Results obtained with carefully characterized samples of different stereoregularity for a number of vinyl polyelectrolytes will then certainly be of wider interest.

Note added in proof: This chapter was submitted in July 1966 and, consequently, only literature published before that date is discussed. Since this volume was delayed due to the lateness of other chapters, the above discussion is not as current as we would wish. However, we feel that incorporation of more recent data in a meaningful form would result in even further delays to publication—A. D. K. and V. C.

REFERENCES

1. A. M. Liquori, *J. Polymer Sci.*, **C12**, 209 (1966).
2. P. De Santis, E. Giglio, A. M. Liquori, and A. Ripamonti, (*a*) *Nuovo Cimento*, **26**, 616 (1962); (*b*) *J. Polymer Sci.*, **A1**, 1383 (1963); (*c*) A. M. Liquori, G. Anzuino, V. M. Coiro, M. D'Alagni, and P. De Santis, *Nature*, **206**, 358 (1965).
3. A. M. Liquori, 2° *Conference Europeenne des Plastiques et du Caoutchou, Paris, May 1966.*
4. C. W. Bunn and E. R. Howells, *Nature*, **174**, 549 (1954).
5. A. M. Liquori, *Acta Cryst.*, **8**, 345 (1955).
6. G. Natta and P. Corradini, *Nuovo Cimento*, **15**, 3 (1960).
7. T. M. Birshtein, *Vysokomolekul. Soedin.*, **1**, 748 (1959).
8. K. Nagai, *J. Chem. Phys.*, **31**, 1169 (1959).
9. G. Allegra, P. Ganis, and P. Corradini, *Makromol. Chem.*, **61**, 225 (1963).
10. P. Pino, *Advan. Polymer Sci.*, **4**, 3 (1966).
11. T. M. Birshtein and P. L. Luisi, *Vysokomolekul. Soedin.*, **6**, 1238 (1964).
12. G. Allegra, P. Corradini, and P. Ganis, *Makromol. Chem.*, **90**, 60 (1966).
13. P. J. Flory, *Principles of Polymer Chemistry*, Cornell Univ. Press, Ithaca, N.Y., 1953.
14. H. Morawetz, *High Polymers*, Vol. XXI, Wiley (Interscience), New York, 1965.
15. B. H. Zimm, *J. Chem. Phys.*, **24**, 269 (1956).
16. P. J. Flory and T. G. Fox, *J. Am. Chem. Soc.*, **83**, 1023 (1961).
17. T. A. Orofino and P. J. Flory, *J. Chem. Phys.*, **26**, 1067 (1957).
18. D. A. Brant and P. J. Flory, *J. Am. Chem. Soc.*, **87**, 2788 (1965).
19. W. H. Stockmayer and M. Fixman, *J. Polymer Sci.*, **1**, 137 (1963).
20. H. Baumann, *J. Polymer Sci.*, **B3**, 1069 (1965).
21. R. Chiang, *J. Phys. Chem.*, **69**, 1645 (1965).
22. C. J. Stacy and R. L. Arnett, *J. Phys. Chem.*, **69**, 3109 (1965).
23. W. Silberszyc, *J. Polymer Sci.*, **B1**, 577 (1963).
23a. P. J. Flory and J. E. Mark, *Makromol. Chem.*, **75**, 11 (1964).
24. F. E. Bailey and R. W. Callard, *J. Appl. Polymer Sci.*, **1**, 56 (1959). F. E. Bailey, J. L. Kucera, and L. G. Inholf, *J. Polymer Sci.*, **32**, 517 (1958).
25. J. E. Mark and P. J. Flory, *J. Am. Chem. Soc.*, **87**, 1415 (1965).
26. V. Crescenzi and P. J. Flory, *J. Am. Chem. Soc.*, **86**, 141 (1964).
27. M. Kurata and W. H. Stockmayer, *Fortschr. Hochpolymer. Forsch.*, **3**, 196 (1963).
28. J. B. Kinsinger and R. E. Hughes, *J. Phys. Chem.*, **67**, 1922 (1963).
29. F. Danusso and G. Moraglio, *Rend. Accad. Nazl. Lincei, Ser. VIII*, **25**, 509 (1958).
30. W. R. Krigbaum, J. E. Kurz, and P. Smith, *J. Phys. Chem.*, **65**, 1984 (1961).
31. J. E. Mark and P. J. Flory, *J. Am. Chem. Soc.*, **87**, 1423 (1965).
32. G. Moraglio and G. Giannotti, *J. Polymer Sci.*, **27**, 374 (1959).
33. G. Moraglio and J. Brzezinski, *J. Polymer Sci.*, **B2**, 1105 (1964).
34. J. E. Mark, R. A. Wessling, and R. E. Hughes, *J. Phys. Chem.*, **70(6)**, 1895 (1966).
35. R. A. Wessling, J. E. Mark, E. Hamori, and R. E. Hughes, *J. Phys. Chem.*, **70(6)**, 1903 (1966).
36. G. V. Schulz, W. Wunderlich, and R. Kirste, *Makromol. Chem.*, **74**, 22 (1964).
37. E. Hamori, L. R. Prusinowski, P. G. Sparks, and R. E. Hughes, *J. Phys. Chem.*, **69**, 1101 (1965).

38. T. G. Fox, *Polymer*, **3**, 111 (1962).
39. H. A. Kramers and G. H. Wannier, *Phys. Rev.*, **60**, 252 (1941).
40. G. F. Newell and E. W. Montroll, *Rev. Mod. Phys.*, **25**, 353 (1953).
41. T. M. Birshtein and O. B. Ptitsyn, *Zh. Tekhn. Fiz.*, **29**, 1048 (1959); T. M. Birshtein, *Vysokomolkul. Soedin.*, **1**, 798, 1086 (1959); O. B. Ptitsyn, *Usp. Fiz. Nauk*, **49**, 371 (1959).
42. S. Lifson, *J. Chem. Phys.*, **30**, 964 (1959).
43. K. Nagai, *J. Chem. Phys.*, **31**, 1169 (1959).
44. C. A. J. Hoeve, *J. Chem. Phys.*, **32**, 888 (1960).
45. C. A. J. Hoeve, *J. Chem. Phys.*, **35**, 1266 (1961).
46. P. J. Flory, V. Crescenzi, and J. E. Mark, *J. Am. Chem. Soc.*, **86**, 146 (1964).
47. P. J. Flory, J. E. Mark, and A. Abe, *J. Am. Chem. Soc.*, **88**, 639 (1966).
48. T. M. Birshtein, *Vysokomolkul. Soedin.*, **5**, 1675 (1963).
48a. G. Natta, E. Lombardi, A. L. Segre, A. Zambelli, and A. Marinangeli, *Chim. Ind. (Milan)*, **47**(4), 378 (1965).
48b. P. J. Flory and J. D. Baldeschwieler, *J. Am. Chem. Soc.*, **88**(12), 2873 (1966).
48c. R. Chiang, *J. Phys. Chem.*, **70**, 2348 (1966).
48d. A. Ciferri, C. A. J. Hoeve, and P. J. Flory, *J. Am. Chem. Soc.*, **83**, 1015 (1961); P. J. Flory, A. Ciferri, and R. Chiang, *J. Am. Chem. Soc.*, **84**, 1023 (1961).
49. F. Danusso and G. Moraglio, *J. Polymer Sci.*, **24**, 161 (1957).
50. F. Danusso and G. Moraglio, *Makromol. Chem.*, **28**, 250 (1958).
51. M. S. Muthana and H. Mark, *J. Polymer Sci.*, **4**, 527 (1949).
52. Q. A. Trementozzi and S. Newman, in *Crystalline Olefin Polymers* (R. A. V. Raff and K. W. Doak, eds.), Vol. XX, Wiley (Interscience), New York, 1965, Chap. 9.
53. V. N. Tsvetkov, V. S. Skazka, and N. M. Krivoruchko, *Vysokomolkul. Soedin.*, **2**, 1045 (1960); *Polymer Sci. USSR English Transl.*, **3**, 229 (1962).
54. H. Utiyama, *J. Phys. Chem.*, **69**, 4138 (1965).
55. J. B. Kinsinger and R. E. Hughes, *J. Phys. Chem.*, **63**, 2002 (1959).
56. G. Allen, C. Booth, and C. Price, *Polymer*, **7**, 167 (1966).
57. J. B. Kinsinger and A. R. Wessling, *J. Am. Chem. Soc.*, **81**, 2908 (1959).
58. I. Sakurada, A. Nakajima, O. Yoshieaki, and K. Nakanal, *Kolloid-Z.*, **B186**, 41 (1962).
59. W. R. Krigbaum, in *Newer Methods of Polymer Characterization* (B. Ke, ed.), Wiley (Interscience), New York, 1964, Chap. 1.
60. K. J. Ivin, H. A. Ende, and G. Meyerhoff, *Polymer*, **3**, 129 (1962).
61. H. G. Elias and O. Etter, *Makromol. Chem.*, **66**, 56 (1963).
62. T. A. Orofino and J. N. Mickey, *J. Chem. Phys.*, **38**, 2512 (1963).
63. U. Bianchi, *J. Polymer Sci.*, **A2**, 3083 (1964).
64. M. Abe and H. Fujita, *J. Phys. Chem.*, **69**, 3262 (1965).
65. F. Danusso, G. Moraglio, and G. Giannotti, *J. Polymer Sci.*, **51**, 475 (1961).
66. W. H. Watanabe, C. F. Ryan, P. C. Fleischer, and B. S. Garrett, *J. Phys. Chem.*, **65**, 896 (1961)
67. C. F. Ryan and P. C. Fleischer, *J. Phys. Chem.*, **69**, 3384 (1965).
68. M. D'Alagni, P. De Santis, A. M. Liquori, and M. Savino, *J. Polymer Sci.*, **B2**, 925 (1964).
69. A. M. Liquori, G. Anzuino, V. M. Coiro, M. D'Alagni, P. De Santis, and M. Savino, *Nature*, **206**, 358 (1965).

70a. A. M. Liquori and F. Quadrifoglio, *Polymer*, **4**, 448 (1963).

70b. G. Moraglio and F. Danusso, *Polymer*, **4**, 445 (1963).

70c. U. Bianchi and C. Rossi, *Polymer*, **4**, 447 (1963).

71. R. Kirste and W. Wunderlich, *Makromol. Chem.*, **73**, 240 (1964).

72. R. Kirste and W. Wunderlich, *J. Polymer Sci.*, **B3**, 851 (1965).

73. G. W. Brady and R. Salovey, *J. Am. Chem. Soc.*, **86**, 3499 (1964).

74. V. Luzzati, M. Cesari, G. Spach, F. Mason, and J. M. Vincent, *J. Mol. Biol.*, **3**, 566 (1961).

75. P. Saludjian and V. Luzzati, *J. Mol. Biol.*, **15**, 681 (1966).

76. G. W. Brady, R. Salovey, and J. M. Reddy, *Biopolymers*, **3**, 573 (1965).

77. W. R. Krigbaum and R. W. Godwin, *J. Chem. Phys.*, **43**, 4523 (1965).

78. M. Szwarc, M. Levy, and R. Milkovich, *J. Am. Chem. Soc.*, **78**, 2656 (1956).

79. F. Bueche, B. J. Kinzing, and C. J. Coven, *J. Polymer Sci.*, **B4**, 399 (1965).

80. M. T. Vala, J. Haebig, and S. A. Rice, *J. Chem. Phys.*, **43**, 886 (1965).

81. S. Yanari, F. A. Bovey, and L. Lumry, *Nature*, **200**, 242 (1963).

82. L. J. Basile, *J. Chem. Phys.*, **36**, 2204 (1962).

83. W. Kauzman, *Advan. Protein Chem.*, **14**, 1 (1959).

84. S. A. Rice and M. Nagasawa, *Polyelectrolyte Solutions*, Academic Press, New York, 1961; A. Katchalsky, Z. Alexandrowicz, and O. Kedem, in *Transactions of the Symposium on Electrolyte Solutions, Toronto, May 1964*, Wiley, New York, 1965.

85. F. Ascoli, C. Botrè, V. Crescenzi, A. M. Liquori, and A. Mele, *J. Polymer Sci.*, **40**, 169 (1959).

86. A. M. Liquori, G. Barone, V. Crescenzi, F. Quadrifoglio, and V. Vitagliano, *J. Macromol. Chem.*, **1**, 287 (1966).

87. M. Nagasawa, T. Murasa, and K. Kondo, *J. Phys. Chem.*, **69**, 4005 (1965).

88. E. M. Loebl and J. J. O'Neill, *J. Polymer Sci.*, **55**, 538 (1960).

89. G. Barone, V. Crescenzi, and F. Quadrifoglio, *Ric. Sci.*, **35**(II-A), 393 (1965).

90. J. C. Leyte and M. Mandel, *J. Polymer Sci.*, **A2**, 1879 (1964).

91. T. M. Birshtein, E. V. Anufrieva, T. N. Nekrasova, O. B. Ptitsyn, and T. V. Sheveleva, *Vysokomolekul. Soedin.*, **7**, 372 (1965).

92. G. Barone, V. Crescenzi, F. Quadrifoglio, and V. Vitagliano, *Ric. Sci.*, **36**, 477 (1966).

93. G. Barone, V. Crescenzi, and F. Quadrifoglio, *Ric. Sci.*, **35**(II-A), 1069 (1965).

94. G. Anzuino, L. Costantino, R. Gallo, and V. Vitagliano, *J. Polymer Sci.*, **B4**, 459 (1966).

95. J. J. O'Neill, E. M. Loebl, A. Y. Kaudanian, and H. Morawetz, *J. Polymer Sci.*, **A3**, 4201 (1965).

96. O. B. Ptitsyn, *Vysokomolekul. Soedin.*, **2**, 463 (1960).

97. M. L. Miller, K. O'Donnell, and J. Skogman, *J. Colloid Sci.*, **67**, 649 (1962).

CHAPTER 7

Macromolecules as Information Storage Systems

A. M. Liquori

CENTRO NAZIONALE DI CHIMICA DELLE MACROMOLECOLE, SEZ. III
ISTITUTO CHIMICO
UNIVERSITÀ DI ROMA
ROME, ITALY

I. INTRODUCTION

With very few exceptions, natural macromolecules may be described from a purely chemical standpoint as linear sequences of monomer units. Even the most complex globular proteins made of several polypeptide chains inter- or intramolecularly cross-linked through S—S bridges may be included in such a description.

An operational subdivision of natural macromolecules into two large classes appears nowadays to be useful, especially in view of their outstanding role in molecular biology. Such a classification is not based on the chemistry of these systems, but rather on their potential ability to carry or not carry information.

An "informational" macromolecule is characterized by a large variety of allowed sequences of chemically distinct monomer units, such as

ABCDACBDDABD
ACDBABCDDABC

On the other hand, a "noninformational" macromolecule corresponds to a simple repetition of identical monomer units or of identical pairs,

287

triplets, etc., of different monomer units. Let us, for instance, consider a linear macromolecule containing only two kinds of monomer units, A and B. The relative frequencies of AA, BB, AB, BA pairs in the chain are represented in the following probability matrix:

$$
\begin{array}{c|c|c|}
 & \text{A} & \text{B} \\
\hline
\text{A} & p_{\text{AA}} & p_{\text{AB}} \\
\hline
\text{B} & p_{\text{BA}} & p_{\text{BB}} \\
\hline
\end{array}
\tag{1}
$$

The amount of information contained in a chain having n monomer units in a given sequence may be measured by its "entropy of information" H, which corresponds to the uncertainty with which such a sequence may be predicted.† This is given by:

$$
H = -\sum_i \sum_j p_i p_{ij} \ln p_{ij}
\tag{2}
$$

where p_i are the a priori probabilities p_A and p_B of the chain starting with A or B and p_{ij} refers to the probabilities contained in the above matrix. Obviously, $\sum_i p_i = 1 \sum_j p_{ij} = 1$.

If $p_{\text{AA}} = p_{\text{BB}} = 0$ and $p_{\text{AB}} = p_{\text{BA}} = 1$, the only allowed sequence of the chain may be represented by:

-A-B-A-B-A-B-A-B-

which corresponds to a repetition of AB units or to an (AB) n polymer. Such a macromolecule is noninformational since its entropy $H = 0$, as may be verified by inserting the stipulated values of p_i and p_{ij} into Eq. (2). This may, for instance, be the case of a polysaccharide. In general, for an informational macromolecule made of n monomer units of m different kinds, it is easy to show that the amount of information corresponding to a given sequence of monomer units is simply:

$$
H = n \log_2 m \qquad \text{bits}
\tag{3}
$$

† *Editor's note*: For a brief but excellent discussion of information theory in general and entropy of information in particular, the reader is referred to *The McGraw-Hill Encyclopedia of Science and Technology*, Vol. 7, McGraw-Hill, New York, 1960, p. 99.

The above considerations clearly indicate that, whereas there are no restrictions on the ways to synthesize a noninformational macromolecule, for an informational one only two processes are possible in theory, namely, (a) replication and (b) programmed biosynthesis. Case (a) corresponds to the synthesis of DNA or RNA through a semiconservative self-duplication and to the synthesis of RNA on a DNA template. Case (b) corresponds to the biosynthesis of proteins which takes place according to a "program" contained in a segment of DNA chain in the form of a specific sequence of the four bases.

If one applies Eq. (3) to calculate the amount of information which is required to synthesize a polypeptide chain of n amino acid residues of 20 different kinds with a given sequence, one finds:

$$H_{\text{prot}} = n \log_2 20 \qquad \text{bits} \tag{4}$$

Therefore, the minimum number n' of monomer units contained in the DNA chain acting as "gene" for the above polypeptide chain may be found by imposing the condition that:

$$H_{\text{DNA}} \geqslant H_{\text{prot}} \tag{5}$$

namely,

$$n' \log_2 4 \geqslant n \log_2 20 \tag{6}$$

Such a condition appears completely satisfied by the assumption that

$$n' = 3n$$

which corresponds to the "triplet code" proposed by Crick (*1*) and largely proved by a number of experimental investigations (*2*).

II. MECHANISM OF TRANSFER OF GENETIC INFORMATION FROM DNA TO PROTEINS

A number of brilliant intuitions, euristic models, and experiments have recently resulted in the formulation of a general scheme describing the mechanism controlling the biosynthesis of a polypeptide chain (*2*). According to this the over-all process may be separated into two distinct

steps, "transcription" and "chemical translation" of the genetic information. In the first step the information contained in a given sequence of the
four bases in one of the DNA chains is transcribed into the information
contained in a chain of messenger RNA. The base sequence of the
messenger RNA is, in fact, complementary to that of the DNA chain.
In the second step the messenger RNA controls the assemblage of
"transfer RNAs" carrying the amino acids. This takes place on the
ribosomes, cytoplasmic particles made of ribosomal RNA and proteins.
The correct sequence of transfer RNAs on the ribosomes is ensured by
the pairing of specific base triplets, available in the transfer RNAs, with
complementary triplets along the messenger RNA. Enzymatic polymerization of the activated amino acids thus results in the translation of the
"genetic message."

This scheme obviously considers the formation of a polypeptide chain
in a space without dimensions. As shall be discussed later, it should be
completed by adding another step corresponding to the "stereochemical
translation," a purely physicochemical process where the polypeptide
chain takes up a three-dimensional unique conformation, namely, the
"tertiary structure" determined by the amino acid sequence or "primary
structure." The complete scheme (Scheme A) should, therefore, be considered.

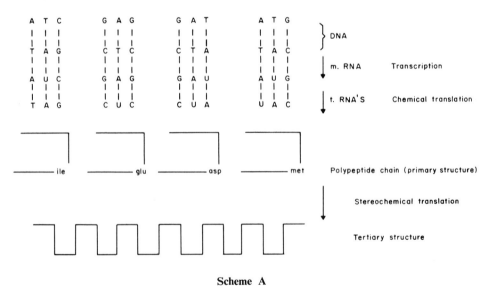

Scheme A

A. Stereochemical Model for Genetic Transcription

Whereas many important details of the chemical translation are still lacking in spite of the very active research which is being carried out, remarkable progress has recently been achieved toward understanding the transcription step. Strong evidence has been accumulated (*3–5*) that RNA synthesis requires the template action of DNA and the presence of RNA polymerase, Mg^{2+} or Mn^{2+} as well as the four monomers ATP, GTP, UTP, and CTP. Polymerization of RNA takes place both in vitro and in vivo and the base sequence of one of the two DNA strands is replicated (*6–8*) with opposite polarity. The transcription is, therefore, considered to be asymmetric. This is shown by the selective ability of RNA to form molecular hybrids with one of the two strands of the DNA acting as a template. On the other hand, the same experiments very strongly suggest that an efficient template action of DNA requires a double-stranded structure. The most convincing proof in this connection lies in the catalytic influence (*9*) of natural polyamines, such as spermidine, which have been shown to stabilize the double-stranded structure of DNA (*10*).

At first sight it might seem difficult to reconcile the condition of a double-stranded structure of the DNA template with the implications stemming from experiments that during polymerization specific pairing takes place between the bases of ribonucleotide triphosphates and those along one DNA strand according to the scheme:

$$A \cdots U$$
$$G \cdots C$$

However, a close examination of the stereochemistry of DNA chains suggests a very satisfactory solution of this problem (*11*).

It will be useful to recall that the Watson and Crick model of DNA consists of two right-handed helical strands with 10 nucleotides per turn with a repeat distance of 3.4 Å along the helical axis, which corresponds to the perpendicular separation between the hydrogen bonded paired bases. There are two helical grooves in the model, a narrow groove and a large groove.

It will be assumed that the RNA replication on the DNA takes place stepwise in the sense that the chain grows one ribonucleotide at a time.

For instance the first step will correspond to the reaction given in Scheme B, which may be schematized as

Scheme B

$$ATP + UTP = A\text{-}p\text{-}U + pp$$

To ensure complementarity between A and U of the ribonucleotide-triphosphates and two consecutive bases T and A of one DNA strand, it is sufficient to assume a local conformational transition of DNA from the

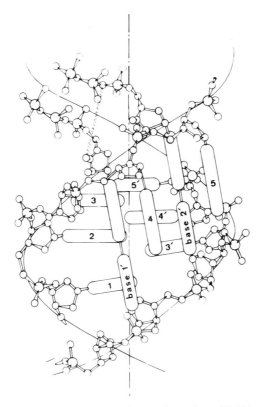

Fig. 1. Schematic drawing of the transcribing conformation of DNA. Two molecules of ribosetriphosphate fixed in the large groove are also shown. Their bases are not numbered and form hydrogen bonds with two consecutive bases 1′ and 2′ of the DNA strand which is being transcribed.

Watson and Crick structure to a new structure which will be called the "transcribing conformation." This transition should involve one-half turn of the Watson and Crick model, namely, 10 nucleotides, 5 in each strand, as shown in Fig. 1.

The "copying" of the bases in one strand is made possible by the following stereochemical aspects of the transcribing conformation.

a. All the hydrogen bonds connecting the five bases 1, 2, 3, 4, and 5 of one DNA strand and the bases 1′, 2′, 3′, 4′, and 5′ in the complementary strand are broken in the transcribing conformation.

b. Two of the bases (1′ and 2′), which will be assumed to be T and A, of one strand in the transcribing conformation are rotated about the bonds connecting them to the D-deoxyribose so that their planes become almost parallel to the molecular axis.

c. The bases 1' and 2' of one strand are perpendicularly separated by about 7 Å. The same distance occurs between bases 4' and 5'.

d. The bases U and A of two ribosetriphosphates can be intercalated between the bases 4' and 5' of one strand and pair with bases 1' and 2' through hydrogen bonding according to the Watson and Crick rule.

e. The other moieties of the two ribosetriphosphates sit in the large groove of the Watson and Crick structure and may take a most appropriate orientation for the reaction shown in scheme B to take place. The direction of growth is from the triphosphate end and the polarity of the growing RNA chain is opposite to that of the DNA strand which is being transcribed.

To explain the asymmetry of the transcription process on the basis of the above stereochemical model, the role played by the enzyme should be considered.

The model provides a wide region in the large groove where the enzyme molecule and DNA may be in contact and this is adjacent to the sites where the ribosetriphosphates are fixed. This region involves the bases 3', 4', and 5' of one DNA strand and the bases 1, 2, and 3 of the other strand. These bases might have a specific affinity for a "recognition site" present in the enzyme together with the catalytic site. This would promote a preferential adsorption of the enzyme in this region which would control both strand selection and initiation of transcription. It is interesting to observe that such a specific region is actually defined by a quintuplet of bases (1, 2, 3, 4, and 5 or 1', 2', 3', 4', and 5') since 3 and 3' are complementary. Such a quintuplet might, therefore, be considered as a universal signal. It would correspond to one of the possible 4^5 sequences of the five bases, and therefore, would impose no significant restriction on the triplet code of the amino acids.

To visualize the dynamics of a transcription process occurring according to the above model, one can consider the formation of the transcribing conformation as a perturbation moving along the Watson and Crick structure as the RNA chain grows. It should always be restricted to a region 17 Å long (one-half turn of a double helix) containing 10 nucleotides (5 on each strand). This would correspond to the minimum required for the formation of only one phosphodiester bond at a time. Such a minimum might conceivably be imposed by energy conservation.

During polymerization, the growing RNA chain should remain bound at one end to DNA until termination occurs. This prediction is compatible with the results reported by Hayashi (8) and with the presence of aggregates between double-stranded DNA and one RNA strand together with free RNA molecules during the process of transcription (12). The resistance to ribonuclease, an enzyme splitting the phosphodiester bonds, of the RNA growing chain may also be explained. The growing RNA chain may, in fact, very well be located in the large groove of the Watson and Crick structure forming nonspecific hydrogen bonds with the paired bases of DNA.

B. Stereochemical Translation

A widely accepted postulate of modern molecular biology implies that the tertiary structure of a globular protein is determined by its primary structure, namely, by the amino acid sequence. Furthermore, a considerable amount of experimental evidence indicates that at least for a protein made of a single polypeptide chain the tertiary structure corresponds to the most stable conformation which such a chain can adopt in water within a restricted range of physicochemical variables.

The structures established in remarkable detail for two globular proteins, myoglobin (13) and lysozyme (14), do not seem to reveal, however, any apparent rule governing, for instance, the unique folding of the polypeptide chain. In both molecules there are segments of the backbone chain of variable lengths having the conformation of a right-handed α-helix connected by segments having irregular but by no means disordered conformations. One feature common to both structures is the typical distribution of the polar side chains on the surface of the macromolecule, whereas the nonpolar side chains are usually not in contact with the water of crystallization but are closely packed in the inside.

The problem concerning the correlation between the primary and tertiary structure of a globular protein, therefore, appears of a formidable complexity, but its importance for the progress of molecular biology obviously justifies any effort toward its elucidation. A solution of this problem might, in fact, provide a set of rules for the "stereochemical translation" of the chemical information contained in a polypeptide chain.

A nonexperimental approach to such a problem was first proposed by our group (15–20) and later followed by other groups (21–24). It is based on an extension of a method which proved valuable in predicting the most stable helical conformations of synthetic polymers with simple skeletons.

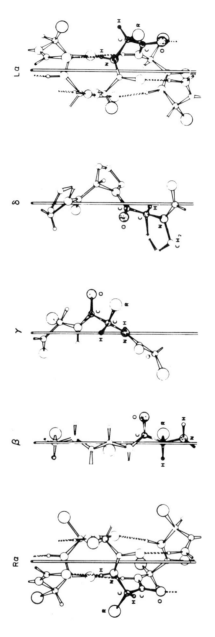

Fig. 2. Allowed helical conformations of a polypeptide chain. The local conformational states of the amino acid residues are also indicated.

A polypeptide chain may be schematized as:

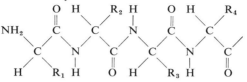

If one first considers a homopolypeptide polymer, that is, a noninformational macromolecule characterized by

$$R_1 = R_2 \cdots R_n$$

the chemical identities between monomer units allows us to impose the
condition of "conformational equivalence," implying that a given amino
acid residue must have the same conformation as the previous one and
the following one. It may now be noticed that the backbone conformation
of an amino acid residue having fixed bond lengths and bond angles is
determined by the angles of rotation about the three skeleton bonds ψ_{C-N},
$\phi_{N-C\alpha}$, and $\psi_{C-\alpha C}$, and the first one can be set in correspondence with
trans planar conformation. It has been shown that when the potential
energy of an infinite homopolypeptide chain made of L-amino acids and
subjected to the condition of conformational equivalence is calculated
as a function of the two angles of rotation $\phi_{N-C\alpha}$ and $\psi_{C\alpha-C}$ about
the nonrigid skeleton bonds, only five minima are found. This implies
that only five helical conformations which may be called Rα, β, γ, δ,
and Lα, are energetically allowed. Conformations Rα and Lα correspond
to a right-handed and to a left-handed α-helix, the first one being more
stable. Conformation β corresponds to the extended twofold helix proposed by Pauling and Corey for silk fibroin. Conformation γ is close
to a right-handed threefold helix and conformation δ may be identified
with the left-handed threefold helix established for *trans*-polyproline and
for polyglycine-II. The five conformations are shown in Fig. 2.
   When a nonhomopolypeptide chain is considered, the lack of chemical
identity between amino acid residues requires that the condition of conformational equivalence be relaxed. One may calculate in this case the
potential energy of the following unit (*25*):

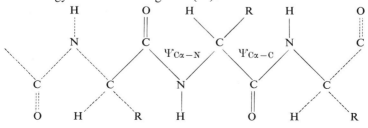

as a function of the angles of rotation $\psi_{C_\alpha-C}$ and ϕ_{N-C_α}. Such a function again contains only five minima corresponding to the five allowed conformations which an amino acid residue can adopt independently from the chemical nature of the previous and following amino acid residue in the chain. These allowed residue conformations may be called Ra, b, c, d, and La (see Fig. 3). It is important to notice that by an infinite repetition

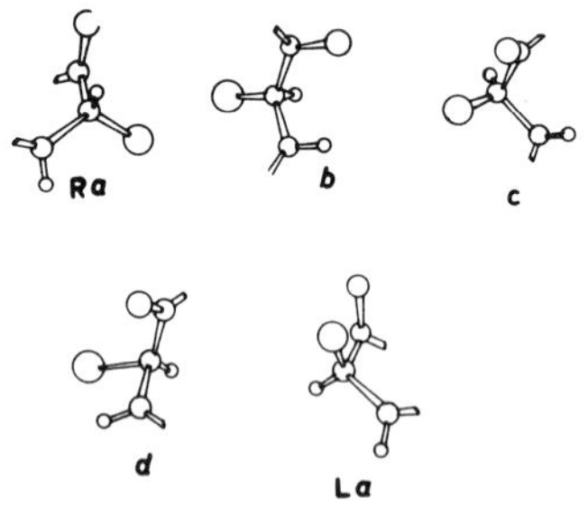

Fig. 3. Allowed conformations of the amino acid residue in a polypeptide chain, corresponding to the elements of the stereochemical code.

of these allowed conformations, the allowed helical conformations Rα, β, γ, δ, and Lα are generated as shown in Fig. 2.

C. Stereochemical Code of Amino Acid Residues

The observation that the allowed conformations Ra, b, c, d, and La of an amino acid residue in a polypeptide chain are not to a first approximation influenced by the side chains of the nearest neighboring monomer units suggests a very useful concept (25). Under the above conditions any conformation of the backbone of a polypeptide chain containing n amino acid residues may be "spelled" as a sequence of $n - 2$ states of five kinds. This is true for all of the 20 amino acids except for glycine for which there are eight allowed states since the enantiomorphous states b^+, c^+, and d^+ are also allowed due to the symmetry of this amino acid. Furthermore, for L-proline only states d and Ra (with some distortion) are allowed. Neglecting these exceptions, the states Ra, b, c, d, and La may now be considered as the elements of a "stereochemical code" or as the "alphabet" of five letters of a stereochemical language which allows a given conformation of a polypeptide chain with n amino acid residues to be represented by a sentence of $n - 2$ characters, such as:

Ra b c La c c d d La c Ra · · ·

One may, therefore, define the "entropy of information" of such a conformation as:

$$S_\infty = -\sum_i \sum_j p_i p_{ij} \ln p_{ij} \qquad (7)$$

and since p_{ij} refers to the probabilities of a consecutive pairs of allowed states, they should be considered as all equal (with exception of proline where the probability p_{aa} is zero). Therefore:

$$S_\infty = -\sum_k p_k \ln p_k \qquad k = 1, 2, 3, 4, 5 \qquad (8)$$

where p_k is the probability of a state k and

$$\sum_k p_k = 1 \qquad (9)$$

Equation (8) strictly holds only if the chain is "ideal" in the sense that there are no attractions between nonnearest-neighbor amino acid residues. This situation is approximated by a randomly coiled polypeptide chain such as a denatured protein.

When the polypeptide chain is folded in a specific way, its "conformational entropy of information" must be zero. This is the case when the chain is helical, namely, when it may be likened to a unidimensional crystal or when it has a stable tertiary structure so that it may be considered as an "aperiodic crystal." The difference of thermodynamic entropy corresponding to a conformational transition from an ordered specific conformation of the chain to a random coil is therefore:

$$\Delta S = -k \sum_k \ln p_k \qquad (10)$$

where k is Boltzmann's constant and

$$p_k = \frac{e^{-(E_k/KT)}}{\sum_k e^{-(E_k/KT)}} \qquad (11)$$

and E_k is the conformational energy corresponding to state k.

D. Stereochemical Translation of the Primary Structure of a "Cyclic Polypeptide" (Gramicidin S)

The stereochemical code of amino acid residues has recently been used to derive the conformation of a cyclic polypeptide, Gramicidin S. The molecule contains 10 amino acid residues of five types which are grouped in two identical sequences: see Scheme C. In general, the stereochemical coding of the amino acid residues, subject to the condition that they are identical in pairs, requires consideration of a very large number of conformations (of the order of 5^5). However, ring closure drastically reduces

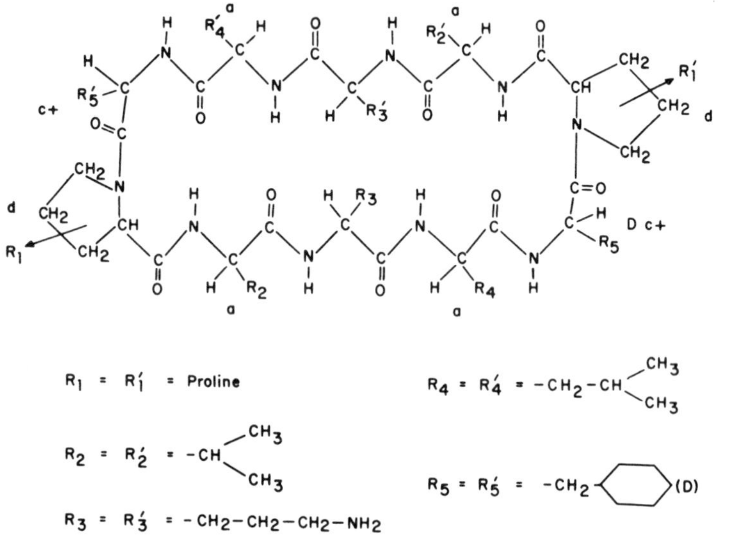

$R_1 = R_1' =$ Proline

$R_2 = R_2' = -CH\begin{smallmatrix}CH_3\\CH_3\end{smallmatrix}$

$R_3 = R_3' = -CH_2-CH_2-CH_2-NH_2$

$R_4 = R_4' = -CH_2-CH\begin{smallmatrix}CH_3\\CH_3\end{smallmatrix}$

$R_5 = R_5' = -CH_2-\bigcirc$ (D)

Scheme C

such a number and a complete satisfactory structure has been derived (25) which corresponds to the following stereochemical translation:

d   Ra   Ra   Ra   c⁺
Pro - Leu - Orn - Val - DPhe
| |
DPhe - Val - Orn - Leu - Pro
c⁺   Ra   Ra   Ra   d

The conformation of the molecule is shown in Fig. 4. It is characterized by two antiparallel α-helical segments related by a dyad axis and connected by two pairs of nonhelical amino acid residues. Its conformational energy is largely negative, which reflects the lack of steric conflicts and a close packing of most of the side chains.

Two other structures have been proposed independently for this molecule by Sheraga et al. (26,27) which appear much less satisfactory. Experimental testing of the models is at present being carried out in various laboratories by X-ray diffraction.

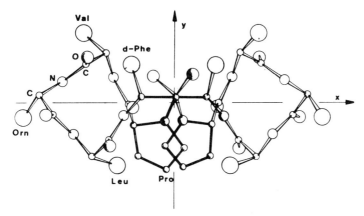

Fig. 4. View of the proposed conformation of Gramicidin S along an axis perpendicular to the dyad axis. Only the β-carbons of the side chains are shown.

III. CONCLUSION

The above considerations lead to very encouraging predictions concerning the possibility of devising a method for translating the primary structure of a protein into its tertiary structure. Both the alphabet of the chemical language (the 20 amino acids) and that of the stereochemical language (the five allowed conformational states of the amino acid residues) are now known. It should, however, be stressed that the problem of converting a sentence from one language to the other does not correspond to a simple "transliteration." It does not only involve one-to-one replacements of letters of one alphabet with letters of the other alphabet, but is a real translation involving the conversion of entire words from one language into the other with the restriction that the number of characters is the same.

As an example, let us consider two segments of the polypeptide chain of lysozyme, namely:

38   39   40   41

Phe - Asn - Thr - Gln

and

47   48   49   50

Thr - Asp - Gly - Ser

From the values of the angles of rotation about the C_α—C and N—C_α bonds of the amino acid residues derived from the X-ray results of

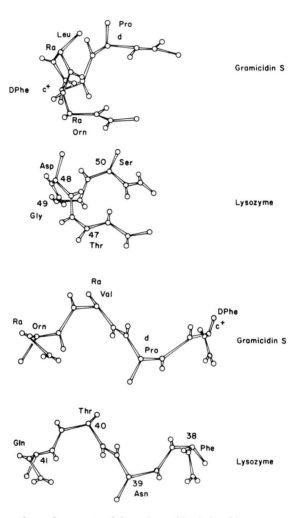

Fig. 5. Conformations of segments of the polypeptide chain of lysozyme as established by X-ray diffraction (*28*) compared with two segments of Gramicidin S in the proposed conformation (*25*). The stereochemical coding of the amino acid residue is indicated in the figure.

Phillips et al. (*28*), the conformations of these segments may be coded as:

$$c^+ \quad d \quad Ra \quad Ra$$
$$Phe - Asp - Thr - Gln$$

and

$$Ra \quad Ra \quad c^+ \quad d$$
$$Thr - Asp - Gly - Ser$$

It, therefore, appears that the stereochemical words

$$c^+ \, d \, Ra \, Ra \quad and \quad Ra \, Ra \, c^+ \, d$$

correspond to the two chemical words Phe-Asn-Thr-Gln and Thr-Asp-Gly-Ser, present in a lysozyme polypeptide chain and to the chemical words:

$$DPhe-Pro-Leu-Orn$$

and

$$Leu-Val-DPhe-Pro$$

present in Gramicidin S, as shown in the previous paragraph. The conformation of the four segments is shown in Fig. 5.

This example may be taken as a very convincing proof that the alphabet of the stereochemical language of a polypeptide chain has been discovered and at the same time as an indication of the complexity involved in the stereochemical translation. Considerable progress is, however, being made at present in our laboratory toward the solution of this fundamental problem.

REFERENCES

1. F. H. C. Crick, J. S. Griffith, and L. E. Orgel, *Proc. Natl. Acad. Sci. U.S.*, **43**, 416 (1957).
2. F. H. C. Crick, in *Progress in Nucleic Acid Research and Molecular Biology*, Vol. I (J. N. Davidson and W. E. Cohn, eds.), Academic Press, New York, 1963, p. 163.
3. M. Chamberlin and P. Berg, *Proc. Natl. Acad. Sci. U.S.*, **48**, 81 (1962).
4. C. F. Fox and S. B. Weiss, *J. Biol. Chem.*, **239**, 175 (1964).
5. J. J. Furth, J. Hurwitz, and M. Anders, *J. Biol. Chem.*, **237**, 2611 (1962).
6. M. Hayashi, M. N. Hayashi, and S. Spiegelman, *Proc. Natl. Acad. Sci. U.S.*, **51**, 351 (1964).
7. E. P. Geidushek, G. P. Tocchini Valentini, and M. L. Sarnat, *Proc. Natl. Acad. Sci. U.S.*, **52**, 486 (1964).
8. M. Hayashi, *Proc. Natl. Acad. Sci. U.S.*, **54**, 1736 (1965).
9. Unpublished results of this laboratory.
10. A. M. Liquori, L. Costantino, V. Crescenzi, V. Elia, E. Giglio, R. Puliti, P. De Santis, M. Savino, and V. Vitagliano, *J. Mol. Biol.*, **24**, 113 (1967).
11. A. M. Liquori, to be published.

12. M. Hayashi and M. N. Hayashi, *Proc. Natl. Acad. Sci. U.S.*, **55**, 635 (1966).

13. J. C. Kendrew, R. E. Dickerson, B. E. Strandberg, R. G. Hart, D. R. Davies, D. C. Phillips, and V. C. Shore, *Nature*, **185**, 422 (1960).

14. C. C. F. Blake, D. F. Koenig, G. A. Mair, A. C. T. North, D. C. Phillips, and V. R. Sarma, *Nature*, **206**, 757 (1965).

15. A. M. Liquori, *Chimica delle Macromolecole*, C. N. R., Rome, 1961.

16. P. De Santis, E. Giglio, A. M. Liquori, and A. Ripamonti, *Nuovo Cimento*, **26**, 616 (1962).

17. P. De Santis, E. Giglio, A. M. Liquori, and A. Ripamonti, *J. Polymer Sci.*, **A1**, 1383 (1961).

18. P. De Santis, E. Giglio, A. M. Liquori, and A. Ripamonti, *Nature*, **206**, 456 (1965).

19. A. M. Liquori, *J. Polymer Sci.*, **C4**, 209 (1966).

20. A. M. Liquori, in *Ciba Foundation Symposium on Principles of Biomolecular Organization*, A. Churchill Ltd., London, 1966, p. 40.

21. C. Ramakrishnan and G. W. Ramachandran, *Biophys. J.*, **5**, 909 (1963).

22. D. A. Brant and P. J. Flory, *J. Am. Chem. Soc.*, **87**, 2788, 2791 (1965).

23. D. A. Brant, W. G. Miller, and P. J. Flory, *J. Mol. Biol.*, **23**, 47 (1967).

24. S. J. Leach, G. Nemethy, and H. A. Scheraga, *Biopolymers*, **4**, 369 (1966).

25. A. M. Liquori, P. De Santis, A. L. Kovacs, and L. Mazzarella, *Nature*, **211**, 1039 (1966).

26. H. A. Scheraga, S. J. Leach, R. A. Scott, and G. Nemethy, *Discussions Faraday Soc.*, **40**, 268 (1965).

27. B. Vanderkood, S. J. Leach, G. Nemethy, R. A. Scott, and H. A. Scheraga, *Biochemistry*, **5**, 2991 (1966).

28. C. C. F. Blake, G. A. Mair, A. C. T. North, D. C. Phillips, and V. R. Sarma, *Proc. Roy. Soc. (London)*, **B167**, 365 (1967).

CHAPTER 8

Automata Theories of Hereditary Tactic Copolymerization

H. H. Pattee

BIOPHYSICS LABORATORY
STANFORD UNIVERSITY
STANFORD, CALIFORNIA

I. BACKGROUND OF THEORY

The discovery of tactic polymerization and topochemical reactions in synthetic chemistry has presented the chemist with a type of detailed control of individual molecular growth which until now was recognized only in biological organisms. A vast gap remains between the limited synthetic control now available to the chemist and the intricate natural control of living cells. Nevertheless, there is a similarity between these two tactic control processes which I believe is more profound and significant than the obvious differences. In particular, the demonstration of controllable eutactic precision in single molecules, even in very simple copolymers, indicates a natural potential for true hereditary propagation at the quantum mechanical level.

The formal mathematics of hereditary processes is now included in what is called automata theory, although its roots lie in formal logic and recursive function theory. Through the early work on the reduction of the most complex sequential symbolic processes to a remarkably small set of elementary operations, by Post (*1*), Turing (*2*), McCulloch and Pitts (*3*), Kleene (*4*), von Neumann (*5*), and others [e.g., see Refs. (*6,7*)], we now can recognize the potential of elementary tactic addition reactions to represent similar hereditary processes in copolymer strings. Our discussion of this theory will be in the following order: (1) the definition of hereditary operations and the general idea of an abstract automaton, (2) the requirements for the extension of this idea to a classical or statistical physical system, and (3) the possible quantum mechanical description of hereditary systems, such as tactic catalysis in copolymer reactions or enzyme catalysis in biological systems.

Not only are hereditary sequences at the foundation of general purpose computing procedures, but at the molecular level such hereditary behavior is the essential prerequisite for the origin and evolution of life as well as the basis of conceptual and symbolic nervous activity. Consequently, experimental and theoretical study of relatively simple and well-defined tactic copolymer systems may be expected to have profound biological significance beyond the obvious practical benefits that such detailed control may provide for the synthetic polymer chemist.

Before discussing some of these fundamental similarities between simple tactic copolymer reactions and abstract hereditary systems, I should point out that my interest in these dynamically constrained chemical reactions did not arise from work in either synthetic polymer chemistry or molecular biology, but began from the point of view of a physicist interested in origin of life (*8–12*). My approach to hereditary tactic reactions will therefore be at a very elementary level with respect to both chemistry and biology. I shall begin with a brief summary of the biological concept of hereditary, since it is in the description of living matter that the word has had the greatest use.

II. BIOLOGICAL CONCEPT OF HEREDITY

It is surprising that in the biological sciences where hereditary control is recognized as absolutely fundamental, it is difficult to find any precise definition of the concept of heredity except as a general process by which some property or character of one system called a parent is transmitted or propagated to another system called an heir (*13,14*). Although this definition is derived from the legal idea of concrete inheritable property, it also applies usefully to the more abstract organizational properties found in living matter. Classically, the science of heredity began only when the particulate nature of hereditary traits was recognized, but it was probably the enormous variety of details in the transmission process of higher organisms that made any precise definition of heredity impractical.

With recent discoveries of molecular biology, the nature of heredity at first appeared to be explained by the eutactic copolymers called nucleic acids. Nucleic acid replication and transcription is generally described as a template process since it is believed to be largely dependent on a stereochemical best-fit between the parent chain monomers and added monomers in the growing chain.

The remarkable new descriptions of the structure of nucleic acids and proteins and the recognition of transcription, coding, and control mechanisms in cells have reduced many biological processes to chemical descriptions at the molecular level, so that recent books in biology often have such titles as *The Molecular Biology of the Gene* (*15*), *The Molecular Control of Cellular Activity* (*16*), and *The Molecular Basis of Evolution* (*17*). The attitude of many molecular biologists has been stated by Watson (*15*): "Until recently, heredity has always seemed the most mysterious of life's characteristics. The current realization that the structure of DNA already allows us to understand practically all its fundamental features at the molecular level is thus most significant. We see not only that the laws of chemistry are sufficient for understanding protein structure, but that also they are consistent with all hereditary phenomena."

It is important to bear in mind, however, that the replication of DNA is still only one facet of what most biologists traditionally call hereditary transmission. Equally important is a "translation" mechanism for converting the genetic DNA description to the specific protein enzymes which express all the crucial phenotypic traits. This translation process in the cell has now been largely identified in terms of its major structures and macromolecular components. Very briefly, the genetic memory storage in the DNA is first transcribed onto messenger RNA under enzyme control. The messenger RNA (mRNA) is then bound to ribosome particles which contain both protein and RNA (rRNA). The actual translation of the DNA message is accomplished by associating each of the 20 amino acids with a corresponding transfer RNA molecule (sRNA) by means of enzymes (amino acyl synthetases), each of which recognizes one type of amino acid and one type of sRNA molecule. Each type of sRNA with its corresponding amino acid can then recognize triplets of adjacent bases on the ribosome-bound mRNA. The rules for this triplet recognition are called the amino acid–nucleotide code and it appears to be the same for all living matter. There has also been expressed the idea that hereditary information passes from nucleic acids to proteins, but never from proteins to nucleic acids. This is the so-called Central Dogma (*18*).

So many reviews of molecular biology are now available [e.g., Refs. (*19–23*)] that further discussion here is not necessary. However, I believe it is correct to say that in spite of all these molecular descriptions, there are still many physicists, chemists, and mathematicians, and even some biologists, who are not entirely satisfied that their own questions about the "secret of life" have been answered by these classical models. It is certainly not yet true that words like *code, memory, control, description, translation,* and *heredity* have been defined in terms of the formal vocabulary of physical and chemical laws or theories, and in this sense at least we do not have a description of the behavior of living matter in physical or chemical terms. To define such words more precisely I believe it will be essential to look more closely at simple tactic and topochemical processes which may be observed in nonliving synthetic molecules. We shall see that template processes are not adequate for representing hereditary reactions, and that tactic catalysts must play the crucial role in replication, transcription, and translation of hereditary information.

III. MATHEMATICAL DEFINITION OF HEREDITARY OPERATIONS

In comparison with these elaborate mechanisms in the cell which appear necessary for what is called hereditary behavior, what meaning can this concept have at the level of ordinary chemical reactions? What is the simplest possible hereditary process in molecules? To answer these questions we must formulate a precise definition of a hereditary event in a physical system. To do this we begin with the more abstract concept of sequential machine or automaton and then proceed to investigate how these formal symbolic hereditary processes can be represented by a real physical system. In particular, we shall see what types of chemical reactions fulfill our conditions for an elementary hereditary event.

The common idea of a hereditary system suggests a dependence on historical events in the distant past which have been transmitted in some form so as to significantly affect the present behavior of the system. This is in contrast to normal events described by physical laws which are predicted only by knowing the immediate past. Hereditary dependence on the distant past therefore requires some form of memory read-out as well as a memory storage to couple this past with the present reactions of the system. By the memory of past events we do not mean simply the accumulated specifications of the states of the system itself over a finite period of time, since this would be redundant data. A memory must be a symbolic or coded description of the past; and a code, even if it is definite and complete, implies some arbitrariness in representation which we associate with all symbolic activity.

An abstract system based on these general ideas requires the concept of classification or a many-to-one mapping. This concept may be formally represented by a semigroup or automaton. For example, we might consider an automaton as an idealized machine with a set n ($n > 1$) of inputs and one output. The allowable inputs and output values form a fixed, finite set of symbols a_i ($i = 1, 2, \ldots, m$; $m > 1$) and the operation of the machine serves to determine the output for any set of inputs which may be arbitrarily supplied. There are therefore n^m distinguishable input states and m outputs. Since any of the m outputs is a possible value for one of the n inputs, the system may be said to have the closure property; but since the machine has no unique set of input states for a given output, no unique inverse operation can be defined.

It is clear that in such a deterministic machine, not only must the location of the output be distinguished from inputs, but the order of the n inputs must be labeled if there are to be n^m distinguishable input states. To accomplish this labeling in a natural way, one might, for example, think of the inputs as a linear string of n symbols fed into the machine like a tape. After the nth input for one elementary operation has entered the machine, the output symbol then appears. The machine may then proceed to read the next n inputs, which leads to a second output symbol, and so on. Many formulations of the automaton idea are possible, [e.g., see Refs. 6,7)], but in any case the operation of the machine results in a many-to-one mapping of each of the n^m possible input states into one of the m outputs.

One fundamental conception of an automaton which gives an even more general picture of its operation is the so-called Post normal tag process (1). The input in this case is again a finite string of symbols, but the operation consists only in removing a fixed number k ($k > 1$) of symbols from one end of the input string and adding a particular string of symbols at the other end of the input string according to a fixed set of substitution rules which associate only the first symbol of the k symbols removed with a definite string to be added at the other end. For example, consider a two-letter alphabet, a,b, and a production rule which says: remove three letters from the left end of the string of letters; if the first left letter is a, add *abbb* on the right end of string; if the first left letter is b, add *aa* on

the right end of string. A starting string *aaababbbababb* would be transformed after four productions to *abbbaaaaabbb*, and after four more will
become periodic, $\{abbbaa\}_n$. The hereditary nature of this process is
particularly evident since the letter which has been on the paper the longest
is the one which determines the next letters to be added, whereas recently
added letters have no immediate effect on the additions. Furthermore,
each production is a many-one mapping and hence has no unique inverse.
Each current event therefore depends on the most distant historical past.
From these basic conceptions a body of elegant theorems has been proved
concerning the equivalence of various automata and the unsolvability of
certain classes of problems [e.g., see Refs. (*24,25*)], but this will not
concern us here.

For the purpose of this discussion of hereditary chemistry, the most significant result of automata theory is that even such elementary processes
as the Post tag system are nevertheless sufficiently general to represent
any computation process which can be formulated with precision. That
is to say, if an explicit procedure or algorithm can be found to solve a
problem, then there exists a suitable code which associates the language of
the problem with the symbols of the automaton so that the operation of
the automaton produces the answer to the problem (*26*). It is this fundamental reduction of all complex sequential computations to elementary
semigroup operations on strings of symbols which suggests the great
potential of simple tactic processes in linear copolymers as molecular
representations of automata or hereditary machines.

So far, however, we have mentioned only abstract symbolic manipula-
tions without regard to the physical laws and initial conditions by which
we predict the behavior of real physical and chemical systems. How can
we characterize real molecular interactions which initate this hereditary
or semigroup property?

IV. CLASSICAL MECHANICAL BASIS OF HEREDITARY
OPERATIONS

It is not immediately obvious how the basic laws of physics are related
to hereditary events as represented by the symbolism of automata theory,
although we take it largely for granted that macroscopic computers obey
all the laws of physics. In an isolated physical system where all the initial
conditions can be measured and all the interactions known, there is
apparently no room for the definition, let alone the hereditary propagation,
of memories or arbitrary variables. From principles of conservation or

invariance, we derive the laws of motion which are therefore independent of particular sets of initial conditions. The initial conditions which represent or define the state of the system at any one time are transformed by these laws of motion to the state immediately following (or preceding) by an infinitesimal time interval. Classically these canonical transformations operate on $2f$ degrees of freedom, f position and f momentum coordinates, whereas in quantum mechanics the corresponding unitary transformations operate on the wave function in f coordinates. Therefore, the state of the system may be predicted knowing only the initial conditions for any *one* given time. In other words, we may say that "memory" of additional initial conditions at some finite time earlier or later will not in any way improve the accuracy of the predictions. For example, if we could specify the initial conditions of a bacterium at one time with sufficient precision, the classical equations of motion lead us to expect that we could in principle predict its behavior in subsequent moments without use of the concepts of memory or heredity. Yet we are still inclined to describe a bacterium as a hereditary system. What precisely then are the physical characteristics which make a hereditary description useful?

Following the automaton definition of a hereditary event, we might propose that a physical hereditary interaction must have no unique inverse and form a semigroup; but unfortunately this is incompatible with the elementary mechanical laws represented by canonical transformations which have unique inverses and form a group. How is it then that a given system can obey all the laws of physics and still be described as hereditary in the sense of an automaton?

In classical mechanics this paradox is apparently evaded by the introduction of additional equations called constraints, resulting from relatively permanent shapes or structures which limit the degrees of freedom of the system. When these equations of constraint represent entirely static or path-independent relationships between the variables, they can be used to reduce the number of degrees of freedom without regard to the equations of motion or the dynamic behavior of the system. Such constraints which can be solved algebraically or integrated directly are called "holonomic." Holonomic constraints reduce the number of degrees of freedom once and for all, independently of the equations of motion, and therefore do not lead to any hereditary behavior.

However, it is also possible to design flexible or dynamic constraints which depend on the motion of the system in such a way that certain degrees of freedom cannot be algebraically eliminated or integrated directly, but which reduce the number of degrees of freedom in the dynamic motion of the system (*27*). These nonintegrable constraints are called "non-holonomic" (*28,29*), and it is only because such dynamic constraints exist that we can construct classical mechanical devices which operate as automata or hereditary systems. Before we consider how similar types of constraints may occur in chemical reactions, it may be instructive to look at an example of a simple nonholonomic constraint in detail, since many of its essential properties can be carried over to the molecular level.

A. Simple Hereditary Machine

To illustrate a physical model approximating the abstract automaton definition of the hereditary property, let us consider a very simple escapement mechanism which can be used to control the rate of flow of balls

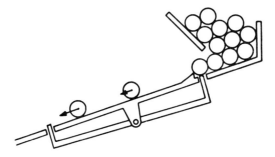

Fig. 1. Escapement clock, a simple hereditary machine. An inclined plane with a potential barrier at the top prevents the balls in the bin from rolling down. An escapement arm allows the kinetic energy of a free-rolling ball to impel one ball over the barrier. The number of balls inside the escapement arm is a hereditary trait.

down an inclined plane. A diagram of this machine is shown in Fig. 1. The operation of the escapement depends upon the potential barrier at the top of the incline which keeps the balls at the top from rolling down until the kinetic energy of one rolling ball is coupled to the ball held by the potential barrier, kicking it over the hump. This coupling is accomplished by the escapement arm which must have both a rigid shape and a flexible motion with respect to the incline. Notice that some initial activation energy is necessary to start the process, and that the number of balls inside the escapement arm is initially arbitrary but constant during the approach to equilibrium. At equilibrium, however, all balls have escaped. The essential hereditary characteristic, as in the Post tag process, is that the dynamics is primarily controlled by the ball which has been rolling the longest time and not the ball just released. We may therefore speak of this delay as a memory storage with respect to the number of balls inside the escapement.

B. Coded Hereditary Machine

This nonholonomic property of memory is certainly a necessary condition of hereditary systems; however, the controlled replacement of one ball by another identical ball is not sufficient to achieve the specific association of different physical elements which we logically associate with codes or symbolic description, or biologically associate with phenotypic expression of the genotype. We wish to find a physical representation not only of memory storage but also of the logical or syntactical rules by which specific memory states may be combined or translated. This is not difficult if one has already accepted the physical realization of nonholonomic constraints, since such dynamic constraints are classically equivalent to extra equations of motion which can be tailored to represent almost any logical function. This "tailoring," however, is a characteristic biological activity which itself has only occurred through billions of years of hereditary evolution.

For example, let us tailor an escapement model to introduce what we may call a coded association of a pair of balls which results in a read-out or translation of the memory storage according to a simple, fixed rule. One simple mechanism to do this might consist of large and small balls each held in a bin by a barrier and two escapement arms, one for the large and one for the small balls, each of which is operated by only one type of ball as it rolls down the incline. In this case we can design the escapement so that, for one example, a rolling large ball will release a small ball and a rolling small ball will release a large ball. In other words, we are associating one type of ball at one end of a string with another type at the other end by a nonholonomic constraint. This is similar to the rules of the Post tag process, except in this example the association is one-to-one.

This coded escapement not only controls the rate of approach to equilibrium, but may be said to select a particular hereditary path to equilibrium as specified by the initial memory state. We shall look at the details of this type of coded rate control when we discuss a similar copolymer model. Notice that the logic or translation code, in this example, is fixed by the structure of the escapement mechanism.

To achieve the versatility of what is called a general purpose computer, it is necessary to provide a constraint which is itself controlled by the memory so that the logic or translation code can be specified in the memory. While this is accomplished in actual computers to a useful approximation, the spontaneous origin of any memory-controlled translation code poses a serious logical problem which is fundamental for the origin of life. However, we shall not discuss here this aspect of the problem [see Ref. (12)].

I should emphasize that these two examples were chosen only to illustrate as simply as possible the basic mechanical principles of hereditary processes; they are not meant to be models of tactic polymerization or biological reactions. I shall try to show, however, that these principles serve to distinguish hereditary events from other ordering processes which are not hereditary in chemical as well as biological reactions. We shall then consider more realistic molecular models of hereditary reactions and show how they are similar and how they differ from these classical mechanical models.

C. Properties of Classical Hereditary Machines

Using these escapement models only as typical examples of hereditary machines, let us try to describe their general behavior in terms of the vocabulary of mechanics. The following three closely related properties are associated with the hereditary aspects of their behavior.

1. *Classification or Many-One Mapping Property*

Considering the elementary operation in both escapement models as the release of a new ball onto the incline, we can then say that there is no unique number or order of the moving balls between the escapement arms corresponding to each deterministic release operation. Thus we can distinguish more input states than output responses at a given time, and in this sense there is no unique inverse state corresponding to a given output. This behavior is, of course, consistent only with a nonequilibrium statistical interpretation of the dynamics, since the detailed laws of motion have a unique inverse and describe group transformations.

2. *Nonholonomic Property*

Stating this property in a slightly different form, we may say that many-one correlations in a physical system imply a greater number of degrees of freedom in the time-independent state description of the system than the number of degrees of freedom in the time-dependent response of the system (27). If this is the case, then there must be time-dependent or rate-determining relations in addition to the equations of motion which are normally considered as the complete and sufficient time-dependent relations which operate on a fixed number of degrees of freedom. If such additional rate-determining relations could be solved or integrated to reduce the number of degrees of freedom independent of the equations of motion, then there would be no difference between the number of static and dynamic degrees of freedom, and the hereditary property could not appear in this description. Therefore, the representation of hereditary events in classical physical systems requires a formulation including non-holonomic constraints.

3. *Multiple Time Scales*

The idea of constraints is entirely classical, arising from the treatment of macroscopic bodies in which we recognize relatively permanent shapes and structures which we treat purely geometrically. However, if we look at matter in more detail, we realize that all macroscopic structure must be represented as a statistical property of large numbers of degrees of freedom. We may then distinguish structures as metastable configurations with relatively long relaxation times compared to our time of observation. Non-holonomic constraints are dynamical conditions which are not integrable; and hence in the statistical mechanical vocabulary, they must appear as correlations in time between stochastic variables. If such dynamic correlations are to appear as a recognizable regularity in the steady state motion of the system, they must in turn be supported by additional correlations with relatively longer relaxation times, as compared to the time necessary to establish the approximately steady state, nonequilibrium constraint dynamics. Thus at least two widely differing relaxation time scales are necessary for the appearance of hereditary behavior in statistical systems, and at least one of these time scales must describe an irreversible system.

Much more can be said about the hereditary behavior of nonequilibrium, nonlinear statistical mechanical systems [e.g., Refs. (*30–32*)], but, as Schrödinger pointed out long ago (*33*), the peculiarity of biological chemistry is that it is based on the dynamics of individual molecules and not statistical averages of vast numbers of molecules. This is also the essential property of tactic catalysis and the primary reason it is of such fundamental importance to our understanding of the difference between living and nonliving molecular hereditary systems.

V. CHEMICAL BASIS OF HEREDITARY REACTIONS

Now we come to the basic question: How can we extend these classical and statistical mechanical ideas of a hereditary process to individual

reactions at the quantum mechanical level? Here we quickly run into
some fundamental difficulties. In the first place, according to the orthodox
interpretation of quantum mechanics, the state vector by which a system
is represented at a given time is a complete description of the system. In
fact, Wigner (*34*) has pointed out that the state vector can be defined as
"a shorthand expression of that part of our information concerning the
past of the system which is relevant for predicting (as far as possible)
the future behavior thereof."

Thus, by common interpretation, the definition of the state vector can
have no hereditary properties, and because of the completeness postulate
no new degrees of freedom may be added to introduce hereditary or any
other extra properties. Furthermore, Wigner (*35*) has shown (in spite of
Watson and Crick) that the fundamental hereditary process of replication
has virtually zero probability according to quantum mechanical equations
of motion. The proof of this result is closely related to the proof of the
limitations on the accuracy of a measurement of any operator which does
not commute with a conserved quantity. Only by assuming a large enough
measuring device so that amplitude interference terms cancel each other
can the accuracy of measurement be improved (*36*).

In addition to these formal mathematical proofs relating replication and
measurement, it is also clear from a practical consideration of actual
measurements that many entirely different physical measuring devices may
interact with a system to give the same observed value, and hence this
value has no unique preceding state, considering the measuring device as
part of the system.

This suggests that the physical conditions for achieving what we have
described as hereditary behavior may be closely related to those conditions
required for a measurement, which may be called a record or "memory"
of an interaction. But if this is the case, we still have a fundamental
problem at the molecular level, since quantum theory of measurement even
after 40 years of discussion remains in a somewhat controversial and
conceptually unsatisfying state.

It would therefore be unproductive here to review the quantum theory
of measurement, especially since many recent papers have appeared on
the subject [e.g., Refs. (*34,36–40*)]. On the other hand, some of the crucial
conditions necessary for defining an actual quantum mechanical measurement interaction or measuring device will also be crucial for interpreting
any hereditary chemical reaction mechanism, and therefore the problem
cannot be completely ignored.

What I can do, however, is proceed in my description of heredity from the classical point of view as far as possible toward the quantum molecular level, in the same way that a physicist must begin (or end) his description of an actual measurement at the classical level, although in both cases, as we shall see, the obscurity of the dynamics will increase as the size of the statistical system is reduced, or as the number of degrees of freedom considered in detail is increased.

This approach may be partly justified by recalling that whether or not a measurement is said to occur within a given collection of physical objects depends on where the observer (or theorist) chooses to separate the quantum mechanical from the classical (or statistical) description of this collection of objects. That is, if we choose to consider the entire collection of objects including what we would commonly call a "measuring device" as only a quantum mechanical system, then we cannot recognize any specific measurement process. Similarly, we shall see that if we choose to consider a collection of molecules including what we would commonly call a "hereditary device" (e.g., a bacterium) only as a quantum mechanical system, then we cannot recognize any specific hereditary reactions. However, let us return to specific examples and consider some concrete polymer reactions which may fulfill our criteria for hereditary behavior.

A. Simple Hereditary Copolymer Model

Consider a growing linear homopolymer situation in which there is an initial monomer addition rate constant K_a. Suppose that it is found that after the polymer chain is long enough it folds into a helical conformation with, e.g., five monomers per turn and that the monomer addition rate then increases to $K_a' > K_a$. Now what could be the mechanism of this rate increase? One would reasonably suppose that the new helical shape would bring the $(n - 4)$th monomer very close to the position to be occupied by the $(n + 1)$st monomer, and that in some way the proximity of the $(n - 4)$th monomer catalyzes the addition reaction. This polymer model is, of course, intended as an analog of the simple clock escapement model. In this model the rate of a reaction is controlled by the interaction of the oldest exposed monomer in the helical chain, and in this sense it has a hereditary property. However, there are essential differences between the escapement and polymer models. The escapement requires two independent kinds of parts, the balls and the nonholonomic constraint, whereas the helical polymer is made out of only one type of monomer. Therefore the shape of the constraint in the polymer depends largely on the nature of the monomers, and the number of monomers per turn (or the delay) is not entirely arbitrary. A more fundamental difference is the nature of the bonds which are being catalyzed. In the ball escapement, the rate control is on the weak bonds between the balls and not on the strong bonds which hold the shape of the balls and the parts of the escapement during the motion. On the other hand, in the growing polymer it is the strong bonds of the linear chain which are being catalyzed by the weaker conformational bonds positioning the catalytic site. We shall return to these differences in a later section.

Such a simple example of a hereditary reaction may not appear to have much evolutionary potential. However, we shall show how natural modifications of such conformation-dependent catalytic effects may produce elaborate hereditary copolymers. It is significant that one observed case of such conformation-dependent catalysis occurs in the N-carboxy-anhydride synthesis of polypeptides (*41,42*).

B. Coded Hereditary Copolymer Model

To obtain the more interesting hereditary behavior of the coded escapement constraint of Sect. IVB in polymers, we must consider controlling the type of monomer as well as the rate of reaction, and this means a tactic catalysis. However, as we saw in the mechanical example, no new principles are required, only a more complex nonholonomic constraint. Similarly, a coded hereditary copolymer model will require only a more complex catalytic interaction which involves some degree of specificity to distinguish monomer types.

As a first step consider a linear copolymer which adds comonomers with initial rates K_a and K_b. Suppose that this chain also folds into a helix with five monomers per turn and that in this configuration the proximity of the $(n - 4)$th monomer to the $(n + 1)$st position catalyses the next addition step as in the previous example. However, now with two types of monomer it is generally unlikely that the catalytic effect of the $(n - 4)$th position is independent of the type of monomer at that position. Assuming a strong (i.e., eutactic) rate-controlling effect of only the $(n - 4)$th monomer, there will be four possible control schemes or codes, as shown in Table 1. The last two codes will of course degenerate into homopolymers no matter what the starting sequence may be; however, the first two codes lead, respectively, to four and eight species of periodic copolymer. The linear sequence of each species is completely determined, for a given code, by any five adjacent monomers in a helix turn. For example, if an *a* or *b* monomer at the $(n - 4)$th position increases the relative rate of addition of the same type of monomer, as shown in the second code of Table 1, then any of the five cyclic permutations sequences *ababa*, *babaa*, *abaab*, *baaba*, and *aabab* are equivalent genetic sequences for one of the species. The other seven species are generated from the two homopolymers, *aaaaa* and *bbbbb*, and the sequences *babab*, *aabaa*, *bbaba*, *baaab*, and *abbba* or their cyclic permutations.

Of course, the specificity or relative catalytic power of the $(n - 4)$th monomer with respect to the types of added monomers will largely determine the inherent rate of mutation in this type of hereditary propagation.

TABLE 1

Possible Eutactic Control Schemes for Monomer Addition Dependent upon Only One Monomer Position in the Chain[a] and Two Types of Monomer

Monomer type in $(n - 4)$th position	Catalyzed monomer in $(n + 1)$st position
a	*b*
b	*a*
a	*a*
b	*b*
a	*a*
b	*a*
a	*b*
b	*b*

[a] In this case the $(n - 4)$th position.

However, the addition of an uncatalyzed monomer, that is, a noncoded monomer, will not necessarily lead to a new species since all cyclic permutations of the end-turn sequence are genetically redundant.

It is experimentally significant to note that the total monomer composition ratio of these polymers is not affected by the degree of tacticity, assuming equal addition rates for each monomer in the starting sequences, and similar error distributions over the tactic additions.

In any case, accurate hereditary propagation requires that the specificity or differential catalytic power for the different types of monomer addition be high. For a given set of monomer types, an increase in specificity would imply an increase in the number of constraints on the monomer being added to the chain, which in turn suggests that more monomer positions in the chain must influence the reaction kinetics for higher specificity or lower error rate.

As a simple example of such multiple-position control of specificity, consider the same five-monomer-per-turn helical copolymer of the last example, but with the last, or nth position, monomer also influencing the specificity of the $(n + 1)$st addition along with the $(n - 4)$th position monomer. This is sterically reasonable since the nth and $(n - 4)$th mono- mer form the step dislocation in the helix where the next monomer will be added. Now instead of only 4 coding schemes as shown in Table 1, there are 16 possible coding schemes, again assuming only eutactic control.†

For one example let us choose a code which catalyzes the addition of an a-type monomer when the nth and $(n - 4)$th monomer are the same type, and a b-type monomer when nth and $(n - 4)$th monomer are a different type. This leads to four species of copolymer:

$$S1 : \{a\}_n$$
$$S2 : \{bba\}_n$$
$$S3 : \{bbbaaba\}_n$$
$$S4 : \{bbbbbababaabbaaabaaaa\}_n$$

Molecules within each species $S2$, $S3$, and $S4$ will differ from each other only in the phase of the starting sequence. The sum of the length of all periods is $2^5 = 32$; therefore no other eutactic species are possible for the given shape and rate table. These four species of copolymer may also be specified by a genetic sequence along with their hereditary code. Again, a genetic memory consists of five consecutive monomers from any part of each chain, for example:

$$S1 : aaaaa$$
$$S2 : abbab$$
$$S3 : baaba$$
$$S4 : bbbbb$$

Clearly, species $S2$, $S3$, and $S4$ have 2, 6, and 20 other equally good starting genetic pentamers, respectively.

It is interesting to consider the average monomer composition of all types of polymer grown under these conditions. For low degrees of polymerization, we assumed equal rates for all additions. The polymer composition would therefore be proportional to the feed ratio at the start. For high degrees of polymerization, the average eutactic composition ratio for all four species is approximately 51.2% type a and 48.8% type b. This

† For eutactic codes and two types of monomers there are 2^{2^n} codes (the number of Boolean functions of n variables) where n is the number of monomers controlling the specificity of the addition step.

is assuming that the continuing eutactic growth rate for each of the 32 starting sequences is equal and that the number of each species is therefore in the ratio $1:3:7:21$.

This near equality of monomer compositions is not peculiar to these examples but is characteristic of a wide range of the so-called autonomous sequence generation configurations (*43*). Furthermore, the detailed sequences generated eutactically by such constraints are not easily distinguishable from random sequences unless the periodicity can be established, or homogeneity of pattern detected. Since the starting sequences are random and the termination sequences equally uncertain, this is not an easy experimental distinction. We shall return to this problem in the last section.

An alternative Markov or state-vector transition matrix description for this chain propagation must list all 32 initial and final states; however, the hereditary property leads to a reducible matrix with four submatrices corresponding to the four species of chain. A part of this matrix is shown in Table 2 with the assignment of numbers to each type of pentamer of our example. This state representation indicates more clearly the significance of the two distinct time scales which we found necessary to explain non-holonomic constraints; i.e., the average state transition time must be very small compared to the average time for a mutation to a different species.

C. Properties of Hereditary Copolymer Reactions

From the state-transition matrix description it appears that the growth space for a given initial five-monomer chain is less than the physically possible state space for five-monomer chains. This is the nature of non-holonomic constraints (*44*). However, such complete eutacticity would correspond physically to perfect reliability of the catalysis and complete isolation of each species so that there is zero probability of a mutation from one to another. This is physically unreasonable both classically and quantum mechanically because of the impossibility of complete isolation from external perturbations. However, there are also inherent errors which are inescapable.

In classical or statistical systems we will find thermal fluctuations producing a mutation from one species to another so that eventually the distribution of states becomes independent of the initial conditions. This would correspond to true equilibrium and a total loss of memory and the hereditary behavior. Nevertheless, we may observe highly tactic reactions in which the metastable, steady state behavior is reached in a time short compared to the relaxation time to true equilibrium. This behavior then

TABLE 2

State Transition Matrix for the Eutactic Copolymer Helical Propagation[a]

Output state / Input state

Input state	1	2	3	4	5	6	7	8	9	10	11	12	13	·	·	·	31	32	State assignments
1	1	$^s1$																	$1 = aaaaa$
2				1	$^s2$														$2 = abbab$
3		1																	$3 = babba$
4			1																$4 = bbabb$
5													1	$^s3$					$5 = abbba$
6					1														$6 = babbb$
7						1													$7 = ababb$
8							1												$8 = aabab$
9								1											$9 = baaba$
10									1										$10 = bbaab$
11										1									$11 = bbbaa$
12																	1	$^s4$	$12 = abbbb$
13								1											$13 = aabbb$
·									1										· ·
·										1									· ·
·																			
31																	1		$31 = bbbba$
32																		1	$32 = bbbbb$

[a] With five monomers per turn and an addition rate as given in the text. The possible pentamers which can initiate this propagation or which form one turn are shown numbered on the right. Each of the four species of copolymer corresponds to one of the reduced submatrices.

appears as a transient hereditary propagation of certain initial conditions. In other words, for a finite time interval the hereditary propagation dominates the long-range statistical behavior.

In individual quantum mechanical systems, such as single enzyme molecules or tactic catalysts, the situation is much more complex and obscure. While the reliability of static memory storage in a single quantum mechanical system may be higher than the corresponding classical system because of the discrete energy levels, as pointed out by Schrödinger (*33*), any nonholonomic hereditary propagation will involve nonclassical relations between the coordinates and conjugate momenta (*45*). Also, as we discussed in Sect. V, if nonholonomic or hereditary reactions are like measurements, then an increase in specificity, considered as a decrease in substrate coordinate uncertainty, or an increase in rate, considered as decrease in substrate interaction time, would increase uncertainty in the corresponding momenta or energy which would in turn increase the probability of a mutation. There may also turn out to be crucial relationships between the size of tactic catalysts and enzymes and their reliability as measuring devices (*36*).

Whatever the quantum mechanical details may turn out to be, the significant fact is that mutations or errors in hereditary propagation will occur. If these mutations are equiprobable in all species and all chain locations, then the average population lifetime of each species will remain the same. However, if external interactions with each species chain are different, then a shift in population ratios may occur without changing monomer addition rates. Such selective changes which do not change the memory storage or the hereditary code may be called natural selection in keeping with biological usage. In fact, the origin of such natural selection in tactic copolymer systems is a condition for the origin of life as we understand it.

In spite of our inability to pursue any details of a quantum mechanical description of catalysis, it is experimentally useful to look for properties of single molecular hereditary catalysts which are crucially different from the properties of macroscopic hereditary machines, or statistical thermodynamic descriptions of chemical reactions involving large numbers of molecules.

1. *Role of Weak and Strong Bonds*

We have already mentioned the difference between the classical escapement model and the helical molecular model with respect to the functions of the weak and strong forces. In the mechanical escapement it is the relatively strong solid state bonds which maintain the three-dimensional structures controlling the rate of weak bond contacts between the one-dimensional string of balls; whereas in the helical copolymer it is the weak bonds which maintain the three-dimensional shape controlling the rate of strong covalent bond formation in the one-dimensional string of monomers At the copolymer level this distinction between strong and weak bonds is already implicit in the concepts of monomer sequence and conformation,

since neither of these terms could be usefully defined if only one type of
bond existed between monomers. Linear sequence may be defined as the
monomer order obtained by following the strong bonds from one end of
the chain to the other, while conformation in linear chains usually refers to
the shapes held by weak bonds as allowed by the rotation or flexibility of
strong bonds, but not by the breaking of strong bonds. Cross-linking
by covalent bonds is, of course, common in enzymes, but the linear sequence is still recognized by the most stable strong-bond path. It is also
generally the case that enzymes catalyze only strong covalent bonds and
that they rely only on weak bonds to recognize the substrate.

2. *Memory Storage and Translation Code Forces*

If we consider only ideal eutactic copolymer reactions which are un-
disturbed by thermal fluctuations or external errors, there is no reason to
choose either a classical or a molecular hereditary machine over the other
with respect to either the function or the number of constrained dimensions
of each type of bond. If the memory storage states are weakly bonded and
the translation code formed from strong bonds, as in the mechanical
clocks, this is just as hereditary, by definition, as the catalytic copolymer
helix which has its memory storage held by strong bonds and its translation
code maintained by weak bonds.

But as systems are heated or subjected to random disturbances, it is
essential for survival to preserve the memory storage rather than the
catalytic structures which might reform spontaneously once the temperature was lowered or the disturbance removed. Therefore we would expect
survival of those hereditary systems which have strong-bond memory
storage and weak bond rate-control mechanisms.

It is no less important that as the temperature increases, the rate-
controlling hereditary mechanisms cease to operate as catalysts before they
lose their translation code structure, otherwise their uncontrolled catalytic
activity would only speed up the destruction of the contents of the memory
storage. For example, the helical copolymer model could preserve species
memory on heating if the helix simply became a random coil and thereby
stopped monomer addition. On the other hand it would destroy the species
if, on heating, the helix pitch changed but the catalytic propagation rule
continued to operate.

For these reasons we may expect survival in hereditary systems in which
the nonholonomic constraints which operate the translation code are
formed from weak-bonded structures while the memory storage is preserved in strong-bonded, metastable structures. This natural hereditary

strategy in some bacterial spores may partly explain why attempts at heat sterilization of satellites often spoil the characteristics of the man-made solid state automata before spoiling the viability of the spores.

The optimum dimensionality of the memory storage structure may also be considered. When we say that a hereditary system has no unique input state for a given output reaction rate, this implies that there is an independent rule or procedure which distinguishes different input states. For example, the n-input, one-output automaton requires an ordering of the n inputs independent of the input values if we are to distinguish all input states. As we pointed out in Sect. III, this ordering is accomplished most simply by linking the inputs directly as a linear chain so that no additional rule is necessary to specify input order. On the contrary, two- or three-dimensional memory storage requires some access syntax which would not appear likely in the simplest natural chemical system. Because of this problem of input state ambiguity, a branched tactic copolymer would cause some additional difficulty as a representation of a spontaneous hereditary reaction process.

3. *Mechanism of Coded Hereditary Catalysis*

These general conditions which may be expected in tactic copolymer reactions exhibiting hereditary control still leave unspecified the nature of the active site of the hereditary catalyst. How would the catalytic reaction mechanism in the simple conformation-controlled copolymerization (Sect. VA) differ from the mechanism of a coded hereditary tactic catalyst (Sect. VB)?

By a mechanism we mean some description of the dynamics involved in controlling the reaction, as contrasted to only the specification of a table of rates, such as given in Table 1 for our helical copolymer model, or a state transition matrix as given in Table 2. While such tables may indicate hereditary behavior by their mapping or reducibility properties, they give no insight into the nature of the forces which are necessary to actually produce such rate control. We are asking what type of reaction mechanism can account for a set of tactic addition rates which have the hereditary property.

One obvious property of a mechanical nonholonomic constraint is a moving part like the escapement arm which is operated by the motion of the masses which it in turn controls to some degree. Such a dynamic constraint is also ascribed to enzyme mechanisms by the so-called induced-fit (46) and allosteric (47) models. It is important to realize that we have derived this flexibility requirement without reference to the known behavior of enzymes, but from a fundamental definition of a hereditary reaction; and, conversely, the induced-fit and allosteric models were derived from experiments on the enzymes without reference to hereditary properties. In fact, according to common molecular biological usage, the template copying of DNA by base pairing would be called the basic hereditary process, whereas enzyme catalysis probably in itself would not be called hereditary at all. By our definition of a hereditary process the pairing of adenine↔thymine and guanosine↔cytosine by hydrogen bonds on DNA, like the pairing of unlike charges in an ionic crystal, is a one-to-one association with no inherent hereditary transmission property. On the other hand, induced-fit or allosteric enzyme models can only be physically described as nonholonomic, rate-controlling constraints which classify possible substrates by the specificity of their interactions.

From this point of view we must also conclude that the Central Dogma (*18*) does not give a fundamentally correct idea of hereditary transmission. While nucleic acids may be said to provide a static memory storage, we would have to say that all hereditary specificity must be propagated through nonholonomic molecular constraints, and the evidence is that these molecules are protein enzymes and not nucleic acids (*12*).

VI. EXPERIMENTAL RECOGNITION OF HEREDITARY COPOLYMERIZATION

There is likely to be great difficulty in obtaining direct experimental confirmation of synthetic tactic copolymerizations with coded hereditary propagation, since the necessary detail in both polymer sequence and conformation is largely beyond the resolution of current techniques and since the crucial aspects of high-speed sequential catalytic reaction mechanisms are not yet clear even for more elementary types of reaction.

Nevertheless, the existence of hereditary propagation in copolymer systems may be expected to produce certain types of behavior which would offer indirect evidence for hereditary reactions. The major difficulty is that the variety of hereditary constraints is unlimited, and even at the threshold of structural complexity which might support nonholonomic rate control, the output tactic sequences may not be easily distinguished from random sequences.

It is therefore important to consider under what general types of experimental conditions it is reasonable to look for evidence of hereditary propagation. This is a problem of the optimum degree of constraint in the reacting components. It is quite clear that homogeneous dilute solution reactions with randomly oriented copolymer chains could not support hereditary constraints. On the other hand, if the copolymer chains have definite conformations such as a helix or other stable folds during the propagation reaction, then hereditary control is conceivable, as in the case of the amino acid N-carboxyanhydride polymerizations (41,42) already mentioned. However, it is not likely that such weak or limited constraints could support a precise coded addition reaction, especially since there is little evidence for strong amino acid side chain interaction in the α-helical conformation.

At the other extreme, it is doubtful that the rigid constraints of the crystalline solids, as in Ziegler catalysts, can provide the flexibility necessary for a nonholonomic or an allosteric type of reaction, although again it is conceivable that the flexibility of the growing polymer itself may be sufficient to support such a hereditary reaction. Similarly, solid state polymerizations are probably too highly constrained to support more than a template type of oriented growth.

Perhaps an optimum degree of constraint for hereditary reactions may be expected at liquid phase boundaries, as in emulsion, suspension, or interfacial copolymerization. At such boundaries both the conformation of the growing copolymer chain and the orientation of the adding monomers may be constrained by weak-bond, side-chain interactions with the phase boundary, but with this two-dimensional constraint leaving flexibility in the chain end to allow the induced sequential motions necessary for the hereditary reaction. Choice of monomer types with widely differing steric or polar interactions may also contribute to the precision of tactic control which is important in preserving any hereditary chain order. However, one of the remarkable properties of some of the existing tactic catalysts is the apparent accuracy with which only isomeric differences in the adding monomers are recognized.

One of the most serious difficulties in the production of hereditary copolymers will be maintaining reasonably steady state conditions over the time of an experiment so that the approach to equilibrium does not wipe out the effects of any hereditary propagation. This may require continuous inputs of monomers and all reactants, as well as continuous removal of polymer in a precipitate or in another natural phase of the reacting system.

The possibility of recognizing hereditary order from chain monomer composition statistics (48) does not appear promising for two reasons. First, as we have shown, even though hereditary chains can be represented as a Markov state-transition matrix, the amount of data necessary to establish its reducibility, which is the necessary condition for hereditary propagation, may be very large. Second, the general composition of simple autonomous hereditary sequences often appears superficially to be near random, since such sequences form permutation groups. The hereditary property is clearly exhibited only because such permutations may be made up of cycles with no common oligomeric characters, as we saw in the pentamers of the helical copolymer model.

However, experimental tests of a coded hereditary reaction cannot rest solely on isolation of one tactic species from different sets of reaction conditions, since this could result also from a simple template mechanism, like crystal growth. A complete test of hereditary propagation must demonstrate dependence of single comonomer addition rates on the chain conformation and sequence such that a nonholonomic condition exists. That is, the rate of addition of each type of monomer must be eutactic, but at the same time each eutactic addition must correspond to no unique chain sequence. A many-one mapping must be represented by the growth.

VII. SUMMARY

The similarities of the eutactic copolymer reactions which form the basis of biological activity and the much simpler and more limited eutactic control discovered in synthetic polymer chemistry suggests the need for a definition of an elementary hereditary reaction derived from fundamental physical principles rather than from descriptive biology. We have proposed a definition of heredity based on the mathematical theory of automata and then extended it to physical and chemical systems.

Mathematically, a symbolic hereditary operation implies some constant relation between an input set of elements and an output element such that the output is uniquely determined for a given set of inputs but no nuique input exists for a given output. Such a many-to-one mapping which obeys certain other conditions may be called an automaton.

To simulate such a symbolic automaton by a real physical system requires a representation of both the symbols as well as the mapping operations. Since physical systems are described by canonical transformations which have unique inverses and form a group, any real automaton is, strictly speaking, only an approximation to the abstract automaton. Therefore, the physical approximation of hereditary behavior must be based on some irreversible structure which can support kinetic constraints restricting the dynamic motion of the system but without corresponding reduction in the number of static degrees of freedom. Such a constraint is called nonholonomic in classical dynamics.

At the chemical level, the concept of constraint loses its clarity, since all structures must depend on chemical bonds, or ultimately on quantum mechanical interactions. Therefore, the appearance of a prolonged dynamic regularity (in addition to the laws of motion themselves) can only result from a metastable steady state which is reached in a subsystem in a time interval which is short compared to the relaxation time of the entire system to equilibrium. This can occur only when two widely different forces and corresponding time scales are involved in the interactions.

In linear copolymers, we define sequence and conformation in terms of strong and weak forces, respectively; and for a stable hereditary behavior in copolymer reactions, the rate of strong bonding of each type of mono-mer must be controlled by the weak-bond interactions associated with the conformation of the chain. Furthermore, this weak interaction must be a dynamic process and not simply a template bonding. These basic conditions for hereditary chemical reactions, derived from automata concepts, appear consistent with the induced-fit and allosteric reaction mechanisms derived from experiments on enzymes but do not appear consistent with the template replication of nucleic acids or the so-called central dogma.

The experimental conditions for hereditary copolymer growth require an optimum degree of constraint which may be characteristic of reactions confined to interphase boundaries. The recognition of such reactions must depend on resolution of the detailed tactic addition mechanism.

ACKNOWLEDGMENTS

This work has been supported by the National Science Foundation, Grant NSF GB-4121 (Environmental Biology), and the Office of Naval Research, Contract Nonr 225(90) (Physics Branch).

REFERENCES

1. E. Post, *Am. J. Math.*, **65**, 197 (1943).

2. A. M. Turing, *Proc. London Math. Soc.*, **2–42**, 230 (1936).

3. W. S. McCulloch and W. Pitts, *Bull. Math. Biophys.*, **5**, 115 (1943).

4. S. C. Kleene, in *Automata Studies* (C. E. Shannon and J. McCarthy, eds.), Princeton Univ. Press, Princeton, N.J., 1956, p. 3.

5. J. von Neumann, in *Automata Studies* (C. E. Shannon and J. McCarthy, eds.), Princeton Univ. Press, Princeton, N.J., 1956, p. 43.

6. J. Fox (ed.), *Mathematical Theory of Automata*, Microwave Research Institute Symposia Series, Vol. XII, Polytechnic Press, Brooklyn, 1963.

7. M. Harrison, *Introduction to Switching and Automata Theory*, McGraw-Hill, New York, 1965.
8. H. H. Pattee, in *The Origin of Prebiological Systems* (S. W. Fox, ed.), Academic Press, New York, 1965, p. 385.
9. H. H. Pattee, *Advan. Enzymol.*, **27**, 381 (1965).
10. H. H. Pattee, in *Natural Automata and Useful Stimulations* (H. H. Pattee, E. A. Edelsack, L. Fein, and A. B. Callahan, eds.), Spartan Books, Washington, D.C., 1966.
11. H. H. Pattee, *J. Theoret. Biol.*, **17**, 410 (1967).
12. H. H. Pattee, *Prolegomena to Theoretical Biology* (C. H. Waddington, ed.), Univ. Edinburgh Press, in press.
13. R. A. Fisher, *The Genetical Theory of Natural Selection*, Dover, New York, 1958, pp. 1–21.
14. T. Dobzhansky, *Evolution, Genetics, and Man*, Wiley, New York, 1955, pp. 23–43.
15. J. D. Watson, *The Molecular Biology of the Gene*, Benjamin, New York, 1965, p. 67.
16. J. M. Allen (ed.), *The Molecular Control of Cellular Activity*, McGraw-Hill, New York, 1963.
17. C. B. Anfisen, *The Molecular Basis of Evolution*, Wiley, New York, 1959, p. 129.
18. F. H. C. Crick, *Symp. Soc. Exptl. Biol.*, **12**, 138 (1958).
19. M. F. Perutz, *Proteins and Nucleic Acids*, Elsevier, Amsterdam, 1962.
20. V. M. Ingram, *The Biosynthesis of Macromolecules*, Benjamin, New York, 1965.
21. G. H. Haggis (ed.), *Introduction to Molecular Biology*, Wiley, New York, 1965.
22. R. F. Steiner, *The Chemical Foundations of Molecular Biology*, Van Nostrand, Princeton, N.J. 1965.
23. J. C. Kendrew, *The Thread of Life*, Harvard Univ. Press, Cambridge, Mass., 1966.
24. M. Davis, *Computability and Unsolvability*, McGraw-Hill, New York, 1958.
25. H. Hermes, *Enumerability, Decidability and Computability*, Academic Press, New York, 1965.
26. B. A. Trakhtenbrot, *Algorithms and Automatic Computing Machines*, Heath and Company, Boston, 1963.
27. A. Sommerfeld, *Mechanics*, Academic Press, New York, 1952, p. 80.
28. E. T. Whittaker, *A Treatise on the Analytical Dynamics of Particles and Rigid Bodies*, 4th ed., Dover, New York, 1944.
29. C. Lanczos, *The Variational Principles of Mechanics*, Univ. Toronto Press, Toronto, 1949.
30. I. Prigogine, *Introduction to Thermodynamics of Irreversible Processes*, 2nd ed., Wiley (Interscience), New York, 1961, p. 107.
31. T. A. Bak, *Advan. Chem. Phys.*, **3**, 33 (1961).
32. M. Sugita, *J. Theoret. Biol.*, **1**, 415 (1961).
33. E. Schrödinger, *What is Life?*, Cambridge Univ. Press, New York, 1944.
34. E. Wigner, *Am. J. Phys.*, **31**, 6 (1963).
35. E. Wigner, *The Logic of Personal Knowledge*, Routledge and Kegan Paul, London, 1961, p. 231.
36. H. Araki and M. M. Yanase, *Phys. Rev.*, **120**, 622 (1960).
37. A. Daneri, A. Loinger, and G. M. Prosperi, *Nucl. Phys.*, **33**, 297 (1962).
38. J. M. Jauch, *Helv. Phys. Acta*, **33**, 711 (1960).
39. H. Wakita, *Progr. Theoret. Phys.*, **23**, 32 (1960); **27**, 139 (1962).

40. J. M. Burgers, *Rev. Mod. Phys.*, **35**, 145 (1963).
41. P. Doty and R. D. Lundberg, *J. Am. Chem. Soc.*, **78**, 4810 (1956).
42. M. Idelson and E. R. Blout, *J. Am. Chem. Soc.*, **80**, 2387 (1958).
43. B. Elspas, *IRE Trans.*, **CT6**, 45 (1949).
44. R. J. Eden, *Proc. Roy. Soc. (London)*, **A205**, 564 (1951).
45. R. J. Eden, *Proc. Roy. Soc. (London)*, **A205**, 583 (1951).
46. D. E. Koshland, Jr., *Fed. Am. Soc. Exptl. Biol. Proc.*, **23**, 719 (1964).
47. J. Monod, J.-P. Changeux, and F. Jacob, *J. Mol. Biol.*, **6**, 306 (1963).
48. G. E. Ham (ed.), *Copolymerization*, Wiley (Interscience), New York, 1964, p. 1.

CHAPTER 9

The Effect of Microtacticity
on the Reactions of Polymers

M. M. Van Beylen†

UNIVERSITY OF LOUVAIN
LOUVAIN, BELGIUM

I. INTRODUCTION

Intramolecular reactions involving groups attached to adjacent units along a polymer chain provide a particularly attractive method to study the influence of the stereochemical structure of the polymer in the immediate vicinity of the functional groups (i.e., of the "microtacticity" of the polymer) on the reaction course and kinetics of polymeric reactions. Obviously, a sharp distinction must therefore be made between reactions that take place at monofunctional sites and reactions affecting two or more neighboring functions attached to the same polymer chain.

Monofunctional reactions on high polymers were often reported to proceed in the same way as do similar reactions on their low molecular weight homologs and to have equivalent activation energies, small differences being compensated for by steric effects.

Thus Hiller (*1*) was able to show by measuring the reaction enthalpy and activation energy of the acetylation of cellulose that this reaction and the reverse one of hydrolysis are both equivalent to those carried out on ordinary alcohols and are both examples of general acid-catalyzed reactions. In cases such as the alkaline hydrolysis of pectinic acids (*2*), where

† Research Associate, N.F.W.O., Belgium.

the electrical potential of the polymer increases as a result of the increasing charge of the chain, this similarity may be disturbed, without, however, necessitating the assumption of another reaction mechanism.

In contrast with this, the different behavior of a polymer and its low molecular weight analog becomes very significant in those reactions where neighboring groups may interact with one another, thereby causing a passage to an intramolecular bi- or multifunctional mechanism in which the relative positions of the interacting groups must necessarily be of great importance. Thus a difference between both types of reaction may be anticipated in view of the fact that, unlike for monofunctional reactions, the functions participating in neighboring group interactions, due to their particular linkage to the polymeric backbone, are found in a more or less prefixed relative steric position toward each other.

Care, however, should be taken to avoid hasty conclusions when it comes to establishing a relation between kinetic effects and different stereochemical configurations or when kinetic data are to be used to characterize the tacticity of a polymer. Some restrictions should thereby be taken into account.

1. It must be emphasized that, if one starts out with a homopolymer, any reaction carried out on such a polymer will necessarily lead to a co-polymer, the composition of which changes progressively with the degree of conversion. Simultaneously, functional interactions between neighboring original and newly created functions may start to occur, giving rise to a change in the functionality of the polymeric reaction. Thus an inter-molecular mechanism involving an external reagent and determined mainly by the accessibility of the functional groups of the polymer rather than by its stereoregularity will interfere with an intramolecular reaction for which the microtacticity can be the rate determining factor. Moreover, even for reactions occurring exclusively or predominantly through an internal mechanism, if the content of both monomers in the copolymer is relatively high, differences in kinetic behavior will be a function not only of stereo-chemical differences but also of the relative importance of different monomer sequences. It is therefore evident that the ideal system would be a copolymer, containing a few units of isolated groups. In this way the functions that are to react intramolecularly with their neighbors will remain in a constant environment throughout the reaction so that any difference in their reactivity can be attributed to steric factors only and not to the chemical nature of the nearest neighbor. On the other hand, the interpretation of data obtained for homopolymers, which are converted in the course of the reaction into copolymers of continuously changing

composition, and for copolymers with relatively high content of both monomers will be much more complicated.

2. A second restriction deals with the fact that it is the steric configuration in the immediate vicinity of the reaction site (i.e., the microtacticity) which is rate determining. However, some of the correlations between reaction rates and tactic structure to be discussed in this chapter were established by means of tacticity estimates, based on physical properties such as crystallinity or solubility, which depend mainly on the presence in the polymer of longer tactic blocks and which are less sensitive to relatively small deviations from randomness. Consequently, they do not permit a detailed analysis of the internal structural elements. In this respect methods such as nuclear magnetic resonance (3) and infrared spectroscopy (4), although the latter is more complicated, are to be considered far more reliable and are therefore to be preferred for the characterization of the microstructure of the polymer.

These considerations should be borne in mind throughout the discussion to follow.

The purpose of this chapter is not to present a general review of chemical reactions of polymers, many of which have already been extensively dealt with in a series of contributions (5), but rather to discuss the influence of the stereochemical structure on both the rate and the attainable degree of conversion on the basis of a number of illustrative examples taken from the literature. Although quite a number of interfunctional reactions have been reported in the literature, this discussion shall be limited to those reactions that have either been studied from the stereochemical viewpoint or for which, at least, data susceptible to be correlated with the internal structure of the polymeric species involved are available.

In this way we shall successively consider the influence of the microtacticity in the case of acrylic and methacrylic polymers and copolymers, poly(vinyl acetals), poly(vinyl acetate), and poly(vinyl chloride).

II. CHEMICAL REACTIONS AND THE MICROTACTICITY OF HIGH POLYMERS

A. Acrylic and Methacrylic Polymers and Copolymers

1. *Polymers Containing Acid and Ester Side Groups*

With the purpose of eventually calculating the electrostatic potential in the neighborhood of polyions by comparing hydrolysis rates of polyelectrolyte derivatives and corresponding uncharged analogs, Morawetz et al.

(6–8) studied the base-catalyzed solvolysis of acrylic acid copolymers containing small proportions of *p*-nitrophenyl methacrylate (1.5–9 mole %) as
compared to the same reaction of *p*-nitrophenyl trimethylacetate in a solution of polyacrylic acid. The hydrolysis of the ester units incorporated into
the polyacrylic acid chain was found to follow first-order kinetics but,
contrary to expectations on electrostatic grounds, the reaction at pH 5–6
proceeded about 1 million times faster than that of the ester of the mono-
carboxylic acid. To interpret their results, the authors assumed that the
rapid hydrolysis is due not to the attack of hydroxyl ions, but to the
internal nucleophilic attack of a neighboring carboxylate ion on the carbonyl carbon of the ester group, with the formation of a six-membered
acid anhydride intermediate according to Eq. (1):

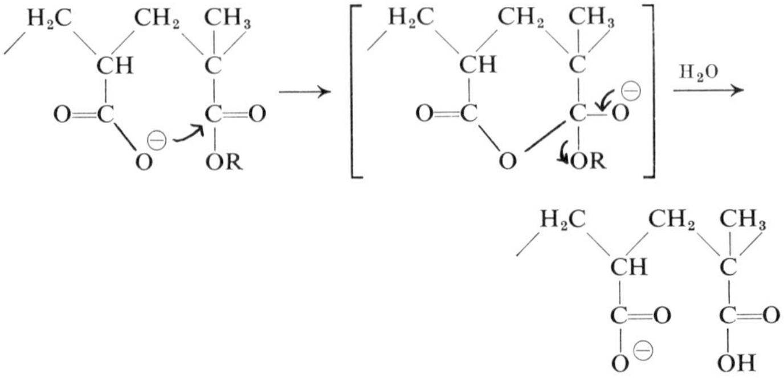

where the formation of the cyclic intermediate is rate determining. Additional evidence supporting this interpretation results from the similarity in
behavior of the phenyl monoesters of succinic and glutaric acid, whose
hydrolysis is very fast compared to the acetate ion-catalyzed hydrolysis of
phenyl esters (7,9). In view of this similarity, the participation in the
reaction of the copolymers of a second neighboring carboxyl group must
be considered unlikely.

Furthermore, the hydrolytic rates in the pH ranges 3–6 both for the
copolymer and the monoesters of the dicarboxylic acids are found to be
proportional to the degree of ionization of the carboxyl groups. The
importance of the proximity of the neighboring catalyzing carboxylate ion
may be illustrated by the fact that the phenyl monoester of succinic acid
reacts 120–200 times more rapidly than the corresponding glutaric acid
monoester (9).

Finally, the hypothesis of an acid anhydride intermediate was confirmed
by the findings of Bender et al., who gave conclusive evidence for the

formation of an anhydride intermediate in the intramolecularly catalyzed hydrolysis of phthalamic acid (*10,11*) and of methyl hydrogen phthalate and aspirin (*12*) as well as in the intermolecular catalysis of hydrolysis of phenyl and *p*-nitrophenyl acetates and 2,4-dinitrophenyl benzoate by acetate ion (*13*). Moreover, these authors were able to demonstrate through comparison of corresponding intermolecular and intramolecular processes that the intramolecular process is much more important. The hypothesis of an anhydride intermediate was further strengthened by the work of Bruice and Pandit (*14*), who studied the effect of geminal substitution, ring size, and conformation of the carbophenoxy and carboxyl groups on the intramolecular nucleophilic catalysis of the hydrolysis of monophenyl esters of dibasic acids and the solvolysis of the intermediate anhydrides.

Although at the time of the findings of Morawetz et al. no stereospecific requirements were postulated besides the direct vicinality of the participating functions, it is clear that the formation of a cyclic intermediate must depend on the relative steric position of the groups and that therefore the results should be related to the microtacticity of the polymeric chain. A more detailed discussion of this correlation shall be dealt with later in this chapter.

In subsequent work Morawetz and Gaetjens (*15,16*) investigated the hydrolysis of copolymers of methacrylic acid and small amounts of either *p*-nitrophenyl methacrylate or *p*-nitrophenyl acrylate. In contrast with the corresponding reactions of acrylic acid copolymers, first-order plots were obtained showing a pronounced curvature and the copolymers behaved as if they contained ester groups of two widely divergent reactivities. Indeed, it was shown that the observed downward curvature could be satisfactorily accounted for if one assumes the presence in the polymer of 18 to 28% of ester groups about 10–14 times as reactive as the remainder. The rate constants corresponding to the two kinds of ester groups were both found to increase monotonically with the ionization of the polymer, indicating that a single neighboring ionized carboxyl is involved in attack on the ester group, since catalysis by two neighboring carboxyl groups has been shown to be a maximum when only one of them is ionized (*17*). It is noteworthy that no change in the fraction of fast ester groups and the ratio of the two rate constants was observed if a *p*-methoxyphenyl ester is used instead of a *p*-nitrophenyl ester. Here an explanation in terms of stereoisomerism was offered by the authors. They believe that the different reactivity of ester groups may reflect a difference in the ease with which a carboxylate ion, in the transition state preceding the formation of the

cyclic anhydride, may approach the carbonyl carbon of the ester, depending on whether the carbons carrying these functions have the same or the
opposite configuration. If the reacting ester group is surrounded by two
carboxylate neighbors, as can safely be assumed in view of the low ester
content of the copolymer, three different steric structures, (1)–(3), may be
visualized.

$$
\begin{array}{ccc}
CH_3 & CH_3 & CH_3 \\
| & | & | \\
-C-CH_2-C-CH_2-C- \\
| & | & | \\
COO^- & COOR & COO^-
\end{array}
\qquad
\begin{array}{ccc}
CH_3 & CH_3 & COO^- \\
| & | & | \\
-C-CH_2-C-CH_2-C- \\
| & | & | \\
COO^- & COOR & CH_3
\end{array}
$$

isotactic triad   heterotactic triad

(1)   (2)

$$
\begin{array}{ccc}
COO^- & CH_3 & COO^- \\
| & | & | \\
-C-CH_2-C-CH_2-C- \\
| & | & | \\
CH_3 & COOR & CH_3
\end{array}
$$

syndiotactic triad

(3)

The occurrence of these three structures in poly(methacrylic acid) prepared by radical polymerization was demonstrated by Bovey and Tiers (18)
and Morawetz and Rubin (19) by nuclear magnetic resonance spectra of
the corresponding poly(methyl methacrylate) into which the acid had
previously been converted. The polymers were found to contain approximately 8–12% isotactic triads, 55% syndiotactic triads, the remaining
groups being heterotactic. The fact that the experimental kinetic data
could nevertheless be satisfactorily explained in terms of only two and not
three different rate constants, as one might expect, was discussed by
Morawetz (20). He suggested either that two of the three rate constants
are too similar to be experimentally distinguishable or that the three steric
configurations occur in the immediate vicinity of the ester residue of the
copolymer in a ratio substantially different from that governing the
distribution along the homopolymer chain. Attention was also called
by this author to the fact that in the copolymer of acrylic acid with
methacrylic ester all ester groups were equally reactive, as evidenced
by their first-order solvolysis, while copolymers of methacrylic acid with
acrylic ester seem to have ester groups of two widely different reactivities.
From this observation he concluded that the conformational differences
between the methacrylic and acrylic chain as a whole would be of greater
importance than the substituents in the immediate neighborhood of the

reacting groups in determining the different behavior of the two copolymers as compared to each other. Although no direct evidence was given, the foregoing data were shown to demonstrate clearly the influence of the microtacticity on the rate of polymeric reactions such as polymeric ester hydrolysis.

To shed more light on this new aspect of polymeric reactions, De Loecker and Smets (*21*) undertook a systematic study of the hydrolysis of several copolymers of methacrylic acid and methacrylic esters of different compositions (acid content: 28.8, 50, 60, 66, 72, 83, and 86.5%) in acidic medium and at different degrees of neutralization. Except for those with the highest acid content, all the copolymers show a two-step hydrolysis in which the second step is about $\frac{1}{6}-\frac{1}{7}$ slower than the first. Kinetically, the reaction is first order in acid and in ester, while from the viewpoint of general catalysis, as suggested by Bronsted, two hydrolysis rate constants of nearly equal magnitude were calculated ($k_{HA} = 1.5 \times 10^{-5}$ and $k_A = 1.0 \times 10^{-5}$) corresponding to the catalytic action of undissociated and neutralized carboxyl groups, respectively, and demonstrating that one is almost as effective as the other in promoting the hydrolysis. As shown in Table 1, the latter is therefore relatively little affected by the degree of neutralization, except when about 25% of the acid groups have been neutralized.

Here, too, the hydrolysis was found to take place mainly through the functional interaction of an ester group with directly neighboring acid and/or carboxylate groups. This intramolecular mechanism was clearly demonstrated by the comparison with the hydrolysis behavior of a water-soluble methyl methacrylate–*N*-vinylpyrrolidone copolymer. As a result of its relatively low methacrylate content (13.5%), it is likely that each ester group is surrounded by vinylpyrrolidone units. This copolymer was used at ester concentrations identical to those used with methyl methacrylate–methacrylic acid copolymers containing 50 and 28 mole % of the ester. Acetic (or polymethacrylic) acid was added and neutralized to a given degree, e.g., 0.5. While the experimental rate constants of the acid–ester copolymers were of the order of 10^{-6} sec^{-1}, that for the ester–vinyl-pyrrolidone copolymer was only about 10^{-8} sec^{-1}. This difference becomes even more pronounced when the greater acid strength of acetic acid, as compared to either poly(methacrylic acid) or the copolymeric acid, is taken into account. These experiments therefore show once more and beyond all doubt that the intermolecular reactions are practically negligible in comparison to the intramolecular functional interactions between an ester group and a directly vicinal acid or carboxylate group.

Another argument in favor of an intramolecular mechanism is given by the experiments carried out at doubled concentrations, as indicated in Table 1. When double amounts of copolymer are taken, obviously both the acid and the ester concentration must be twice as high. Nevertheless, the rate of hydrolysis is only doubled and not quadrupled, thus demonstrating that an acid–ester pair operates as a single kinetic entity and that the reaction must be thought of as occurring between neighboring groups.

TABLE 1

Influence of Copolymer Concentration on the Rate of Hydrolysis of Methacrylic Acid–Methyl Methacrylate Copolymers at $110°C^a$

Neutralization ratio = acid groups/carboxylate groups	Acid content, mole %	Rate (mole/liter), $sec^{-1} \times 10^8$	
		Ester concn., 0.0312 mole/liter	Ester concn., 0.0624 mole/liter
1	72	3.0	
	83	5.8	
2	72	3.5	
	83	6.3	
3	72	7.6	15.5
	83	13.6	26.5
7	72	3.5	7.4
	83	6.9	13.0

^{a} Reprinted by permission from *Angewandte Chemie—International Edition in English*, Volume 1, No. 6, p. 308 (1962).

From Table 1 it can also be seen that at a ratio of neutralization equal to 3 (i.e., one carboxylate against three carboxyl groups) the rate of hydrolysis is approximately twice as high as at any other ratio. This maximum rate is characterized by an appreciably lower activation energy, namely, 16 kcal/mole instead of 23 kcal/mole. Furthermore, by means of structural probability calculations, the distribution of monomeric units 1 and 2 along the polymer chain was evaluated and the first more rapid step was ascribed to the intervention of 121 triads, which can be present, depending on the degree of neutralization, as acid–ester–acid, carboxylate–ester–acid, or carboxylate–ester–carboxylate sequences. The second step, on the other hand, must be related to 122 triads. The twofold increase in rate for copolymers with high acid content at a neutralization ratio equal to three is explained in terms of a predominant acid–ester–carboxylate sequence, for which a concerted reaction mechanism is assumed.

In this system, too, a mechanism similar to the one proposed by Morawetz may be assumed, with the understanding, however, that in this case the ester function can interact not only with a neighboring ionized carboxylate group but with an adjacent undissociated carboxylic acid group as well, and that in this case also a second neighboring carboxyl group favorably affects the anhydride formation between the ester group and the first carboxyl group, except at neutralization ratio = 3, where a concerted mechanism is probably involved. This favorable influence may, however, have a negative rather than a positive character in the sense that a second neighboring carboxyl displays a much lesser steric hindrance for the formation of this intermediary anhydride link than does a second ester group directly neighboring the reacting ester group. Ester groups surrounded by a carboxyl and another ester group therefore undergo much slower hydrolysis, as evidenced by the second slow step. Such an effect could obviously not be detected in the copolymers studied by Morawetz et al., where all ester functions, owing to the low ester content, were flanked by two carboxyls.

Compared to the previously given scheme of Morawetz for the internal carboxylate-catalyzed hydrolysis of an ester group and in direct analogy with the scheme given by Bender et al. (*11*) for the internal hydrolysis of phthalamic acid, the intramolecular mechanism in which the ester group interacts with an undissociated neighboring carboxylic acid group may be represented by:

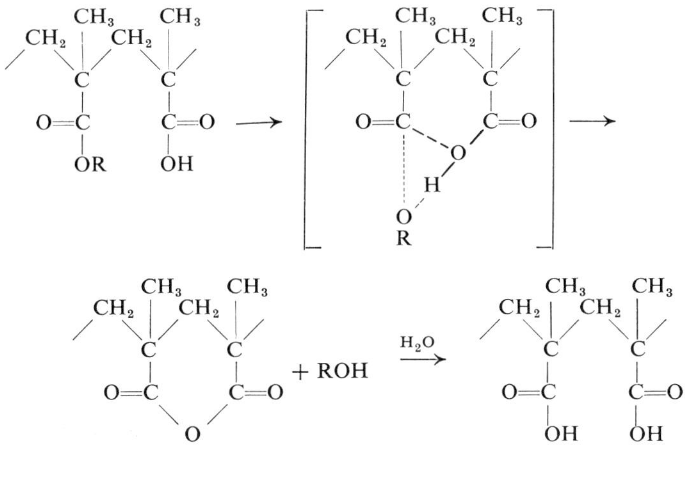

$$(2)$$

In this mechanism, the undissociated carboxylic acid group simultaneously attacks the carbonyl carbon atom of the ester function and donates a proton to the departing alcohol molecule.

As in the experiments reported by Morawetz and Oreskes (17) on intramolecular bifunctional catalysis of ester hydrolysis, the concerted mechanism postulated in this system, when about 2.5% of the carboxyl groups are ionized, is probably also related to the principle of bifunctional catalysis, as described by Swain and Brown (22).

As much as the above-mentioned distributions of monomeric units 1 and 2 along the chain are able to provide an interpretation for the occurrence of either one or two steps during the hydrolysis of the copolymers examined by Smets et al., they fail to explain the limited degree of conversion of the reaction, which is always considerably lower than the total amount of 1,2 configurations. In a copolymer, for instance, with 86.5 mole % of acid, theoretically 90% of the reactive groups are present as 1,2 pairs and should therefore be hydrolyzable, yet experimentally only 45% could be hydrolyzed. To understand this phenomenon, the distribution of the monomeric units along the copolymer chain cannot suffice and the stereochemical structure of the copolymers must be taken into consideration. The fact that the chemical composition of these copolymers cannot be solely responsible for their kinetic behavior was clearly and directly demonstrated in the following experiments.

When a copolymer containing 60 mole % of methacrylic acid groups is hydrolyzed at a degree of neutralization equal to 0.5, the reaction is at first rapid, but slows down later on in the second step, before attaining 72% of acid groups. If, next, a copolymer containing 72 mole % of acid groups and obtained by direct copolymerization is subjected to the hydrolysis, a rapid step is again observed which is considerably faster than the second step in the hydrolysis of the copolymer containing 60 mole % of the acid. The rate of hydrolysis of the 72% copolymer also drops progressively and, when 83 mole % of acid is attained, this rate is again appreciably lower than that of a directly synthesized copolymer with 83 mole % of acid. This successive behavior, as illustrated in Fig. 1, shows unambiguously that an identical chemical composition of two statistical copolymers is insufficient to ensure an equal reaction rate and that some stereospecific interactions must be assumed.

These data on the acid hydrolysis of methacrylic acid–methyl methacrylate copolymers were completed with a study of their alkaline hydrolysis (23) in which an intramolecular mechanism was also shown to prevail at pH values smaller than 12.5. Only in strongly alkaline medium did the hydrolysis occur through the external attack of hydroxyl ions. The limited degree of conversion was again found to depend not only on the over-all chemical composition but also on the stereochemical configuration of the polymeric chain.

Similar results have also been found for acrylic acid–ethyl ethacrylate copolymers with varying molar acid content by Smets and Van Humbeek (*24*). The rate of hydrolysis was examined at different degrees of neutralization in buffered aqueous solutions and was directly proportional to the

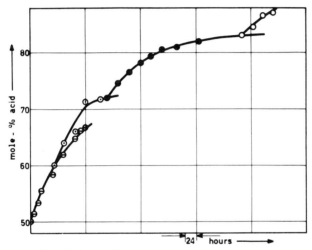

Fig. 1. Successive hydrolysis of different methacrylic acid–ester copolymers. Influence of the stereochemical composition. ⊖, 50 mole % acid; ○, 60 mole % acid; ●, 72 mole % acid; ○, 83 mole % acid. [Reprinted by permission from Ref. (*21*).]

concentration of 1,2,1 triads and practically insensitive to variation of concentration of 1,2,2 triads. In these systems the steric hindrance due to the direct neighboring of two ester groups must be considered so strong that with acid–ester–ester or carboxylate–ester–ester triads the formation of an intermediary anhydride link is practically rendered impossible, whereas for the methacrylic acid–methyl methacrylate copolymers, with a less sterically hindered methyl ester, a second slow step could still be observed. Moreover, depending on the degree of neutralization, the following decreasing order of reactivity has been found: acid–ester–carboxylate > carboxylate–ester–carboxylate ≫ acid–ester–acid. When the degree of neutralization is equal to 0.5, the rate is maximum and corresponds to a minimum of the activation energy (17 kcal/mole), resulting probably from a concerted reaction of the predominant acid–ester–carboxylate triad. In this system, too, the final degree of conversion is, however, limited because of the existence of different stereochemical arrangements of these 1,2,1 triads; a diagram similar to that given in Fig. 1 may be established. The complete data on the hydrolysis of acrylic and methacrylic copolymers shows incontestably that direct vicinality of the interacting functions alone cannot constitute a general basis for the explanation of the observed phenomena but that some steric factors must be operative which are related to the stereochemical arrangements in the immediate neighborhood of the reacting groups. In this respect it is easily understood that, as pointed out previously, the formation in the course of the reaction of a 1,3 disubstituted six-membered cyclic intermediate must necessarily depend on the positions which the groups directly involved in the cyclization occupy relative to one another, and therefore on the microtacticity of the polymeric chain.

In this connection it is worth mentioning an interesting and clarifying discussion of this problem that was presented by Smets (25), who made a comparison between 1,3-dialkylcyclohexane derivatives and the ring structures under discussion. Indeed, it had been recognized earlier (26) that, in view of the similarity in bond length of carbon-carbon and carbon oxygen bonds as well as in the C—C—C and C—O—C angles, cyclohexane and six-membered rings containing oxygen should be stereochemically very similar. Apart from a slight effect on the hexaatomic ring structure due to the carbonyl carbon atoms with sp^2 configuration, Smets therefore felt that the conclusions concerning the stereochemistry of 1,3-dialkylcyclohexanes can be applied without serious error to these intermediate rings.

In 1,3-dimethylcyclohexanes, the *cis* isomer (meso variety) corresponding to an isotactic structure must be diequatorial in order for the interaction energy to be negligible. Indeed, a diaxial *cis* conformation is not favored because the substituents crowd each other strongly and the resulting steric interaction gives rise to a repulsive energy term of 5.5 kcal/ mole (27). In the *trans* isomer, on the other hand, which is the d,l-racemic variety and which corresponds to a syndiotactic structure, the substituents will predominantly occur as follows: one in the equatorial and the other in the axial position. In this form there exists an interaction between the axial methyl group and the syn-axial hydrogen atoms which is of the same type as the interaction in the *gauche* form of butane and may be computed at 0.9 kcal/mole each. On this basis the diequatorial *cis* isomer (isotactic) in which no such interactions are present should be more stable by 1.8 kcal/ mole than the axial–equatorial *trans* isomer (syndiotactic) presenting two such interactions. It must, however, be pointed out that in the case of a cyclized poly(acrylic anhydride) intermediate there can exist only one 1,3 interaction between a hydrogen and the chain to which the ring is attached, since an oxygen has been incorporated into the ring. The difference in stability may therefore be estimated to amount to approximately 1 kcal, taking into account the trend occurring in the conformational free energy differences for monosubstituted cyclohexanes (in kilocalories per mole) when the alkyl chain length or the bulkiness of the substituent increases. These differences were calculated to increase in the following order: methyl 1.7, ethyl 1.8, isopropyl 2.1. For *n*-propyl, *n*-butyl, and neo-pentyl the values are estimated to be 2.0–2.1.

From these considerations it can be seen that, in as far as an intermediate cyclic anhydride intervenes in the hydrolytic reaction mechanism, an isotactic placement in the polyacrylic chain will always be more reactive than a syndiotactic one because a diequatorially substituted ring is more easily formed due to its greater stability. This is illustrated in structures (**4**) and (**5**).

isotactic   syndiotactic
(*cis*)   (*trans*)
(**4**)   (**5**)

reaction intermediate

A direct verification of these assumptions may be found in the work of Smets and Van Humbeek (*24*) who compared conventional and isotactic acrylic acid–methyl acrylate copolymers of roughly the same over-all chemical composition. The conventional copolymer was obtained by direct copolymerization of the two monomers in benzene with azobisisobutyronitrile as an initiator. The isotactic copolymer was prepared by hydrolyzing isotactic poly-tert-butyl acrylate, which was prepared with a phenylmagnesium bromide catalyst at −60°C, as described by Fox et al. (*28*), and by partially methylating the resulting isotactic polyacrylic acid with diazomethane. From the rates of hydrolysis measured at 103°C in buffered aqueous solutions, it becomes evident that the isotactic polymers hydrolyze three to five times faster than the conventional polymers. Simultaneously, in the isotactic copolymer a much higher percentage of ester groups appears to be hydrolyzable than in the conventional one. The pertinent data are summarized in Table 2.

TABLE 2

Rate Constants of Hydrolysis of Acid–Ester Copolymers of Different Tacticities[a]

	Acrylic acid–methyl acrylate (t^0: 103°C)		
Acid content, mole %	$r = \dfrac{acid}{carboxylate}$	Apparent first-order rate constants $\times 10^6$	
		Conventional	Isotactic
64.5 (conventional) ⎫	0	5.1	14
	1	5.4	15
67 (isotactic) ⎭	2	6.7	17
80.5 (conventional) ⎫	0	3.1	14
	1	5.8	21.5
80 (isotactic) ⎭	2	7.9	19

	Methacrylic acid–methyl methacrylate (t^0: 110°C)			
Acid content, mole %	$r = \dfrac{acid}{carboxylate}$	Apparent first-order rate constants $\times 10^6$		
		Conventional	Isotactic	Syndiotactic
40.6	1			0.8
	3			0.8
50	1	1.3		
	3	1.0		
60	1	1.3		0.3
	3			0.3
72	1	0.9	4.2	
	3	2.6		
78.3	1		5.3	
83	1	1.1	5.6	0
	3	3.0	16.8	0

[a] Reprinted from *Pure and Applied Chemistry*, **12**, 214 (1966), by permission of the International Union of Pure and Applied Chemistry and Butterworths Scientific Publications [data adapted from Refs. (*24,29*)].

In the methacrylic copolymers, the intermediate six-membered ring is tetrasubstituted in 1,1' and 3,3' because of the presence in the α position with respect to the carbonyl groups not only of the two chain segments but also of two methyl groups replacing the two hydrogen atoms. By means of models it can be shown that both the isotactic (**6**) and the syndiotactic (**7**) configuration are characterized by a considerable steric hindrance. Nevertheless it is the isotactic polymer which is the least hindered.

isotactic   syndiotactic
(6)   (7)

Although no quantitative data for similar model homologous substances are available as yet, it was argued by Smets that in view of the steric interaction between the two axial substituents, the formation of a cyclic intermediate will be much more difficult than in the acrylic series. This was illustrated with data (Table 2) obtained by Smets and De Loecker (29) for methacrylic acid–methyl methacrylate copolymers. At the same degree of neutralization and taking into account the difference in reaction temperature for the two series of experiments (110°C instead of 103°C), the methacrylic copolymers always hydrolyze about 10–12 times more slowly than the acrylic copolymers of about the same molar composition. The influence of the tacticity within the methacrylic series, on the other hand, was first, although merely qualitatively, illustrated in the experiments reported by Glavis (30) concerning the alkaline hydrolysis of poly(methyl methacrylate) samples of various tacticities. On the basis of some conversion-time data, he demonstrated that conventional and syndiotactic poly-(methyl methacrylates) are hydrolyzed relatively slowly but that the isotactic species is hydrolyzed very rapidly and to a higher final conversion than is either one of the other two types. This different reactivity to alkaline hydrolysis could even be utilized for the separation of mixtures of polymers of different types. While these experiments were carried out in heterogeneous alkaline medium, greater reactivity of the isotactic-type polymers was also manifested in the acid-catalyzed hydrolysis in homogeneous solution.

These qualitative data were later confirmed in a more quantitative way by the results of Smets and De Loecker (29) concerning the rate of hydrolysis in homogeneous aqueous medium of methacrylic acid–methyl methacrylate copolymers of nearly the same chemical composition but of different tacticity. The copolymers used in these experiments were prepared by partial hydrolysis of the tactically corresponding poly(methyl methacrylates), no direct synthesis of such copolymers being available. The structure of the polymers had been examined earlier by Fox et al. (*31–34*). It was implicitly assumed that the tacticity of the polymeric chain remains unchanged in the course of the hydrolysis. In this series again it is seen that the isotactic copolymer obtained by partial sulfuric acid hydrolysis of isotactic poly(methyl methacrylate) (prepared in toluene with Grignard reagent) hydrolyzes four or five times faster than the conventional copolymer and also that a higher degree of conversion may be attained with the isotactic species. On the other hand, copolymers derived by acid hydrolysis from poly(methyl methacrylates) mainly of syndiotactic structure (prepared photochemically at $-20°C$ in the presence of benzoin) hydrolyze very slowly and at high acid content cannot be hydrolyzed further. For both isotactic and conventional copolymers, the reaction rates, although different, were increased about threefold at a degree of neutralization equal to 0.25, indicating an intramolecular concerted mechanism.

In all the cases considered so far, an intramolecular mechanism was always operative for which the stereochemical arrangement of the interacting functions is of decisive importance. As soon, however, as this intramolecular mechanism is replaced by a bimolecular mechanism with an external reagent, the accessibility of the reacting functions becomes the predominant factor in determining the rate and a reversal in the observed order of reactivities may well occur. Thus one may explain the results reported by Sakurada et al. (*35*) on the saponification reaction of poly-(methyl acrylates) prepared by various methods of radical polymerization. It was observed that one of the poly(methyl acrylate) samples, which differed markedly from the others in potentiometric titration behavior and seemed to be more syndiotactic, showed an initial rate of saponification with sodium hydroxide about 20 times higher than that of the other samples that were comparatively more isotactic. The lower initial rates of the more isotactic samples clearly show the greater steric hindrance toward external reagents inherent in an isotactic configuration.

2. *Polymers Containing Acid and Amide Groups*

A similar behavior to that of the acrylic and methacrylic acid–ester copolymers is displayed in the hydrolysis of polyacrylamides and acrylic acid–acrylamide copolymers. Thus during the hydrolysis of polyacrylamide in buffered aqueous solution (acetic acid–sodium acetate), Smets and

Hesbain (*36*) observed a slow initial rate proportional to the concentration of acetic acid followed by an autocatalytic acceleration of the reaction as soon as about 3 % of the amide groups were hydrolyzed. This acceleration, illustrated in Fig. 2, is again ascribed to the intramolecular reaction of internal (acrylic) acid, resulting from the hydrolysis, and neighboring amide groups. This reaction proceeds at a much higher rate than that between external (acetic) acid and amide groups. In the acid hydrolysis

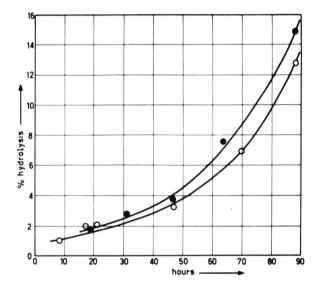

Fig. 2. Autoacceleration in the hydrolysis of polyacrylamide in the presence of maleic acid (open circle) or acetic acid (filled circle). [Reprinted by permission from Ref. (*36*).]

of copolymers of acrylic acid and acrylamide of different composition (70, 74.5, 85, and 88 mole % acid) and at various degrees of neutralization, two steps may be distinguished, as in the case of the copolymers of methacrylic acid–methyl methacrylate. The first step was characterized by a rate constant about 300 times higher than both the rate constant for polyacrylamide in the presence of acetic acid and the constant for the second step. The first rapid step results from the interaction between an amide group and an undissociated directly neighboring acid group, whereas the second slow step, whose rate is similar to that of polyacrylamide hydrolysis in the presence of acetic acid, is due to external acid.

The intramolecular hydrolysis of the acrylic acid–acrylamide copolymer may be visualized by the Eq. (3), which is similar to the mechanism proposed by Bender for the hydrolysis of phthalamic acid (11).

$$\tag{3}$$

When the number of amide groups directly vicinal to an acid group is calculated, it is seen that only about 40% of them hydrolyze rapidly, the other 60% behaving much in the same way as the small fraction of amide groups not adjacent to acid groups. From this observation it was again concluded that direct vicinality of the interacting undissociated acid and amide groups is not a sufficient guarantee for a rapid hydrolysis. The two groups must also occur in a well-determined stereochemical position. This stereospecificity of the reaction, thus postulated, was again proved by the same method as with the polyacid–ester copolymers, namely, by comparing two copolymers of the same over-all chemical composition (90% acid), one of which was prepared by direct copolymerization of both monomers and the other by hydrolysis of a copolymer initially containing 85% acid. This comparative behavior is illustrated in Fig. 3. It is seen that the hydrolysis of a copolymer containing 85 mole % of acrylic acid starts out rapidly in a first step, slowing down afterward before 90% of acid groups is attained. On the other hand, when a copolymer containing 90 mole % acid groups but prepared by direct copolymerization is hydrolyzed, the reaction proceeds much faster than the second slow step observed in the hydrolysis of the copolymer containing 85 mole % of acid.

It is obvious that in so far as an acid anhydride must also be assumed to be the intermediate in the hydrolysis of acrylamide-containing copolymers, the same stereochemical arguments as given above for the acid–ester copolymers must also hold in the present case.

The difference in the type of intramolecular catalysis of hydrolysis of *p*-nitrophenyl esters, methyl esters, and acrylamides incorporated in a poly-acid chain is noteworthy at this point. Indeed, whereas catalysis in the hydrolysis of *p*-nitrophenyl esters incorporated in a polyacrylic or meth-acrylic acid chain was due exclusively to adjacent carboxylate groups, it was shown that the hydrolysis of methacrylic acid–methyl methacrylate copolymers was catalyzed by neighboring undissociated carboxylic acid groups as well as by vicinal carboxylate groups. Finally, the undissociated

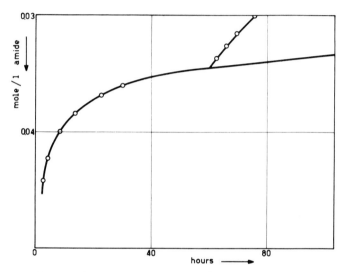

Fig. 3. Rate of hydrolysis of acrylamide–acrylic acid copolymers. Influence of stereo-specificity. Upper curve, 90% acid; lower curve, 85% acid. [Reprinted by permission from Ref. (*36*).]

neighboring carboxylic acid group was found to catalyze the hydrolysis of acrylamide units. These differences in the relative importance of un-dissociated adjacent carboxylic acid or ionized carboxylate groups can probably be associated with differences in basicity, increasing along the series carbophenoxy–carbomethoxy–amide group. A similar interpreta-tion was given by Bender et al. in the case of the hydrolysis of methyl hydrogen phthalate (*12*), catalyzed by an internal *o*-carboxylic acid group, and that of phthalamic acid, in which the carboxylate ion is the catalytic species.

In connection with the hydrolysis of polyacrylamides and acrylamide copolymers, it may be of interest to consider also the results of Morawetz and Westhead (7,8,37) obtained for the hydrolysis of copolymers of p-nitroacrylanilide with acrylic acid between pH 2 and 8 and for the hydrolysis in strong base solution of copolymers of p-nitroacrylanilide or p-nitromethacrylanilide with acrylic or methacrylic acid. Although this study did not concern itself with the stereochemical structure of the polymer, it is nevertheless interesting not only from a comparative viewpoint but also because it illustrates how neighboring groups may be differently involved in a polymeric reaction, depending upon the conditions, so that accordingly a different effect of the microtacticity may be expected.

The pH dependence of the hydrolysis rate of the acrylic acid–p-nitroacrylanilide copolymer, examined, respectively, in hydrochloric acid solution and in sodium acetate and disodium hydrogen phosphate buffers, showed that the rate first decreases with rising pH and that from pH 2 to 6 it remains nearly constant and then decreases again in more alkaline solution. In view of the difficulty of accurately estimating the pH at the reaction temperature (135.4°), the dependence of the rate on the degree of neutralization was investigated in runs carried out in partially neutralized polyacrylic acid solution. Neither method established with certainty whether after the initial stage up to pH 2, where the hydrogen ion is probably the catalytic species, the hydrolysis is catalyzed by an undissociated carboxyl group, as was the case for the hydrolysis of phthalamic acid (10, 11) or whether two ionized carboxylate groups inhibit the uncatalyzed hydrolysis of the nitroanilide. The absence of a neighboring group effect in the hydrolysis of the mono-p-nitroanilide of glutaric acid favors the second hypothesis. This observation could, according to the authors, also be explained alternatively by the presence of two neighboring carboxyl groups in the copolymer or in terms of a higher flexibility of the molecule as compared to phthalamic acid or the copolymer.

In strongly alkaline solution, on the other hand, inhibition of the hydrolysis reaction by two neighboring ionized carboxylate groups is almost certainly the rate-determining factor. Kinetic data in strongly basic solution for copolymers of p-nitroacrylanilide or p-nitromethacrylanilide with acrylic or methacrylic acid showed, indeed, that the nitroanilide groups incorporated in the copolymer hydrolyzed two to four orders of magnitude slower than the nitroanilides of trimethylacetic, glutaric, or succinic acids. This stabilization of the nitroanilide groups toward NaOH was ascribed mainly to hydrogen bonding with neighboring ionized carboxyl groups, electrostatic repulsion of the catalytic OH ion by the polyanion contributing only to a small extent.

This assumption was confirmed by the strongly accelerating effect on the hydrolytic rate of small amounts of Ba^{2+} ions, which through chelate formation with a pair of carboxylates on each side of the anilide group (**8**) eliminate the stabilizing hydrogen bonds, thus again setting this function free.

(8)

It was also noted that this effect of Ba^{2+} ions depends on the degree of dissociation. Thus the addition of 0.0025 M barium chloride was found to reduce the rate of hydrolysis of the copolymer by 25% at $\alpha = 0.12$ and by 35% at $\alpha = 0.51$, whereas an acceleration of 15% was observed at $\alpha = 0.78$ and of 53% at $\alpha = 0.9$. This seemed to indicate in the hydrolysis of these nitroanilides that both catalysis by neighboring undissociated carboxyls and inhibition of the reaction by adjacent carboxylates through hydrogen bonding may be operative, depending on the experimental conditions. Thus in the range where the catalysis of hydrolysis is governed by the attack of an unionized carboxyl on the anilide, barium ion reduces the rate by interfering with this catalysis, whereas in the range where external attack on the anilide by either water or hydroxyl takes place, barium ion accelerates the hydrolysis by eliminating the possibility of hydrogen bonding with neighboring carboxylates through chelation with these groups.

Still another type of intramolecular interaction, similar again to the bifunctional catalysis of Swain and Brown (*22*) but occurring intramolecularly, was observed with nitroanilides formed by condensing *p*-nitroaniline with a methacrylic acid–maleic anhydride copolymer (*8,37*). No hydrolysis was observed, but instead the nitroanilide group was found to condense with one of the neighboring carboxyls to form an imide. The observation that the reaction rate was maximum when the pH was such that the anilide function was flanked by an ionized carboxyl on one side and an unionized one on the other side favors the assumption of a concerted mechanism, as represented by Eq. (4):

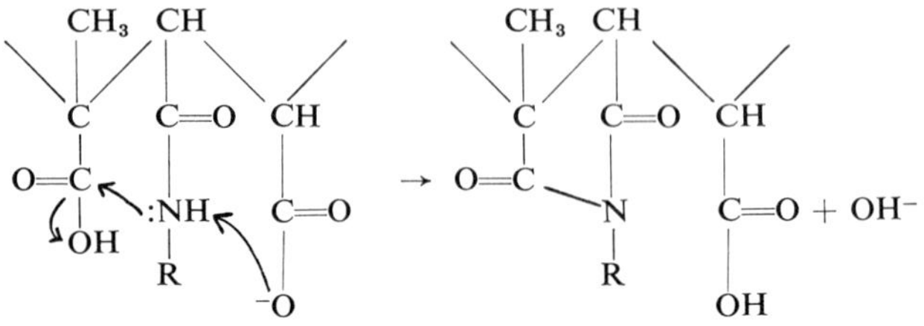

$$
\text{(4)}
$$

Although no evidence was given in these experiments for the influence of stereoregularity, which, however, must evidently be very important in these systems, we believe that the experiments are nevertheless very significant in that they clearly show that a detailed understanding of the intimate mechanism of the intramolecular reaction is often required before any unambiguous conclusions can be drawn as to the effect of the micro-tacticity on the reaction.

Direct evidence of this effect, confirming the interpretation proposed by Smets and Hesbain for the hydrolysis of polyacrylamides and acrylic acid–acrylamide copolymers, was given by Chapman in a study of the acid-catalyzed hydrolysis of tactic and atactic poly-N,N-dimethylacrylamides (38). It was shown that the crystalline tactic polymer hydrolyzed at a higher rate than the atactic one and that samples of lower tacticity, as established by solubility experiments, were hydrolyzed at rates intermediate between the two extremes. An autocatalytic acceleration was observed in this system also similar to that in the rate measurements on polyacrylamides reported by Smets and Hesbain (36). Here too an explanation was offered in terms of two different mechanisms one occurring at random and catalyzed by external $H_3O^\oplus$ attack and another by internal stereospecific attack of suitably placed neighboring carboxylic acid groups on the amide function with formation of an intermediate acid anhydride as shown in Eqs. (5) and (6):

$$-\text{CON(CH}_3)_2 + \text{H}_3\text{O}^\oplus \xrightarrow{k_1} -\text{COOH} + \text{H}_2\text{N}^\oplus(\text{CH}_3)_2 \qquad (5)$$

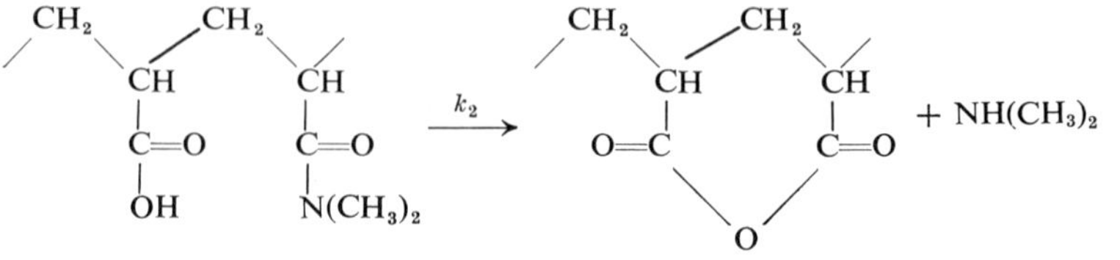

$$
\xrightarrow{k_2} \quad + \text{NH(CH}_3)_2 \quad (6)
$$

On this basis the initial stages were represented by a kinetic expression of the form

$$dx/dt = k_1(a - x) + k_2 fx$$

in which a stands for the initial concentration of amide groups and x for the concentration of acid groups at time t, and k_1 and k_2 are the rate constants, respectively, for the external and intramolecular reaction. The term f was introduced to account for the fact that the intramolecular reaction of an amide group with an adjacent carboxyl group must be limited by their relative steric configuration. Hence this term was defined by Chapman to express the probability that a vicinal carboxyl group is in the proper configuration for the intramolecular reaction with the amide to occur and is therefore a function of the tacticity constant. According to Chapman, this tacticity constant must itself be defined in terms of isotactic or syndiotactic sequences, depending upon which better fulfills the steric requirements of the intramolecular reaction. In view of the conformational stability considerations of the 1,3 disubstituted hexaatomic rings discussed above, this is presumably the isotactic configuration.

In this way Chapman used the obtained kinetic result to calculate the term f and thus the corresponding tacticity constants of different samples of varying tacticity and of different mixtures of tactic and atactic polymer relative to that of the most crystalline polymer. In spite of the relative character of this method, this work must nevertheless be considered as an important contribution to the quantitative characterization of the tacticity of polymer molecules on the basis of kinetic data.

3. *Polymers Containing Anhydride Linkages*

It is self-evident that the considerations given above concerning the stability of 1,3 disubstituted six-membered rings must be valid also in the case of the cyclization of polymeric acids into the corresponding polyanhydrides. Such transformations therefore also constitute an interesting example of the dependence of chemical reactions on the tacticity of the chain.

The synthesis of poly(acrylic anhydride) by cyclopolymerizing acrylic anhydride was described by Jones (*39*) and Crawshaw and Butler (*40*), who showed that the reaction proceeds through alternate propagation and cyclization steps and who ascribed a completely cyclized structure to these polymers (*9*).

The chemical structure of these polymers was thoroughly investigated by Mercier and Smets (*41*), who indicated on the basis of spectrometric and chemical analyses that besides some vinyl unsaturation the polymer contains mainly hexaatomic rings present in two different stereochemical structures, depending on the reaction conditions (solvent, temperature), pentaatomic rings being formed only at higher temperatures.

$$\left[\begin{array}{c} \text{CH}_2 \quad \text{CH}_2 \\ \text{CH} \quad \text{CH} \\ \text{O=C} \quad \text{C=O} \\ \text{O} \end{array} \right]_x$$

(9)

By comparison of the relevant IR spectra with those of the meso and racemic varieties of α,α'-dimethylglutaric anhydride, it was established that the polymer prepared at 35° in cyclohexanone has the syndiotactic structure. By heating at 97°C in cyclohexanone or at 35°C in the presence of traces of acrylic acid or by carrying out the cyclopolymerization in strong polar solvents such as dimethylformamide, the syndiotactic form isomerizes to the isotactic form, which is apparently the more stable one because of the higher stability of the cis-1,3 diequatorial rings compared to the axial–equatorial trans conformation. It seems, therefore, that the cyclic polymerization mechanism exerts some stereoregulating control that results in the initial formation of the less stable syndiotactic configuration.

The isomerization was assumed to involve enolization of the α-hydrogen with respect to the carbonyl group. Furthermore, it was shown (42) that hydrolysis of syndiotactic polyanhydride prepared by low conversion cyclopolymerization at 35°C yields the polymeric acid of the same tacticity but that this syndiotactic acid, when treated with thionyl chloride, cannot be recyclized into anhydride and therefore does not revert to the original cyclopolymer.

On the other hand, it was found that conventional poly(acrylic acid) prepared by radical polymerization of its monomer in the presence of AIBN as initiator could be dehydrated in two successive steps, of which the first was about five times more rapid than the second. The rapid step in these dehydration reactions was again ascribed to the presence in the polymer of some 30–40% of isotactic acid pairs, while the subsequent slow step was assumed to be due to the syndiotactic pairs, the dehydration of which would require a preliminary slow isomerization.

A similar study was made on the structure of poly(methacrylic anhydride) by Smets et al. (43). Infrared spectrometry and bromometric analyses revealed the presence mainly of hexaatomic rings, again of two types, depending on whether the cyclopolymerization was carried out in cyclohexanone solution at 36.6°C or in bulk at 100°C, and of some open anhydride units with unsaturated side groups. In this case, however, the authors remarked that the interpretation of the infrared spectra and the band assignments for the two isomers remained unclear. On the other hand, by nuclear magnetic resonance examination of the poly(methyl methacrylate) derived from the polyanhydride by hydrolysis and esterification, Miller et al. (44) studied the polymerization of methacrylic anhydride under various conditions. They were able to show that the cyclic mechanism does exert a steric control on the reaction and that there is an undeniable increase in the percentage of isotactic character with an increase of the polymerization temperature, more random distributions prevailing at lower temperatures.

In a similar way Sakurada et al. (45) demonstrated that the infrared spectra of poly(methyl methacrylate) derived from a poly(methacrylic anhydride) which was prepared at relatively low temperature corresponded closely to that of conventional poly(methyl methacrylate), while the spectra of polymers prepared at higher temperature and lower monomer concentration were almost the same as those of isotactic poly(methyl methacrylate).

As pointed out by Miller et al., these results seem to indicate that the steric placements are kinetically controlled or, if both kinetic and equilibrium considerations are involved, that the syndiotactic structure is kinetically more readily formed, while the isotactic configuration is the thermodynamically more stable one.

4. *Epimerization; Equilibrium vs. Kinetic Factors*

It is obvious that the considerations concerning conformational stability, valid for the preceding systems, must by nature be limited to those cases in which a cyclic structure intervenes at least as an intermediate. For an open chain, however, it has been suggested that vinyl polymers containing electron-withdrawing substituents and an α-hydrogen may well undergo a change in their steric structure by epimerization after their formation, whereby an equilibrium configurational arrangement is established in which the steric and polarity effects of two adjacent units on each pseudo-asymmetric center are at a minimum.

This problem was investigated by Clark (46,47) on the basis of the diastereoisomers of short-chain models of acrylic polymers, namely, the 2,4-dimethylglutaric acid and its methyl ester, which were separated into the meso and racemic form and correspond to monomer diads, and heptane-2,4,6-tricarboxylic acid, its salt, and its methyl ester, which were separated into their isomers which correspond to isotactic, heterotactic, and syndiotactic triads in a polymeric chain. The separated diastereo-isomers of the methyl esters were brought to a common equilibrium concentration by treatment with alkoxide, those of the acids and salts by heating their aqueous solutions at 180° in the presence, respectively, of acid or base as a catalyst. Similar runs were carried out on a synthetic isotactic-rich mixture of ethyl and isopropyl esters (28:57:15, isotactic–heterotactic–syndiotactic). The equilibrium concentrations were determined by gas chromatography. Some of the results are given in Table 3.

TABLE 3

Steric Equilibration of $H+CH_2$—CH--$)_\overline{3}$--CH_3 Derivatives[a]

COOR

	Ester epimerization, (t^0: 25°C), alcohol solution			Acid and salt epimerization, (t^0: 180°C), aqueous solution	
R	Catalyst, mole/liter	K^b	R	Catalyst, mole/liter	K^b
Me	0.45 NaOCH$_3$	1.47	H	6.0 HCl	1.13
Et	0.45 NaOC$_2$H$_5$	1.84	NH$_4^+$	8.0 NH$_4$OH	1.12
i-Pr	0.11 NaOCH(CH$_3$)$_2$	3.40	Na$^+$	1.5 NaOH	1.52

[a] Reprinted from *Pure and Applied Chemistry*, **12**, 215 (1966), by permission of the International Union of Pure and Applied Chemistry and Butterworths Scientific Publications [data adapted from Ref. (47)].

[b] K = (syndio)/(isotactic).

In all cases it was seen that the syndiotactic form is favored over the iso-tactic one. Steric factors were found to be more important than polarity effects.

These data, obtained for the steric equilibria of model compounds, are believed to be valid also in a first approximation for the corresponding equilibria in high polymers. It was further pointed out by Clark that these model substances were often heated over 100°C for longer periods. It was only for the carboxylic acids at 180°C that some interconversion of the steric forms occurred in the absence of alkaline catalysts. On the other hand, at 100°C the acids did not change in relative concentration even in the presence of either acid or base. It thus seems that polymeric esters, except when treated with strong alkali, are capable of retaining their stereochemical configuration after their formation. However, the above data clearly demonstrate that, in general, caution is required during the isolation and treatment of polyacrylic polymers, if their physical properties or their chemical behavior are to be correlated with their internal structure.

B. Poly(vinyl acetals)

Group interactions and chain microtacticity also seem to be involved in the hydrolysis of poly(vinyl acetals). Thus Smets and Petit (*48*) noticed that the hydrolysis of acetalyzed poly(vinyl alcohols) of various degrees of acetalization (10, 20, 27, and 51%) in water–dioxane solution proceeds differently depending on the acidity of the reaction medium.

In $N/2$ sulfuric acid solution the rate was found to be directly proportional to the acetal concentration and independent of the concentration of alcohol. The rate-determining step was therefore believed to consist in the opening of the conjugated acid of the acetal ring, setting free an alcohol function and an unstable hemiacetal carbonium ion:

$$\text{(chemical structure)} \longrightarrow \text{(chemical structure)} \tag{7}$$

By contrast, in more dilute acid solution (e.g., sulfuric acid $N/200$) the reaction mechanism appears to be much more complicated. Indeed, it was found that for the same polymer solution (e.g., a 51% acetal polymer solution), the over-all rate of acetal hydrolysis increased with dilution, thus giving rise to an apparent negative order with respect to the acetal concentration. On the other hand, the rate of hydrolysis for copolymers of different composition at the same acetal concentration was shown to increase with increasing alcohol content of the copolymer, the increase being most pronounced for the most concentrated solutions. Furthermore, the addition of foreign poly(vinyl alcohol) brought about an even stronger increase in rate than the alcohol units incorporated in the acetal copolymer. These observations were explained by taking into account both intra- and intermolecular association of the alcohol units, which are absent in strong acidic medium, and by again assuming a rate-enhancing effect on the acetal group by directly neighboring hydroxyl groups. This activation by neighboring hydroxyl groups may be interpreted in terms of hydrogen bonding with the ether oxygen of the acetal, as represented by (**10**).

An alternative explanation would be the one given by Sakurada and Sakaguchi for the autoacceleration observed during the hydrolysis of poly(vinyl acetate) (49). In this work the autocatalytic increase in hydrolysis rate with conversion was attributed by the authors to "adsorption" of the catalyst on the free hydroxyl groups of the chain and it was further

(10)

assumed that hydroxyl groups exert an influence only on the directly neighboring ester groups. Such adsorption would indeed produce a higher local catalyst concentration in the immediate neighborhood of the reacting function, and directly adjacent hydroxyl groups would thus facilitate the action of the catalyst on this function.

If a catalytic effect of neighboring alcohol groups, regardless of whether it is due to hydrogen bonding or to catalyst adsorption is also assumed in the case of acetal alcohol copolymers, it is obvious that the probability of an acetal having one or two hydroxyl neighbors increases with the alcohol content of the copolymer, resulting in an increasing rate. As for the rate-accelerating effect of dilution, it was assumed that dilution diminishes the intermolecular association, thus liberating a greater number of neighboring hydroxyl groups. In as much as this effect is more important than the simultaneous decrease in concentration of acetal groups upon dilution, a higher rate results. The influence of foreign poly(vinyl alcohol) may result from the formation of new hydrogen links with the added molecules in such a way as to set free an alcohol group directly neighboring an acetal group.

On the basis of this data, showing once more a passage from a purely external mechanism to one in which neighboring groups may participate because of the polymeric nature of the substrate, it could be expected that the tacticity of the polymer exerts an influence on the reaction rate and on the equilibrium degree of hydrolysis.

Direct information on the effect of chain stereoregularity on the reactivity of poly(vinyl acetals) is available from the data obtained by Fujii et al. for the acid-catalyzed hydrolysis of poly(vinyl acetals) derived from poly(vinyl alcohols) of various tacticities (*50*). The experiments were carried out in dioxane–water mixtures containing hydroxylamine hydrochloride to bind the acetaldehyde liberated during the reaction, so that any reverse reaction of acetalization could be neglected and the reaction could be followed by titration of the hydrochloric acid formed from the hydroxylamine hydrochloride. On the other hand, due to this liberation of hydrochloric acid, the catalyst concentration increases with conversion in this system.

It was found that as the syndiotactic content (determined on the basis of the infrared absorbance ratio D_{916}/D_{850}) of the starting poly(vinyl alcohol) increases, the acetal derived therefrom becomes more easily hydrolyzable.

Three different factors were invoked to interpret the different hydrolysis rates:

1. Reactivity of the acetal ring itself
2. Influence of directly neighboring hydroxyl groups
3. Influence of hydroxyl group association

The first should be of decisive importance at least in the initial stages of the reaction, involving still highly acetalized samples. As the reaction goes on, producing an increasing number of hydroxyl groups, the two other factors may start contributing but they were not examined in this work.

Conformational considerations analogous to those made above in the case of polyacrylic and polymethacrylic derivatives also provide an explanation for the lower stability and consequently the higher reactivity of the syndiotactic acetals (**12**) which are characterized by a 1,3 axial–equatorial orientation of the two chain segments in the hexaatomic ring as compared to the more stable diequatorial orientation characteristic of the isotactic acetals (**11**).

isotactic   syndiotactic

(**11**)   (**12**)

In this case there are, however, two ring oxygen atoms and the difference in stability may be even more pronounced than for the acrylic copolymers since there are two chain–hydrogen interactions (1,3 and 1,5) here instead of only one in the acrylic series. Similar conclusions were arrived at by Fujii et al., who compared the isotactic portions to the *cis*-4,6 derivative of *m*-dioxane and the syndiotactic ones to the *trans* derivative.

To further confirm these data, use was made of the reversibility of the reaction to study the equilibrium degree of acetalization of poly(vinyl alcohols) of different tacticities as compared to that of stereoisomeric dimer and trimer model compounds, namely, *dl* (syndiotactic) and meso (isotactic) pentane-2,4-diols (*51*) and heptane-2,4,6-triols (*52*). The acetalized poly(vinyl alcohols) and acetals of the model compounds were subjected to equilibrium hydrolysis by heating for 24 hr at 60°C in the presence of 0.02 *N* hydrochloric acid. The relevant data are summarized in Table 4.

TABLE 4

Equilibrium Hydrolyses of Various Acetals[a]

Compound	Stereostructure	Initial	At equilibrium	K (equilibrium constant)
Pentane-2,4-diol-α	Meso (isotactic)	100	86.33	8.7×10^3
Heptane-2,4,6-triol	Isotactic		84.5	
Poly(vinyl alcohol)	Isotactic	85.4	66	3.01×10^3
Poly(vinyl alcohol)	Conventional	82.7	55.8	1.14×10^3
Poly(vinyl alcohol)	Syndiotactic	77.5	50.6	7.96×10^2
Pentane-2,4-diol-β	*dl* (syndiotactic)	100	49.8	3.7×10^2
Heptane-2,4,6-triol	Syndiotactic		53.4	

[a] Reprinted from *Pure and Applied Chemistry*, **12**, 217 (1966), by permission of the International Union of Pure and Applied Chemistry and Butterworths Scientific Publications [data adapted from Refs. (*51,52*)].

As seen in Table 4, the syndiotactic varieties are the least stable for the model compounds as well as for the polymers.

The higher stability of the isotactic acetals is also illustrated by the acetalization reaction of poly(vinyl alcohols) of different tacticity as described by Sakurada et al. (*53*). They showed that isotactic poly(vinyl alcohol), derived from isotactic poly(vinyl ether), is acetalized more readily with acetaldehyde than either syndiotactic poly(vinyl alcohol) derived from poly(vinyl trifluoroacetate) or poly(vinyl alcohols) derived from radical polymerized poly(vinyl acetate), apparently because a diequatorially substituted ring is more easily formed. The last two polymers showed nearly the same rate.

The reactivities of isotactic poly(vinyl alcohol) with boric acid and borax were also found to be larger than those of the other poly(vinyl alcohols).

C. Poly(vinyl acetate)

As already mentioned above, it had been found by Sakurada and Sakaguchi (49) that the rate of hydrolysis of poly(vinyl acetate) in the presence of acid or alkali catalyst increased autocatalytically with increasing degree of hydrolysis, while the acetylation rate of poly(vinyl alcohol) decreased with increasing degree of acetylation. To explain these phenomena, it was assumed by the authors that alkali or acid was adsorbed on the free hydroxyl groups of the chain and that an influence on the acetyl group is exerted only by hydroxyl groups directly adjacent. Here, too, an alternative explanation in terms of hydrogen bonding between the hydroxyl group and the oxygen atom of the ester may be given.

To investigate a possible influence of the tactic structure of the polymer on the degree of autocatalytic acceleration, Fujii et al. (54) studied the alkali-catalyzed hydrolysis of poly(vinyl acetate) samples prepared by acetylation of poly(vinyl alcohols) of various tacticities. It was shown on the basis of s-shaped time-conversion data that the rate of hydrolysis of poly(vinyl acetates) is relatively insensitive to the tacticity of the polymer as compared to the corresponding poly(vinyl acetals). Only when isotactic sequences above some critical length were present did the effect of the tactic structure become noticeable.

The initial rate constant of the isotactic sample was calculated to be the same as that of conventional and syndiotactic samples but the degree of acceleration during the reaction was lower for the isotactic one.

In contrast, it was found by Sakurada et al. (55) that isotactic poly(vinyl acetate) derived from isotactic poly(vinyl ether) showed a lower initial rate of saponification with sodium hydroxide but a larger autocatalytic effect than the syndiotactic variety, derived from poly(vinyl trifluoroacetate). It was also noted by the authors that the differences between both polymers were not as large as those between poly(methyl acrylates) of different steric configurations. The rates of hydrolysis of different poly(vinyl acetates) prepared by radical polymerization under various conditions were practically equal and nearly the same as that of syndiotactic poly(vinyl acetate). These results were interpreted by the authors by taking into account that the distance between neighboring groups is smaller in isotactic polymers than in syndiotactic varieties. As for the smaller differences observed between the tactic varieties of poly(vinyl acetate) compared to those of poly(methyl acrylate), it was argued by the authors that in the case of poly(vinyl acetate) the carbonyl group is not directly linked to the chain and consequently presents a higher mobility in comparison with the poly(methyl acrylate). As a result a smaller effect of the stereostructure of the poly(vinyl acetate) on the kinetics could be expected.

The fact that the differences in hydrolysis rates of isotactic and syndiotactic poly(vinyl acetates) are much less pronounced than for the corresponding acetals must probably be related to the occurrence in the latter of six-membered rings, the stability of which depends on their tacticity. In as much as the previously suggested intramolecular hydrogen bonding between an adjacent hydroxyl group and the acetal and ester alkyl oxygen, respectively, as illustrated in (13) and (14), may be involved in these phenomena, this also could constitute a difference between the poly(vinyl acetals) and the poly(vinyl alcohols), the acetal oxygen having a higher electron availability than the ester alkyl oxygen bonded to an electron-withdrawing carbonyl group. This effect, however, is likely to contribute less than the presence of six-membered rings in polyacetals.

acetal   ester
(13)   (14)

As already emphasized by Smets (25), it is obvious that a regularly alternating structure of the polymeric chain and a correct determination of the tactic structure of the polymer are prerequisites for these conclusions and the interpretation of the results presented so far. This becomes particularly important for polymers of less reactive monomers such as vinyl acetate and for the poly(vinyl alcohols) derived therefrom, in which head-to-head or tail-to-tail structures may occur as a result of occasional vicinal additions. For poly(vinyl alcohol), the number of 1,2-glycol units was shown to be unimportant (56,57). On the other hand, the high degree of syndiotacticity for poly(vinyl trifluoroacetate) was claimed to be incorrect (58). As a result some of the conclusions given above should be regarded with reserve.

D. Poly(vinyl chloride)

Recently, the stability of poly(vinyl chlorides), prepared by different methods, toward zinc metal was examined by Millan and Smets (59) as a function of the method of synthesis, and an attempt was made to take into account the effect of the internal structure of the different polymers.

For poly(vinyl chloride) prepared both by emulsion polymerization and in bulk, a rapid dechlorination was observed upon treatment with zinc with simultaneous formation of cyclopropane units. On the other hand, for poly(vinyl chloride) prepared in n-butyraldehyde solution and containing a higher percentage of syndiotactic placements, as shown by infrared spectrometry, the formation of double bonds becomes more important than that of cyclopropane units from a certain time of reaction on, thus causing an increasing divergency between dechlorination reaction and cyclopropane ring formation. Simultaneously, the absorption ascribed to the syndiotactic arrangements (604 cm^{-1}) disappears in the course of the reaction.

III. EFFECT OF MICROTACTICITY ON PHYSICOCHEMICAL PROPERTIES

In connection with the thermodynamic considerations frequently dealt with throughout this chapter, it may be worthwhile at this point to mention that the microtacticity of the chain not only affects the kinetics and the course of reactions on polymers, but also exerts an influence on some physicochemical properties of these substances, such as ionization equilibria of polymeric acids, through neighboring group interactions.

Thus it was recognized that the potentiometric titration behavior of polyacids could not be completely accounted for in terms of the average electrostatic potential only but that first- and possibly second-neighbor interactions may well have to be taken into account. Polyacids differing only in their stereochemical structure have therefore been examined. Whereas Miller et al. (60) did not find a difference in potentiometric titration between solutions of stereoregular and atactic poly(acrylic acids), it was reported by Loebl and O'Neill (61) that solutions of "atactic" and isotactic poly(methacrylic acids) showed significant differences in titration behavior (acid dissociation constant), enthalpy of dissociation, and copper binding. The isotactic form was shown to be a weaker acid than the atactic one, their apparent acid dissociation constant differing by about 0.3 pK units. This difference was found not to depend on the degree of neutralization and very little on the concentration of added salt.

The dissociation enthalpy of the isotactic acid is approximately zero at all degrees of neutralization, while that of the atactic one is negative and decreases with increasing neutralization.

Similar results were obtained by Sakurada et al. (62), who carried out potentiometric titrations on isotactic, syndiotactic, and atactic poly(methyl methacrylates), hydrolyzed up to 70 mole %. At the same degree of neutralization, the isotactic acid solution showed a higher pH value than the syndiotactic and atactic polymers, both of which had nearly the same titration curve.

The fact that, in contrast with this significant difference in potentiometric titration behavior between isotactic and atactic poly(methacrylic acid), Miller et al. did not observe any such difference in the case of stereoregular and atactic poly(acrylic acid) was tentatively attributed by Loebl and O'Neill to special steric effects in the case of poly(methacrylic acid) and its derivatives. Sakurada and Sakaguchi (63), on the other hand, showed that poly(acrylic acid), prepared in aqueous solution at pH = 7 and a monomer concentration = 0.1 mole/liter, is a stronger acid than either the polyacid obtained by hydrolyzing conventional radical polymerized poly(methyl acrylate) or that prepared by direct radical polymerization of acrylic acid at 60°C in 10% benzene solution.

Since at pH = 7 and low monomer concentrations the polymerization in aqueous solution of acrylic acid is very slow, mainly because of electrostatic repulsion between the carboxyl groups, these authors felt that the poly(acrylic acid), prepared under these conditions, might be fairly syndiotactic and that the so-called atactic poly(acrylic acid), in view of its higher pH value, might in fact be rather isotactic. This constitutes another explanation for the fact that Miller et al. did not observe any difference between the so-called atactic and the stereoregular (presumably isotactic) poly(acrylic acid).

In connection with the above-mentioned influence of tacticity on the potentiometric titration behavior of polymeric acids, it should be pointed out that a similar difference in titration behavior can sometimes also occur for polymers differing from each other in the distribution of carboxylic acid groups along the polymer chain. Thus polymers prepared by partially hydrolyzing poly(methyl acrylates) in an acetone–water mixture with a high concentration of the first component, which have carboxyl groups regularly distributed along the chain, had a higher pK value than polymers prepared in a mixture with high water content for which the carboxyl groups were assembled in small blocks along the chain (64).

The electrolytic behavior of aqueous solutions of maleic anhydride copolymers with several unionizable vinyl monomers was also investigated at different degrees of neutralization and interpreted in terms of coiling of the chain at low degrees of neutralization and near-neighbor interactions in the region of higher neutralization (65,66).

IV. CONCLUSION

In conclusion it can be said that the correlation between microtacticity and kinetics or physicochemical properties, when used with caution, affords a valuable means to elucidate apparently exceptional kinetic results or physicochemical behavior. Conversely, kinetic studies of reactions involving groups attached to neighboring chain units as well as the examination of those physicochemical properties which also depend on such interactions, may make an important contribution to the characterization of the stereoregularity of polymeric chains.

ACKNOWLEDGMENT

The author wishes to thank Professor G. Smets for critical review of the manuscript.

REFERENCES

1. L. A. Hiller, Jr., *J. Polymer Sci.*, **10**, 385 (1953).
2. A. Katchalsky and J. Feitelson, *J. Polymer Sci.*, **13**, 385 (1957).
3. U. Johnsen, paper presented at the *Bunsen-Diskussionstagung, Ludwigshafen, 1965.*
4. G. Schnell, paper presented at the *Bunsen-Diskussionstagung, Ludwigshafen, 1965.*
5. E. M. Fettes (ed.), *Chemical Reactions of Polymers*, Wiley (Interscience), New York, 1965.
6. H. Morawetz and P. E. Zimmering, *J. Phys. Chem.*, **58**, 753 (1954).
7. H. Morawetz and E. W. Westhead, Jr., *J. Polymer Sci.*, **16**, 273 (1955).
8. P. E. Zimmering, E. W. Westhead, Jr., and H. Morawetz, *Biochim. Biophys. Acta*, **25**, 376 (1957); *C. A.*, **51**, 16617d (1957).
9. E. Gaetjens and H. Morawetz, *J. Am. Chem. Soc.*, **82**, 5328 (1958).
10. M. L. Bender, *J. Am. Chem. Soc.*, **79**, 1258 (1957).
11. M. L. Bender, Y. L. Chow, and F. Chloupek, *J. Am. Chem. Soc.*, **80**, 5380 (1958).
12. M. L. Bender, F. Chloupek, and M. C. Neveu, *J. Am. Chem. Soc.*, **80**, 5384 (1958).
13. M. L. Bender and M. C. Neveu, *J. Am. Chem. Soc.*, **80**, 5388 (1958).
14. T. C. Bruice and U. K. Pandit, *J. Am. Chem. Soc.*, **82**, 5858 (1960).
15. H. Morawetz and E. Gaetjens, *J. Polymer Sci.*, **32**, 526 (1958).
16. E. Gaetjens and H. Morawetz, *J. Am. Chem. Soc.*, **83**, 1738 (1961).
17. H. Morawetz and I. Oreskes, *J. Am. Chem. Soc.*, **80**, 2591 (1958).
18. F. A. Bovey and G. V. D. Tiers, *J. Polymer Sci.*, **44**, 173 (1960).
19. H. Morawetz and I. D. Rubin, *J. Polymer Sci.*, **57**, 687 (1962).
20. H. Morawetz, in *Chemical Reactions of Polymers* (E. Fettes, ed.), Wiley (Interscience), New York, 1965, Part B, Chap. 1, p. 27.
21. W. De Loecker and G. Smets, *J. Polymer Sci.*, **40**, 203 (1959).
22. C. G. Swain and J. F. Brown, Jr., *J. Am. Chem. Soc.*, **74**, 2538 (1958).
23. G. Smets and W. De Loecker, *J. Polymer Sci.*, **41**, 375 (1959).
24. G. Smets and W. Van Humbeeck, *J. Polymer Sci.*, **A1**, 1227 (1963).

25. G. Smets, paper presented at the *IUPAC Symposium on Macromolecular Chemistry, Prague, 1965; Pure Appl. Chem.*, **12**, 211 (1966).
26. E. L. Eliel, *Stereochemistry of Carbon Compounds*, McGraw-Hill, New York, 1962, p. 246.
27. E. L. Eliel, N. L. Allinger, S. J. Angyal, and G. A. Morrison, *Conformational Analysis*, Wiley (Interscience), New York, 1965, p. 53.
28. T. G. Fox, Jr., J. W. E. Goode, and J. D. Stroupe, Brit. Pat. 566,713, to Rohm and Haas Co., 1957.
29. G. Smets and W. De Loecker, *J. Polymer Sci.*, **45**, 461 (1960).
30. F. J. Glavis, *J. Polymer Sci.*, **36**, 547 (1959).
31. R. G. J. Miller, B. Mills, P. A. Small, A. Turner-Jones, and D. G. M. Wood, *Chem. Ind. (London)*, **1958**, 1323.
32. T. G. Fox, W. E. Goode, and J. D. Stroupe, U.S. Pat. 652,267, to Rohm and Haas, Co. 1957.
33. J. D. Stroupe and R. E. Hughes, *J. Am. Chem. Soc.*, **80**, 2341 (1958).
34. T. G. Fox, W. E. Goode, S. Gratch, G. M. Hugget, J. F. Kincaid, A. Spell, and J. D. Stroupe, *J. Polymer Sci.*, **31**, 173 (1960).
35. I. Sakurada, Y. Sakaguchi, T. Iwagaki, and Y. Mikuzu, *Chem. High Polymers Japan*, **21**(231), 426 (1964); *Makromol. Chem.*, **80**, 254 (1964).
36. G. Smets and A. M. Hesbain, *J. Polymer Sci.*, **40**, 217 (1959).
37. E. W. Westhead, Jr., and H. Morawetz, *J. Am. Chem. Soc.*, **80**, 237 (1958).
38. C. B. Chapman, *J. Polymer Sci.*, **45**, 237 (1960).
39. J. F. Jones, *J. Polymer Sci.*, **33**, 15 (1958).
40. A. Crawshaw and G. B. Butler, *J. Am. Chem. Soc.*, **80**, 5464 (1958).
41. J. Mercier and G. Smets, *J. Polymer Sci.*, **A1**, 1491 (1963).
42. A. Poot, private communication.
43. G. Smets, P. Hous, and N. Deval, *J. Polymer Sci.*, **A2**, 4825 (1964).
44. W. L. Miller, W. S. Brey, Jr., and G. B. Butler, *J. Polymer Sci.*, **54**, 329 (1961).
45. I. Sakurada, T. Iwagaki, and Y. Sakaguchi, *Chem. High Polymers Japan*, **21**(228), 270 (1964); *Makromol. Chem.*, **78**, 241 (1964).
46. H. G. Clark, *Makromol. Chem.*, **86**, 107 (1965).
47. H. G. Clark, paper presented at the *IUPAC Symposium on Macromolecular Chemistry, Prague, 1965*.
48. G. Smets and B. Petit, *Makromol. Chem.*, **33**, 41 (1959).
49. I. Sakurada and Y. Sakaguchi, *Kobunshi Kagaku*, **13**, 441 (1956); *CA*, **51**, 17365g (1957).
50. K. Fujii, J. Ukida, and M. Matsumoto, *Makromol. Chem.*, **65**, 86 (1963).
51. K. Fujii, J. Ukida, and M. Matsumoto, *J. Polymer Sci.*, **B1**, 693 (1963).
52. K. Fujii, *J. Polymer Sci.*, **B3**, 375 (1965).
53. I. Sakurada, Y. Sakaguchi, and Z. Shiiki, *Chem. High Polymers Japan*, **21**(229), 289 (1964); *Makromol. Chem.*, **79**, 230 (1964).
54. K. Fujii, J. Ukida, and M. Matsumoto, *J. Polymer Sci.*, **B1**, 687 (1963).
55. I. Sakurada, Y. Sakaguchi, Z. Shiiki, and J. Nishino, *Chem. High Polymers Japan*, **21**(228) 241 (1964); *Makromol. Chem.*, **78**, 239 (1964).
56. P. J. Flory and F. S. Leutner, *J. Polymer Sci.*, **3**, 880 (1948).
57. H. E. Harris and J. G. Pritchard, *J. Polymer Sci.*, **A2**, 3673 (1964).
58. K. C. Ramey and N. D. Field, *J. Polymer Sci.*, **B3**, 63 (1965)
59. J. Millan and G. Smets, *Makromol. Chem.*, in press.

60. M. L. Miller, M. C. Botty, and C. E. Rauhut, *J. Colloid Sci.*, **15,** 83 (1960).

61. E. M. Loebl and J. J. O'Neill, *J. Polymer Sci.*, **45,** 538 (1960).

62. I. Sakurada, Y. Sakaguchi, and O. Ohara, *Chem. High Polymers Japan*, **19**(211), 704 (1962); *Makromol. Chem.*, **63,** 226 (1963).

63. I. Sakurada and Y. Sakaguchi, *Makromol. Chem.*, **61,** 1 (1963).

64. I. Sakurada, Y. Sakaguchi, K. Fukami, and K. Takashima, *Chem. High Polymers Japan*, **20**(213), (1963); *Makromol. Chem.*, **64,** 236 (1963).

65. Y. Sakaguchi, J. Nishino, K. Sakai, and M. Tsuda, *Chem. High Polymers Japan*, **21**(235), 673 (1964); *Makromol. Chem.*, **83,** 296 (1965).

66. Y. Sakaguchi, M. Tsuda, and J. Nishino, *Chem. High Polymers Japan*, **21**(235), 678 (1964); *Makromol. Chem.*, **83,** 296 (1965).

CHAPTER 10

Degradation of Stereoregular Polymers

H. H. G. Jellinek

DEPARTMENT OF CHEMISTRY
CLARKSON COLLEGE OF TECHNOLOGY
POTSDAM, NEW YORK

I. INTRODUCTION

Degradation studies of stereoregular polymers are in their initial stages. The available literature is still quite limited; however, it is to be expected that considerable work will be done on these polymers in the near future.

Degradation of polymers is concerned with any type of modification of a polymer molecule affecting the main-chain backbone or the side groups.

Changes can be brought about by heat, light, high energy radiation, shearing forces, ultrasonic vibrations [the latter is a mechanical type of degradation caused by cavitation (*1*)], degradation by repeated and rapid freezing of the solvent of a polymer solution (*2*), chemical agents, high speed stirring (*1*), and a number of other means. Two of the most important types of degradation are the random degradation of polymers and the depolymerization process; the latter is a reversal of the polymerization process.

In the simplest case, depolymerization consists of an initiation, depropagation, and termination reaction. In the depropagation step, monomer is formed, instead of being consumed, as is the case in the propagation step. Under certain conditions, an equilibrium can exist between propagation and depropagation leading to so-called ceiling temperatures. Above the ceiling temperature, polymer cannot be produced from monomer below a definite concentration. Another reaction, which is of great importance, is cross-linking. This reaction eventually leads to a gel point and a three-dimensional network. From a purely chemical point of view, random degradation and cross-linking are reactions of almost infinitesimal extent. They are so noticeable because of the linear nature of the polymer molecules. Thus, rupture of one main-chain bond or formation of one cross-link between two polymer chains will, on the average, either halve or double the original chain length.

It is to be expected that stereospecific polymers will show some differences in their degradation characteristics from those of their atactic isomers due to their inherently different structure. Thus, rate constants and energies of activation are expected to differ somewhat. However, the mechanism probably will remain the same, unless, due to their different mode of preparation, abnormal structures or alien groups are either introduced into the chain molecule or prevented from being incorporated. Thus, the existence of a double bond near the end of a polymer molecule may alter its mechanism of breakdown completely. Such cases will be discussed below. At low temperatures, the degree of crystallinity will also have an influence on the degradation characteristics.

II. BRIEF SURVEY OF DEGRADATION KINETICS

Only a brief survey will be given here as this topic has been repeatedly dealt with elsewhere (1,4).

A. Random Degradation

Polymers, which have tertiary hydrogen atoms in their structure, degrade preferentially by a random degradation process. This process is characterized by rupture of main-chain links purely according to the laws of probability, each main-chain link being equivalent as far as bond strength and position are concerned.

This chain scission reaction is very sensitive to detection, as the rupture of one main-chain link near the middle of the polymer chain has a profound effect on the average molecular weight. The following relationship holds for the random degradation process of a monodisperse polymer caused by any type of agency (high energy radiation, photolysis, oxidation thermal degradation, hydrolysis), at least as far as the primary reactions are concerned:

$$\ln \left(1 - \frac{1}{DP_0}\right) - \ln \left(1 - \frac{1}{DP_t}\right) = k_{ir}t \tag{1}$$

where DP_0 is the initial number-average chain length or degree of polymerization and $\overline{DP_t}$ that at time t; k_{ir} is a rate constant. Equation (1) is derived under the assumption that the rate of breaking main-chain links is proportional to the number of main-chain links at time t. For moderate degrees of degradation, Eq. (1) simplifies to

$$\frac{1}{\overline{DP_t}} - \frac{1}{DP_0} = k_{ir}t = \alpha = \frac{s}{DP_0} \tag{2}$$

where α is the degree of degradation and s is the average number of broken main-chain links in each original chain molecule. Monomer is produced purely statistically in this type of degradation and the average chain length shows a large and very rapid drop in the beginning of the process, while the amount of monomer formed during this period is very small indeed. The rate of monomer formation is given by (4):

$$\frac{dm_1}{dt} = 2k_{ir}(m_1^{1/2} - m_1) \tag{3}$$

where m_1 is the number of moles of monomer produced at time t. Equation (3) has a maximum at $m_{1,\text{max.}} = 0.25$ and $(dm_1/dt)_{\text{max}} = 0.5$.

In photolysis reactions, where the primary reaction is usually of a random nature and for high energy irradiation, which also is initiated at random, k_{ir} is given, for weak absorption in either case, by:

$$\text{Photolysis} \quad k_{ir} = \phi_s \frac{2.303E}{[n]_0 l} = k_2\phi_s \tag{4}$$

$$\begin{array}{c} \text{High energy} \\ \text{radiation} \end{array} \quad k_{ir} = \frac{r'M_1}{E_d N_A} \tag{5}$$

where ϕ_s is the quantum yield for chain scission (ϕ_s = number of chain scissions/number of quanta absorbed), E the extinction of the polymer solution or very thin polymer film, $[n]_0$ the initial concentration of main-chain links (α values are moderately small), and l the length of the reaction cell (i.e., cylindrical cell) or the thickness of the film, provided the light absorption is quite small. E increases linearly with $[n]_0$, hence $(E/[n]_0 l) = k_2$, which shows that the rate constant is independent of the polymer concentration in solution and of the shape of the reaction vessel. Of course, k_2 will have different numerical values for different reaction vessels. I_0 is the incident light intensity (e.g., quanta sec^{-1} cm^{-2}). In Eq. (5), r' is the radiation dose (time^{-1} g^{-1}), M_1 the molecular weight of the monomer, E_a the energy required to rupture one main-chain link, and N_A Avogadro's number.

There exist, of course, more complicated degradation processes than the simple random breakdown. Thus, the initiation reaction may be random, followed by a depropagation reaction where the radicals formed are unzipped, forming monomer units and constituting the reverse of the propagation reaction. The process may be terminated by a second-order process such as disproportionation, or the number-average kinetic chain length (number of monomers produced per initiation act) may be so large that once the chain is initiated, it depolymerizes completely to monomer. The rates of monomer formation for homodisperse polymer are given by:

$$\bar{\varepsilon} < DP_0 \qquad \frac{dm_{1,tot}}{dt} = k_d \left(\frac{2k_{ir}}{k_{td}}\right)^{1/2} \left(\frac{1}{V_m}\right)^{1/2} V_m(m_0 - m_{1,tot}) \qquad (6)$$

Integrated:

$$\ln \frac{m_0}{m_0 - m_{1,tot}} = k_d \left(\frac{2k_{ir}}{k_{td}}\right)^{1/2} V_m^{1/2} t \qquad (7)$$

$$\bar{\varepsilon} \gg DP_0 \qquad \frac{dm_{1,tot}}{dt} = k_{ir}(DP_0 - 1)(m_0 - m_{1,tot}) \qquad (8)$$

Integrated:

$$\ln \frac{m_0}{m_0 - m_{1,tot}} = k_{ir}(DP_0 - 1)t \qquad (9)$$

In these equations, $\bar{\varepsilon}$ is the number-average kinetic chain length; k_d, k_{ir}, and k_{td} the rate constants for depropagation, random initiation, and disproportionation; V_m the monomeric unit molar volume; and m_0 the initial amount of polymer in monomeric unit moles. The number-average chain length at any time t follows Eq. (1); however, the random initiation rate constant for $\bar{\varepsilon} \gg DP_0$ is given by:

$$k_{ir} = \left(\frac{kd}{\bar{\varepsilon}}\right)^2 \frac{V_m}{2k_{td}}$$

Molecular size distributions at any stage of the degradation process can also be calculated for the pure random degradation process. After about five breaks, on the average, in each original chain, starting with a monodisperse sample, the so-called random distribution is obtained, which is practically the same as the most probable distribution:

$$n_{DP} = \alpha^2(1 - \alpha)^{DP-1} \cong \alpha^2 e^{-\alpha(DP-1)} \tag{10}$$

Here n_{DP} is the number of moles of DP chains, starting with one monomeric unit mole of polymer. Once this distribution is reached, it is maintained during a large part of the degradation process. The ratio of weight to number-average chain length for this distribution is $DP_{w,t}/DP_{n,t} = 2$. Simple relationships are obtained when starting the process with a sample initially having the most probable distribution (4).

B. Depolymerization

At the opposite end of the degradation spectrum is the pure depolymerization process. In between, transfer processes, various termination reactions, simultaneous random and chain end initiations, and other reactions occur. The pure depolymerization process consists of chain end initiation, depropagation, and usually second-order termination, such as disproportionation or combination. The depropagation reaction may have a number-average kinetic chain length $\bar{\varepsilon}_1$ which is smaller or larger than the original chain length of the homodisperse sample. The rate of monomer formation is given with disproportionation as the termination reaction by (4):

$$\bar{\varepsilon} < DP_0 \qquad \frac{dm_{1,\text{tot}}}{dt} = 2k_d \left(\frac{k_{ie}}{k_{td}}\right)^{1/2} \left(\frac{m_0 V_m}{DP_0}\right)^{1/2} (m_0 - m_{1,\text{tot}})^{1/2} \tag{11}$$

Integrated:

$$m_0^{1/2} - (m_0 - m_{1,\text{tot}})^{1/2} = k_d \left(\frac{k_{ie}}{k_{td}}\right)^{1/2} V_m^{1/2} \left(\frac{m_0}{DP_0}\right)^{1/2} t \tag{12}$$

$$\bar{\varepsilon} \gg DP_0 \qquad \frac{dm_{1,\text{tot}}}{dt} = 2k_{ie}(m_0 - m_{1,\text{tot}}) \tag{13}$$

Integrated:

$$\ln \frac{m_0}{m_0 - m_{1,\text{tot}}} = 2k_{ie}t \tag{14}$$

In the above equations, k_{ie} is the rate constant for depolymerization.

In contrast to Eq. (8) and (9), where $(dm_{1,\text{tot}}/dt)$ and $m_{1,\text{tot}}$ are proportional to $(DP_0 - 1)$, $(dm_{1,\text{tot}}/dt)$ and $m_{1,\text{tot}}$ in Eqs. (13) and (14) are independent of initial chain length of the monodisperse sample. The residual polymer chain length in either case remains constant and equal to DP_0.

A few remarks may be made about the ceiling temperature. In a closed system containing polymer and its monomer of a definite concentration, there is a certain temperature, the ceiling temperature T_c, where equilibrium between monomer formation and consumption is established. Here the free energy $\Delta G_{p,x}$ of polymerization is zero, hence

$$\Delta G_{p,x} = 0 = \Delta H_{p,x} - T_c \Delta S_{p,x} \tag{15}$$

or

$$T_c = \frac{\Delta H_{p,x}}{\Delta S_{p,x}} \quad \text{and} \quad \left(\frac{dm_1}{dt}\right)_{\text{over-all}} = 0 \tag{16}$$

As $E_p - E_d \simeq \Delta H_{p,x}$, where E_p and E_d are the energies of activation for propagation and depropagation, respectively, one obtains the following equations:

$$T_c = \frac{E_p - E_d}{R\left(\ln \dfrac{A_p}{A_d} + \ln [m_1]_e\right)} \tag{17}$$

or

$$\ln [m_1]_e = \frac{-\Delta H_{p,x}}{RT_c} + \frac{\Delta S_{p,x}}{R} \tag{18}$$

Here $m_{1,e}$ is the equilibrium monomer concentration.

C. Cross-linking

It is of importance to discuss, very briefly, cross-linking and simultaneous main-chain rupture. As already pointed out above, polymers which have tertiary hydrogen atoms such as

$$\begin{array}{c} \text{H} \quad \text{H} \quad \text{H} \\ | \quad\; | \quad\; | \\ \sim\!\text{C}\!-\!\text{C}\!-\!\text{C}\!\sim \\ | \quad\; | \quad\; | \\ \text{H} \quad \text{R} \quad \text{H} \end{array}$$

tend to degrade randomly and/or cross-link, whereas polymers having a structure

$$\begin{array}{ccc} H & R_1 & H \\ | & | & | \\ \sim C - C - C \sim \\ | & | & | \\ H & R_2 & H \end{array}$$

tend to degrade via depolymerization reactions.

Cross-linking reactions can be followed by changes in molecular weight, solubility, swelling, and mechanical properties. A number of parameters are of interest in this context. The cross-linking density q is defined as the fraction of the total amount of monomer in the sample, which is cross-linked. The number of cross-linked monomers in the systems is then qm_0, where m_0 is the number of monomers in the polymer sample. The number of cross-links is half that number. Cross-linking is a random process.

If, on the average, one monomer in each original chain is cross-linked, the gel point is reached. This is true for a monodisperse sample. In a heterodisperse sample, the gel point is reached when there is one cross-linked monomer, on the average, for each weight-average chain length. At this point, an insoluble fraction, the gel fraction, appears. This fraction increases with increase in cross-linking, while the sol fraction decreases. The cross-linking index δ is defined, in terms of weight-average molecular weight, by:

$$p_c DP_w = \delta \tag{19}$$

where p_c is the probability of one monomer being cross-linked in each original chain. At the gel point $p_c = p_{c,\mathrm{crit}} = 1/(DP_w - 1)$ and

$$p_{c,\mathrm{crit}} DP_w = \delta_{\mathrm{crit}} = 1 \tag{20}$$

The cross-linking index is defined, in terms of number-average molecular weight, by $p_c \overline{DP_0} = \gamma$. For a monodisperse sample $DP_0 = DP_w$ and $\delta = \gamma$, and for a sample of initial random distribution $DP_w = 2 DP_0$ and $\delta = 2\gamma$. The number-average molecular weight between cross-links M_c is given by:

$$M_c = M_1/q \tag{21}$$

where M_1 is the molecular weight of the monomer.

If high energy radiation is the cause of cross-linking, the extent of cross-linking can be expressed by G values. These are defined as the number of individual acts of any one kind taking place for each 100 eV absorbed by the irradiated system. Thus G (cross-linking) is the number of cross-links formed per 100 eV absorbed, G (main-chain scissions) the number of main-chain scissions per 100 eV absorbed, and $G(CO_2)$ the number of CO_2 molecules evolved per 100 eV absorbed.

If cross-linking and chain rupture take place simultaneously at random in a polymer which initially has a random distribution, a relationship derived by Charlesby and Pinner (5) is valid:

$$S + S^{1/2} = \beta/\alpha + 1/(\alpha \overline{DP}_{n,0} r) \tag{22}$$

or

$$S + S^{1/2} = G(S)/2G(X) + \frac{100 N_A}{r M_{w,0} G(X)} \tag{23}$$

where S is the sol fraction; α and β constants of proportionality; r the radiation dose g^{-1}; $G(S)$ and $G(X)$ the G values for chain rupture and cross-linking, respectively; and $\overline{DP}_{n,0}$ the initial number-average chain length. α and β are given by the following relationships:

$$p_c = \alpha r$$

$$p_d = \beta r$$

Here p_c and p_d are the probabilities of cross-linking and main-chain rupture, respectively, which are assumed to be proportional to the radiation dose r. P_d is actually equal to the degree of degradation s/DP_0. Hence, the ratio β/α remains constant with increasing r. $S + S^{1/2}$ plotted against $1/r$ should give a straight line, whose intercept on the ordinate gives β/α. If $\beta/\alpha = 0$, only cross-linking takes place. It is important to note that the ratio β/α applies only to the polymer system after the gel point has been reached; in other words, the sol fractions have to be determined after attainment of the gel point. If the initial molecular size distribution of the polymer is not random, the plot of S against $1/r$ is only linear for part of the $1/r$ range. More details concerning these topics can be found elsewhere (6).

III. THERMAL DEGRADATION

A. Poly(methyl methacrylate)

Thermal degradation of isotactic and syndiotactic poly(methyl methacrylate) in a closed reaction vessel was recently studied by Jellinek and Luh (7). The reaction vessel consisted of a quartz spoon gauge; recording volatiles evolved during degradation in terms of pressure (8). Thin polymer films (ca. 50 μ thick) were degraded over a temperature range from 275 to 400°C. Monomer evolution and chain lengths were measured.

One fractionated and one unfractionated isotactic polymer and one syndiotactic polymer sample were degraded; the chain length of the latter was about 10 and 20 times smaller, respectively, than those of the isotactic samples. The unfractionated sample was prepared with phenylmagnesium bromide in toluene and had a very broad molecular weight distribution ($\bar{M}_v/\bar{M}_n \simeq 12.5$; $\overline{DP}_v = 1.26 \times 10^4$.) The other isotactic sample was made with Grignard reagent and fractionated; a fraction of $\overline{DP}_v = 2.45 \times 10^4$ was taken for the experiments. The syndiotactic polymer was prepared in liquid ammonia with lithium at $-70°C$; its chain length was $\overline{DP}_v = 1.28 \times 10^3$ and its molecular weight ratio $\bar{M}_v/\bar{M}_n = 1.4$.

The thermal degradation of atactic poly(methyl methacrylate) has been investigated in detail by various workers (9). The results show clearly that two reactions are operative simultaneously in poly(methyl methacrylate), polymerized with benzoyl peroxide as initiator. It is known that this type of poly(methyl methacrylate) has a certain percentage of polymer chains (up to about 50%) which have one double bond near one of their chain ends, probably due to a disproportionation reaction which terminates the polymerization. The chains containing double bonds degrade by chain end initiation, depropagation, and disproportionation with an energy of activation of about 22.5 kcal/mole (10) for monomer formation as long as the kinetic chain length is smaller than the polymer chains. At the same time, a much slower reaction with an energy of activation around 64 kcal/mole (10), consisting of random initiation, depropagation, and disproportionation, takes place for chains without double-bond chain ends.

The stereoregular polymers studied by Jellinek and Luh were prepared in such a way that negligible amounts of chains with double-bond ends were formed. Hence, these polymer chains should only show one reaction corresponding to the slow one in the atactic polymer, consisting of random initiation, depropagation, and disproportionation. This has, indeed, been found to be the case, as will be shown below.

Decrease in viscosity number-average chain lengths as a function of time for the isotactic samples and the syndiotactic polymers are shown in Figs. 1 and 2. The initial molecular weight of the syndiotactic polymer was relatively small and the curves are typical of a degradation process, where the kinetic chain length is of similar magnitude to that of the polymer chains. The curves for the isotactic polymers are typical for random initiation reactions. The rate constants for monomer formation can be expressed for various extents of conversion from polymer to monomer by

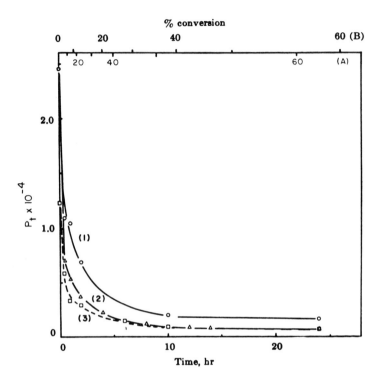

Fig. 1. Viscosity- and number-average chain lengths as function of time and percentage conversion for isotactic poly(methyl methacrylate) at 300°C: (1) $\overline{DP}'_{v,t}$ for fractionated PMMA; (2) $\overline{DP}'_{n,t}$ for fractionated PMMA; (3) $\overline{DP}'_{v,t}$ for unfractionated PMMA; (A) % conversion for fractionated PMMA; (B) % conversion for unfractionated PMMA (7).

the following Arrhenius equations:

a. Isotactic PMMA (unfractionated):

Initial range

$$k = (2.83 \pm 0.38) \times 10^{22} \exp \frac{(66900 \pm 3180) \text{ cal/mole}}{RT} \text{ min}^{-1}\dagger$$

Final range

$$k = (5.64 \pm 1.18) \times 10^{21} \exp \frac{(65570 \pm 1870) \text{ cal/mole}}{RT} \text{ min}^{-1}$$

† ± are standard deviations.

b. Isotactic PMMA (fractionated):

Initial range

$$k = (5.08 \pm 0.18) \times 10^{21} \exp \frac{(64150 \pm 577) \text{ cal/mole}}{RT} \text{ min}^{-1}$$

Final range

$$k = (1.13 \pm 0.36) \times 10^{20} \exp \frac{(61480 \pm 4793) \text{ cal/mole}}{RT} \text{ min}^{-1}$$

c. Syndiotactic PMMA:

Initial range

$$k = (8.36 \pm 0.41) \times 10^{21} \exp \frac{(65760 \pm 830) \text{ cal/mole}}{RT} \text{ min}^{-1}$$

Final range

$$k = (2.93 \pm 0.38) \times 10^{21} \exp \frac{(64940 \pm 2004) \text{ cal/mole}}{RT} \text{ min}^{-1}$$

The energies of activation correspond fairly closely to those for the slow reaction of the atactic polymer. There is no indication of a second reaction as there is in the case for the atactic polymer.

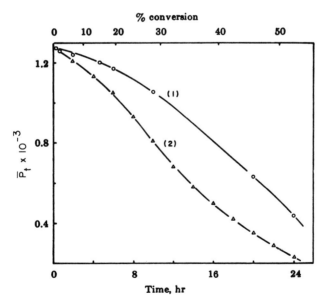

Fig. 2. Viscosity- and number-average chain lengths as function of time and percentage conversion for syndiotactic poly(methyl methacrylate) at 300°C: (1) $\overline{DP}'_{v,t}$; (2) $\overline{DP}'_{n,t}$ (7).

TABLE 1

Rate Constants for Random Initiation k_{ir}, Monomer Formation K, and Number-Average Kinetic Chain Lengths $\bar{\varepsilon}$, for Isotactic, Syndiotactic, and Atactic Poly(methyl methacrylate)

Sample	$\bar{M}_{n,o}$	K/k_{ir} from Eq. (25)	K (min^{-1}) from Eqs. (7), (24), and (25); initial and medium ranges of reaction	k_{ir}, min^{-1} From Eq. (2) only	k_{ir}, min^{-1} From K/k_{ir}, Eq. (25), and K, Eqs. (7) and (24)	Number-average kinetic chain length $\bar{\varepsilon}$ From $\frac{1}{2}(K/k_{ir})$, Eqs. (25) and (26)	Number-average kinetic chain length $\bar{\varepsilon}$ From K, Eqs. (6) or (7), and k_{ir}, Eq. (2)
Isotactic fraction (values for 300°C)	2.45×10^6	9.21×10^2	1.82×10^{-3}	1.62×10^{-6}	1.97×10^{-6}	460	563
Syndiotactic, narrow size distribution $M_w/M_n = 1.4$ (values for initial stages and 300°C)	1.28×10^5	1.8×10^3 (approx.)	0.70×10^{-3}	4.1×10^{-7}	3.9×10^{-7}	900	875
Atactic[a]	$\bar{M}_{w,o}$ (weight average, 5.03×10^6)						
300°C		4.60×10^3	0.96×10^{-3}	3.2×10^{-7}	2.1×10^{-7}	2.3×10^{3b}	1.5×10^{3b}
320°C		2.26×10^3	4.5×10^{-3}	1.8×10^{-6}	2.0×10^{-6}	1.2×10^{3b}	1.3×10^{3b}
340°C		2.02×10^3	4.2×10^{-2}	1.8×10^{-5}	2.1×10^{-5}	1.0×10^{3b}	1.2×10^{3b}

[a] All values refer to weight-average MW or chain length.
[b] To obtain number average $\bar{\varepsilon}$, divide by two.

For a random initiation process, followed by depropagation and dis-proportionation, Eqs. (1) or (2), (6), and (7) are valid; for $\bar{\varepsilon} \gg DP_0$, Eqs. (8) and (9) hold. Actually, an experimental rate constant K is obtained, which in this particular case is given by:

$$K = k_d \left(\frac{2k_{ir}}{k_{td}}\right)^{1/2} V_m^{1/2} \tag{24}$$

Equations (2) and (7) can be combined, yielding:

$$\ln \frac{m_0}{m_0 - m_{1,\text{tot}}} = \frac{K}{k_{ir}}\left(\frac{1}{\overline{DP}_t'} - \frac{1}{DP_0}\right) \tag{25}$$

k_{ir} can be obtained from Eq. (2) and also from the ratio K/k_{ir} (Eq. (25)) together with the experimental value for monomer formation K (Eqs. (7) and (24) for $\bar{\varepsilon} < DP_0$). If $\bar{\varepsilon} \gg DP_0$, k_{ir} can be obtained directly from Eq. (9); however, in the case of the syndiotactic polymer, $\bar{\varepsilon}$ is not much larger than DP_0, but of a similar magnitude. The number-average kinetic chain length $\bar{\varepsilon}$ is given by:

$$\bar{\varepsilon} = \frac{K}{2k_{ir}} \tag{26}$$

The relevant numerical values are contained in Table 1.

It would be desirable to compare the data for the stereoregular polymers, especially the kinetic chain lengths, with data for the corresponding reactions of atactic poly(methyl methacrylate) without interference by the reaction due to double-bond chain ends. To do this, data has to be available for chain lengths at various stages of the degradation process and for monomer formation as a function of time. The investigations by Hart (11) of an atactic polymer of fairly high molecular weight, prepared by polymerization in vacuum at -25 to $-35°C$ without catalyst, appear to be suitable for this purpose. The polymer had an average molecular weight of 5.03×10^6 measured by light scattering (Hart's sample B). The decrease of chain length or molecular weight with time gave a curve typical for random initiation. The values given in Table 1 for the atactic polymer were obtained by evaluating Hart's experimental results by means of the relationships given here in the various equations, as was similarly done for the stereoregular polymers. These equations hold satisfactorily for this atactic polymer, except for a short initial period. This indicates that the percentage of chain ends having double bonds is quite small. Moreover, for a high molecular weight sample, as used by Hart, the total number of chain ends in a given amount of polymer is relatively small. Thus, the longer the polymer chains are, the more dominant the random initiation reaction will become.

It was noted by Hart (11) that the energy of activation abruptly increased at about 320°C. Such a discontinuity appears also in the present evaluation by plotting log K and log k_{ir}, respectively, against $1/T$.

The energy of activation becomes very large in the range from 320 to 340°C (100 kcal/mole for K and 190 kcal/mole for k_{ir}). However, if only the range from 300 to 320°C is taken into account, reasonable energies of activation are obtained. The reason for the discontinuity is not clear. The Arrhenius equations for the range from 300 to 320°C are as follows:

$$k_{ir} = 1.58 \times 10^{21} e^{-73500/RT} \text{ min}^{-1}$$

and

$$K = 1.26 \times 10^{17} e^{-53000/RT} \text{ min}^{-1}$$

The energy of activation for K is about 10 kcal/mole smaller than those found for the K values of the stereoregular polymers. However, recent results by Jellinek and Luh (10) for atactic polymer fractions indicate that the energy of activation for the slow reaction is quite similar to those for the stereoregular polymers (ca. 65 kcal/mole). Hart's polymer sample was unfractionated.

The k_{ir} values of the atactic polymer in Table 1 have to be multiplied by 2 as they are derived from weight-average chain lengths. (This is valid provided the distribution is of the random type; this distribution is reached quickly on degradation as the initial ratio of $\bar{M}_w/\bar{M}_n$ for this type of polymer is usually 1.5.)

The data presented in Table 1 are neither numerous nor accurate enough to allow definite conclusions to be drawn concerning differences in degradation of the various polymers. However, some trends seem to be indicated. At 300°C, the rate constants for random initiation, k_{ir}, are quite similar for the syndiotactic and atactic polymers, whereas the value for the isotactic polymer is about three to four times larger than those for the others. The kinetic chain lengths (the values for the atactic polymer have to be halved as they are weight-average values) for the atactic and syndiotactic polymers are larger than those of the isotactic one. It has been asserted that during polymerization, the energy of activation for the propagation step of the polymerization process for the isotactic polymer is about 1 kcal/mole larger than that for the syndiotactic one (12).

The Arrhenius equations of the rate constants for monomer formation from the stereoregular polymers are quite similar to those for the "slow" random reaction of the atactic PMMA fractions degraded under comparable conditions. There is no doubt that the stereoregular polymers are more heat stable than the atactic one, which has a certain percentage of double-bond-ended chains. This difference in heat stability is not due to stereoregularity but to the different chain ends which result from the various modes of polymerization.

The energy of activation of 73.5 kcal/mole for the random initiation rate constant is entirely reasonable.

B. Poly(alkylene oxides)

Thermal degradation of atactic and isotactic poly(propylene oxide) was investigated by Madorsky and Straus (13). The atactic polymer consisted of glassy material of molecular weight 1.6×10^4 and the isotactic polymer was crystalline of molecular weight 2.15×10^5. Rate measurements were carried out in a tungsten spring balance and the reaction products were analyzed in a mass spectrometer. The pyrolyses were followed for 30 min after a 5-min heating-up period. The percentage weight loss for the period prior to reaching the desired temperature was 1 to 2% and 16 to 22% for the isotactic and atactic polymers, respectively. Only 3.55 and 2.83% of the gaseous products from the atactic and isotactic samples, respectively, consisted of monomer.

The rate of volatile production is appreciably different for the two polymers. Whereas the atactic polymer shows a very rapid decrease in rate with conversion, slowing down after about 35 to 65% weight loss, depending on the temperature (265 to 285°C), the isotactic rate of volatilization vs. conversion curves pass through maxima between 8 and 15% conversion.

The rate vs. conversion curves of the atactic polymer appear to be typical of a random degradation of a branched polymer, whereas those for the isotactic polymer are typical of random degradation where all original molecules below about a molecular weight of 600 are volatile (this corresponds to a chain length of about 10).

The rate of volatilization for such a case is given by an expression as follows (4):

$$\frac{d \sum_{DP=1}^{L} m_{DP}}{d\tau} = \frac{dC}{d\tau} = 2\left[\sum_{DP=1}^{L} m_{DP} \left(\sum_{DP=1}^{L} e^{-(DP-1)\tau} \right)^{1/2} - \sum_{DP=1}^{L} m_{DP} \right]$$
$$- \sum_{DP=1}^{L} m_{DP} \frac{\sum_{DP=1}^{L} (DP-1)e^{-(DP-1)\tau}}{\sum_{DP=1}^{L} e^{-(DP-1)\tau}} \qquad (27)$$

where m_{DP} is the amount of chains of length DP which volatilize; $\tau = k_{ir}t$, where k_{ir} is the random initiation rate constant; L is the chain length of the largest chains, which can vaporize without degrading; C is the fractional conversion: (m_t/m_0); m_0 is the initial amount of monomeric unit moles and m_t the total amount of volatiles in monomeric unit moles at time t.

The chain length as a function of time for such a process is given by (4):

$$\frac{1}{2L + 1}\left\{\ln\left(1 - \frac{2L + 1}{DP_0}\right) - \ln\left(1 - \frac{2L + 1}{\overline{DP}_{n,\tau}}\right)\right\} = \tau \qquad (28)$$

Experiments showed that the isotactic polymer is more heat resistant than the atactic one; this is probably due to the branches of the latter, as degradation occurs readily at branch points.

The temperature at which a polymer loses half its weight in 35 min (including a 15-min heating-up period) for a number of polymers is as follows: atactic poly(propylene oxide), 295°C; isotactic poly(propylene oxide), 312°C; poly(ethylene oxide), 345°C; and polypropylene, 387°C. Poly(propylene oxide) is less thermally stable than polypropylene as the C—O bond is weaker than the C—C bond.

The over-all energies of activation calculated from straight-line parts of the rate curves amount to 20 kcal/mole for atactic poly(propylene oxide), 45 kcal/mole for isotactic poly(propylene oxide), and 46 kcal/mole for poly(ethylene oxide). The assumed branches in the atactic polymer account for the low over-all energy of activation for this polymer.

C. Polystyrene

Nakajima et al. (14) carried out an interesting study of the thermal degradation of isotactic polystyrene. In particular, they investigated the molecular size distributions as a function of degree of degradation. The polymer was degraded in vacuum over a range of temperatures from 290 to 330°C. The loss of weight over a period of about 12 hr was not more than 3%.

Before degradation, the sample had a molecular weight distribution of the normal logarithmic type (15), which is also typical of Ziegler polyethylene:

$$m_{DP} = \frac{1}{DP}\frac{1}{\beta(\pi)^{1/2}}\exp\left\{-\frac{1}{\beta^2}\left(\ln\frac{DP}{N_0}\right)^2\right\} \qquad (29)$$

where m_{DP} is the weight fraction (or the amount of P chains in grams in 1 g of polymer) of chain length DP, $\beta/\sqrt{2}$ is the standard deviation for this

Gaussian distribution, and N_0 is the degree of polymerization, where the integral weight distribution M_{DP} is equal to 0.5. The latter is given by:

$$M_{DP} = \frac{1}{\beta(\pi)^{1/2}} \int_0^{DP} \frac{1}{DP} \exp\left\{-\frac{1}{\beta^2}\left(\ln\frac{DP}{N_0}\right)^2\right\} dDP \qquad (30)$$

The various average chain lengths are given by the following expressions:

$$\overline{DP}_n = N_0 \exp\left(-\beta^2/4\right) \qquad \overline{DP}_w = N_0 \exp\left(+\beta^2/4\right)$$
$$\overline{DP}_v = N_0 \exp\left(\alpha'\beta^2/4\right) \qquad (31)$$

where α' is the exponent in the Mark–Houwink relationship $[\eta] = K\overline{DP}_v^{\alpha'}$. The ratio $\overline{DP}_w/\overline{DP}_n = e^{\beta^2/2}$. The actual distribution is quite a broad one. The weight fraction for a degree of degradation α is given by (14); (16).

$$m_{DP,\alpha} = e^{-\alpha DP}\left(\frac{1}{\beta(\pi)^{1/2}DP}\exp\left\{-\frac{1}{\beta^2}\left(\ln\frac{DP}{N_0}\right)^2\right\}\right.$$
$$+\frac{\alpha^2 DP}{2}\left(1-\frac{2}{\pi^{1/2}}\int_0^{(1/\beta)\ln(DP/N_0)} e^{-x_2}\,dx\right)$$
$$+\frac{(2-\alpha DP)\alpha DP}{2N_0}\exp\left(\frac{\beta^2}{4}\right)$$
$$\times\left.\left\{1-\frac{2}{\pi^{1/2}}\int_0^{(1/\beta)\ln DP/N_0 \exp(-\beta^2/2)]} e^{-x_2}\,dx\right\}\right) \qquad (32)$$

The probability integrals are tabulated. Furthermore:

$$\frac{[\eta]_0}{[\eta]_\alpha} = \frac{DP_0^{\alpha'}}{DP^{\alpha'}} = \frac{\displaystyle\int_0^\infty m_{DP}DP^{\alpha'}\,dDP}{\displaystyle\int_0^\infty m_{DP,\alpha}DP^{\alpha'}\,dDP} \qquad (33)$$

$$\overline{DP}_{n,\alpha} = \left(\int_0^\infty \frac{m_{DP,\alpha}}{DP}\,dDP\right)^{-1} \qquad (34)$$

$$\overline{DP}_{w,\alpha} = \int_0^\infty m_{DP,\alpha}DP\,dDP \qquad (35)$$

$$\overline{DP}_v = \left(\int_0^\infty m_{DP}DP^{\alpha'}\,dDP\right)^{1/\alpha'} \qquad (36)$$

β is given by:

$$\beta = \sigma\sqrt{2} = \sqrt{2}\,\frac{\log DP_b - \log DP_a}{2}$$

where σ is the standard deviation and DP_a and DP_b the chain lengths corresponding to integral distribution values of $M_{DP} = 0.5$ and 0.977, respectively.

The original polymer and some of the degraded samples were fractionated. The distributions can be represented quite well by normal logarithmic distributions. The typical trend during degradation to pass from wide distributions to random distributions due to random chain scission is well brought out. Some numerical values of various average chain lengths are given in Table 2.

TABLE 2

Average Chain Lengths of Original and Degraded Isotactic Polystyrene, 310°C (*14*)

	N_0	β	$\overline{DP}_{n,\alpha}$	$\overline{DP}_{w,\alpha}$	$\overline{DP}_{w,\alpha}/\overline{DP}_{n,\alpha}$	$\overline{DP}_v$ calc. Eq. (*36*)	$\overline{DP}_v$ observed
Original	3500	2.10	1162	10540	9.07	7373	7460
30 min	2000	1.76	922	4340	4.71	3380	4000
5 hr	530	1.26	356	788	2.21	693	744
10 hr	400	1.20	279	572	2.06	510	425

It is of interest to note that after 5 hr of degradation, a random distribution is obtained; α for this stage of degradation is 1.98×10^{-3}, corresponding to 2.3 chain scissions on the average for each original number-average chain length. Thus the random distribution is very quickly reached even when starting with a wide distribution, as was the case here.

The results were compared by these authors with experiments carried out by Jellinek, who postulated the existence of "weak links" in atactic polystyrene as early as 1944 (*17*). The term "weak links," often misinterpreted, is meant to convey that there are some structural features or some abnormal groups in the polymer molecules, which lead to scissioning of main-chain links with an energy of activation considerably lower than that required for the normal structure. A long-standing controversy has developed over the existence of these weak links in polystyrene. Grassie and co-workers (*18*) have verified that weak links are actually present in the polymer molecule. The nature of these weak links is still not established with any certainty; however, Cameron and Grassie (*19*) suggest that they may be due to unsaturated structures analogous to the ketenimine structures in polymethacrylonitrile. These structures act as weak links in the polystyrene polymer, i.e.,

$$\sim CH_2-CH$$

However, the weak links may still be simply hydroperoxide groups (17).

A different view was taken by Wall and co-workers (20), who maintained that the rates for main-chain rupture can be accounted for by assuming intermolecular transfer instead of weak links. The experimental data can be fitted well with the help of a computer by kinetic schemes consisting of random initiation, depropagation, intermolecular transfer, and termination by disproportionation (second-order termination). However, it must be pointed out that fitting experimental data to curves by equations containing a number of parameters does not constitute proof of a mechanism; at best, such fitting of curves can increase the probability that a proposed mechanism is correct. Proper proof can be obtained only from additional experimental data such as those, for instance, which Grassie and co-workers have accumulated.

The data given in the paper under discussion give additional experimental proof for the existence of weak links in atactic polystyrene. The proof is rather definitive and should bring an end to this long-standing controversy. Nakajima et al. determined the intrinsic viscosity of isotactic polystyrene as a function of degradation time, as was also done by Jellinek in the case of atactic polystyrene. The degree of degradation could be evaluated from these data as a function of time for either polymer. Figure 3 shows α as a function of time for the isotactic polymer and Fig. 4 the same relationship for atactic polystyrene. It is clear that isotactic polystyrene gives straight lines, according to Eq. (2), without indication of weak links, whereas atactic polystyrene shows a distinct decrease in the rate of α with time.

Jellinek (17) found for the atactic polymer an energy of activation of 24.5 kcal/mole for the initial degradation process, rising to 39 kcal/mole after consumption of the weak links, whereas the energy of activation for the isotactic polymer according to the Japanese workers is 42 kcal/mole from the beginning of the degradation reaction. It is very unlikely, indeed, that isotactic and atactic polystyrene would show different kinetics due to stereoregular structure. Thus there must be abnormal structures or groups in the atactic polymer. However, it is to be expected that there are some

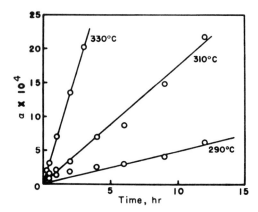

Fig. 3. Degree of degradation α against degradation time for isotactic polystyrene (*14*).

relatively small differences in the numerical values of the rate constants, energies of activation, and kinetic chain lengths due only to stereoregular structure.

Jellinek assumed an exponent $\alpha' = 1$ in the Mark–Houwink equation for his polystyrene, but it is known now that α' is smaller than 1. Thus the ratio $[\eta]_\alpha/[\eta]_0$ for a monodisperse sample is not equal to $\overline{DP}_{w,\alpha}/\overline{DP}_{w,0}$ but is rather given by $\overline{DP}_{n,\alpha}^{\alpha'}/\overline{DP}_{n,0}^{\alpha'}$ where $[\eta] = 1.06 \times 10^{-4}$, $\overline{M}_n^{0.735}$ deciliters/g (*21*) in benzene solution at 30°C.

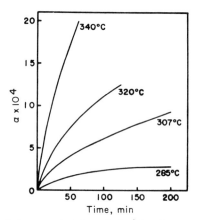

Fig. 4. Degree of degradation α against degradation time for atactic polystyrene obtained from the data of Jellinek (*14,17*).

Thus $[\eta]_\alpha/[\eta]_0$ for an initially monodisperse polymer obeying an equation $[\eta] = KM^{\alpha'}$ is given for small values, according to Matsumoto (22) by:

$$[\eta]_\alpha/[\eta]_0 = s(s + 2)\left\{\frac{1}{(\alpha' + 2)} - \frac{s}{(\alpha' + 3)} + \frac{s^2}{2!}\frac{1}{(\alpha' + 4)} - \frac{s^3}{3!}\frac{1}{(\alpha' + 5)} \cdots\right\}$$
$$- s^2\left\{\frac{1}{\alpha' + 3} - \frac{s}{(\alpha' + 4)} + \frac{s^2}{2!}\frac{1}{(\alpha' + 5)} - \frac{s^3}{3!}(\alpha' + 6) + \cdots\right\} + e^{-s}$$

(37)

For relatively large s values, this becomes:

$$[\eta]_\alpha/[\eta]_0 = \frac{1}{s^{\alpha'+1}}\{(s + 2)\Gamma(\alpha' + 2) - \Gamma(\alpha' + 3)\}$$

(38)

where s is the average number of breaks in each original chain. $s = (DP_0/DP_t) - 1$ and $s/P_0 = \alpha$.

If $\alpha' = 1$,

$$[\eta]_\alpha/[\eta]_0 = \frac{2}{s^2}(s - 1 + e^{-s})$$

(39)

or

$$\frac{\overline{DP}_{w,\alpha}}{\overline{DP}_{n,\alpha}} = \frac{2(s + 1)}{s^2}(s - 1 + e^{-s})$$

(40)

For $s = 2$, this ratio is 1.92.

D. Poly(α-methylstyrene)

Poly(α-methylstyrene) has been investigated by a number of workers. Brown and Wall (23) studied fractions of a polymer prepared with sodium as catalyst by the Dow Chemical Company. It is not unlikely that this polymer was to a large extent syndiotactic. The range of degradation temperature was from 254 to 292°C. The apparatus was similar to that previously used by Grassie and Melville (24). It took about 15 to 20 min to reach the desired temperature; thus measurements were started only after about 20% loss of weight. In this way indications of a maximum in the rate of weight loss against conversion were neglected and the curves were extrapolated back to zero. However, recent experiments by Jellinek and Kachi (25) indicate that these different initial rates are real. The heating-up times in the apparatus of the latter workers were less than 30 sec. The energy of activation derived by Wall and Brown from the zero time values was 65 kcal/mole. The initial rates increased linearly for quite a large range of molecular weights with chain length up to a length of about 1500. It must not be overlooked that this extrapolation to zero time is not permissible as the reaction does not follow the extrapolated curves. Thus these "initial" rates do not pertain to DP_0 but to smaller chain lengths.

Thus the experimental results indicate that $\bar{\varepsilon} \gg DP_t$ [see Eq. (8)], where $\overline{DP_t}$ is the chain length corresponding to a conversion to monomer just past the maximum of the weight loss rate vs. conversion curve. The over-all energy of activation for such a mechanism is equal to the energy of activation for the initiation process, i.e., $E_a = E_i$ ($\bar{\varepsilon} = 1340$, $E_a = 65$ kcal/mole). Madorsky (26) carried out similar experiments (229–247°C) suggesting the same mechanism; however, he obtained an over-all energy of activation of 58 kcal/mole.

An interesting study was made by Grant et al. (27) of the degradation of poly(α-methylstyrene) in decalin and diphenylether solutions. Two types of polymer were used: One was prepared between 0 and -78°C with $SnCl_4$ in ethyl chloride and the other at -78°C in tetrahydrofuran solution with sodium naphthenide as catalyst. The latter type of polymer had a very sharp molecular weight distribution ($M_w/M_n \cong 1.05$). According to Braun and Heufer (28), the first type of polymer is about 95% syndiotactic and 5% isotactic and the second type probably about 40% isotactic and 60% syndiotactic. Only conversions smaller than 10% were investigated over a temperature range from about 213 to 239°C. Polymer concentrations (up to about 1.0×10^{-2} g/liter) and solvent had no effect on the rate of weight loss. The monomer formation rate was directly proportional to molecular weight up to about 6×10^5. The reaction fits the same mechanism as that proposed by Brown and Wall (23) with the exception that up to about 20% conversion, Wall's experimental data did not follow this mechanism, while it fits the data of Bywater et al. even below 10% conversion. The kinetic chain length in solution is larger than that in bulk. There is no difference due to the different degrees of tacticity or different modes of preparation. The energy of activation is 62 ± 2 kcal/mole for all the polymers investigated in solution. It was observed by these authors that an anionically produced polymer sample of MW 428,000 with a very sharp distribution ($M_w/M_v = 1.05$) showed a decrease in chain length of about 6% after 9% conversion, but the sharpness of the distribution was preserved. This can only mean that there is a chain-end-initiation component with a number-average kinetic chain length smaller than the polymer chain length. The rate of monomer formation for such a case is proportional to $(1/DP_0)$ for a first-order reaction, which would occur if termination takes place by solvent molecules, or to $(1/DP_0)^{1/2}$ for second-order termination. If this reaction represents only a small percentage of the total reaction, the rate of monomer formation will still be practically linearly proportional to chain length. But there should be a small intercept on the monomer rate axis. For small molecular weights, where the kinetic chain length is larger than the number-average polymer chain length, the monomer formation due to chain end initiation becomes independent of DP_0. In this case, the rate of monomer formation will be strictly proportional to chain length, but again there will be an intercept on the rate axis. This will be discussed below in more detail.

An interesting study was made recently by Braun and Heufer (28). A number of unfractionated and fractionated samples of poly(α-methylstyrene) of various percentages of iso- and syndiotacticity having a variety of different end groups were degraded in a temperature range from 220 to 240°C. The molecular weights were relatively small ($<78,000$) and the conversions were less than 20%. Appreciable differences in the rate of monomer formation were found with polymers having different end groups. The rate of monomer formation or the amount of monomer formed during a small initial and constant time interval (2 hr) at 230°C was proportional to the initial chain lengths of the fractions; however, depending on the type of end group and mode of preparation, different intercepts were obtained on the percentage weight loss axis.

These results indicate that random initiation with $\bar{\varepsilon} > DP_0$ and chain end initiation take place simultaneously. Whether $\bar{\varepsilon}$ for chain end initiation is smaller or larger than the various initial polymer chain lengths is not clear, but there are indications that $\bar{\varepsilon} < DP_0$. These authors did not attempt to formulate any kinetics but concluded that the different stabilities are to a certain extent due to the various degrees of stereoregularity. However, the present author believes that the different thermal stabilities are due to the mode of polymerization (i.e., different end groups) rather than to the different stereoregularities, which appear only to have a small effect on stability. The rate of total monomer formation for $\bar{\varepsilon} > DP_0$ is given by the following relationship:

$$\left(\frac{dm_1}{dt}\right)_{\text{tot}} = k_{ie}(Fm_0 - m_{1,e}) + k_{ir}DP_0(m_0 - m_1) \tag{41}$$

where k_{ie} and k_{ir} are the rate constants for chain end and random initiation, respectively; F the fraction of the total initial monomeric unit moles with chain ends susceptible to degradation; $m_{1,e}$ the amount of monomer formed from chain end degradation; and m_1 the total amount of monomer formed at time t. For a small initial time interval ($\Delta t = $ constant), Eq. (41) can be written:

$$(\Delta m_1)_{\text{tot}} = \Delta t[k_{ie}Fm_0 + k_{ir}DP_0m_0] \tag{42}$$

Equation (42) gives a straight line when Δm_1 is plotted against DP_0 for various fractions. Experimental data followed Eq. (42). The intercept on the percentage weight loss axis is given by $\Delta t k_{ie} F m_0$. If the kinetic chain length for chain end initiation is $\varepsilon < DP_0$, but for the random process $\varepsilon > DP$, one obtains (4):

$$\frac{dm_1}{dt} = K \left(\frac{m_0}{DP_0}\right)^{1/2} (Fm_0 - m_e)^{1/2} + k_{ir} DP_0 (m_0 - m_1) \qquad (43)$$

It would be difficult to detect a curvature in the Δm_1 vs. DP_0 curve if the chain end initiation component is small compared with the random initiation component; hence, for a small Δt:

$$\Delta m_{1,\text{tot}} = \Delta t \left\{ K \left(\frac{m_0}{DP_0}\right)^{1/2} (Fm_0^{1/2} + k_{ir} DP_0 m_0) \right\} \qquad (44)$$

Equation (42) would still be almost a straight line. Actually, $(1/DP_0)^{1/2}$ varies from 0.14 to 0.025, whereas DP_0 varies from 506 to 1600 for the case under discussion. The slope was found to be practically the same for various samples, but the intercepts varied.

E. Polypropylene

The thermal degradation of polypropylene in vacuo was investigated by Schooten and Wijga (29). They do not state clearly whether the polymer was isotactic, although it is likely that it was. At relatively low temperatures (230 to 300°C) there are indications of weak links in the polymer, believed to be hydroperoxide groups. At higher temperatures, volatile products were formed and chain scission proceeded, possibly by random initiation, depropagation, and second-order termination; however, there was not enough data to justify such conclusions. Kinetic measurements, which would prove such a mechanism, were not carried out. The energy of activation at relatively low temperatures, where the hydroperoxide groups are believed to lead to chain scission, was 30 to 40 kcal/mole, whereas Madorsky and Straus found 58 kcal/mole at about 336°C. Copper accelerated the rupture of weak links; this is in accord with the assumption that hydroperoxide groups are present, as it is known that copper accelerates their decomposition.

Davis et al. (30) also studied the thermal degradation of polypropylene in absence of air by determining the molecular size distributions and the decrease in intrinsic viscosities at various stages of the degradation process. The polypropylene was prepared with triethyl aluminum and titanium trichloride as a catalyst and hence must have been isotactic, although this was not stated explicitly. 0.1-g samples were sealed in ampoules and degraded over a range of temperatures from 250 to 302°C. Samples weighing 0.3 to 0.5 g gave similar results. The original distribution of the polymer was logarithmic normal. The experimental size distribution at various stages of the degradation process obtained by fractionation were compared

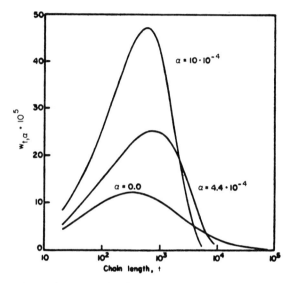

Fig. 5. Differential chain length distributions for random degradation of polypropylene (30).

with theoretical distributions expected from the random theory of breaking links. Some of the mathematical aspects have been discussed above in connection with isotactic polystyrene (14). Very good agreement was found between experiment and theory. Intrinsic viscosities were transformed into number- and weight-average molecular weights and chain lengths via the random theory using an intrinsic viscosity–molecular weight relationship by Kinsinger (31). Some of the distributions are shown in Fig. 5 and the decrease in number and weight average is shown in Fig. 6, including the ratio M_w/M_n. The degrees of degradation are small and $\alpha = 10^{-3}$ corresponds to about 0.7 broken main-chain links on the average for each original chain (see Fig. 6). At this stage of random degradation, the initially very wide distribution ($M_w/M_n = 9$) reached a ratio $M_w/M_n \cong 2.5$, which is fairly close to that for a random distribution

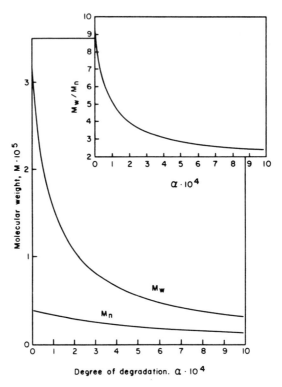

Degree of degradation. $\alpha \cdot 10^4$

Fig. 6. Change in $\overline{M}_w$, $\overline{M}_n$, and $\overline{M}_w/\overline{M}_n$ for random degradation of polypropylene (30).

$(\overline{M}_w/\overline{M}_n = 2)$. The weight loss should be quite small, but was not measured; for $\alpha = 10^{-3}$ it should be less than 0.3%. The α values obtained from viscosity measurements and those derived from molecular size distributions agreed quite satisfactorily, giving an internal check of the calculations. The relevant values are as follows:

Temperature, °C:	250	295	302	302	302
Time, hours:	88	8	2	24	48
$[\eta]_t/[\eta]_0$:	0.676	0.464	0.535	0.285	0.206
$\alpha \cdot 10^4$ from distributions:	0.5	1.5	1.3	4.0	7.0
$\alpha \cdot 10^4$ from $[\eta]_t/[\eta]_0$ vs. $\alpha = s/DP_0$:	0.59	1.57	1.13	4.05	6.98

If the number of links broken on the average in each original chain is plotted against time, curves are obtained which indicate that more than one type of link is involved in the degradation. The authors claim that the energies of activation calculated from two temperatures (265 and 280°C) are 60 and 53 kcal/mole for normal and weak links, respectively.

Satisfactory plots for the Arrhenius energy of activation were obtained by the present author by using all three temperatures (250, 265, 280°C).† Thus it appears that both types of links are abnormal; this is not unlikely since the degradation was only studied in its very initial stages up to about $\alpha = 10^{-3}$ or an average number of breaks in each original chain of about 0.7. However, there is no doubt that the breakdown is a random degradation process; transfer, depropagation, and termination do not need to be invoked.

Schooten and Wijga, as already pointed out above, reported an energy of activation of 33 kcal/mole for a range of temperatures from 230 to 250°C. These authors came to the conclusion that different types of bonds are broken in a lower temperature range than those which are broken at higher temperatures, as used by Madorsky (26), for instance, (336°C).

IV. PHOTOLYSIS

The photolyses in aqueous solutions of atactic and isotactic poly(methacrylic acid) show a number of interesting differences. They were investigated by Jellinek and Chou (32) and Jellinek and Lipovac (33), respectively. The two acids show many similarities in their random chain scission process. However, they differ quantitatively due to the fact that the atactic acid is about 100 times stronger than the isotactic acid. The changes in the ultraviolet absorption spectra as a function of irradiation time are also qualitatively different; apparently, different reactions are involved.

Both acids were irradiated with light of $\lambda = 2537$ Å and degradation measured as a function of pH values, polymer concentration, and chain length. pH values were changed by using HCl acid solutions of various concentrations, phosphate, and borax buffers. The isotactic acid becomes insoluble below a pH value of about 5.5.

To evaluate chain scission reactions obtained at different pH values, each reaction must be referred to a reference standard. In the case of the atactic acid, all chain scissions were obtained by converting intrinsic

† The energy of activation derived in this way is 31 kcal/mole. Similarly, the initial slopes gave very good Arrhenius plots, yielding 43.5 kcal/mole.

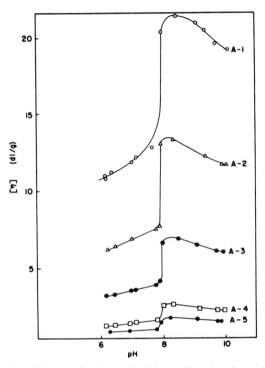

Fig. 7. Intrinsic viscosities as a function of pH for various fractions of isotactic poly-(methacrylic acid): A-1, $DP_0 = 3.34 \times 10^4$; A-2, $DP_0 = 1.01 \times 10^4$; A-3, $DP_0 = 4.48 \times 10^3$; A-4, $DP_0 = 1.66 \times 10^3$; A-5, $DP_0 = 1.04 \times 10^3$ [pH 6.3 to 8, phosphate buffer, 8 to 10 Borax buffer (33)].

viscosities to those corresponding to 2×10^{-3} M HCl solutions by means of calibration curves. In the case of the isotactic polymer, the procedure was somewhat different. Calibration curves were obtained as follows: Isotactic poly(methyl methacrylate) was fractionated and the molecular weights of the fractions were ascertained. Then the fractions were hydrolyzed to the acid with concentrated sulfuric acid. Intrinsic viscosities of each acid fraction were measured as a function of pH. In this way a calibration curve was obtained for each pH value by plotting the chain lengths of the ester fractions against the intrinsic viscosities of the corresponding acid fractions. Thus on photolysis at a definite pH value, the corresponding chain length could be obtained from the calibration curve and the degree of degradation could be evaluated.

Both polymers follow Eq. (2) and (4) for random degradation, i.e.,

$$\frac{1}{\overline{DP}_t} - \frac{1}{\overline{DP}_0} = k_{ir}t = \frac{\phi_s(1 - e^{-E})I_0 t}{[n]_0 l} = \frac{\phi_s I_{abs} t}{c' N_A} \qquad (45)$$

where ϕ_s is the quantum yield for chain scission; I_{abs} the light intensity on the average absorbed by 1 volume unit of the polymer solution, and c' its concentration in monomeric unit moles.

The intrinsic viscosities before irradiation of some of the isotactic acid fractions as a function of pH values are shown in Fig. 7. A steep rise in intrinsic viscosity occurs at about pH 8. Figure 8 gives the experimental photolysis rate constants for atactic and isotactic PMA as a function of pH values based on intrinsic viscosities.

Experiments showed that the chain scission reaction is independent of polymer concentration for either acid. This is to be expected for a pure random degradation process, according to Eq. (45), for moderate degrees of degradation and weak light absorption [see Eq. (4)], as I_{abs} is linearly proportional to the polymer concentration.

The photolysis of the isotactic acid was observed to be dependent on chain length, whereas that of the atactic acid was not (although the latter may also be dependent on chain length, the range of chain lengths investigated for atactic acid was not as large as that for isotactic acid). The quantum yields for the isotactic acid are directly proportional to the

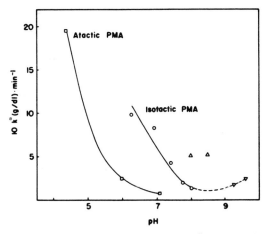

Fig. 8. Experimental rate constants for chain scission k'' as a function of pH derived from $1/[\eta]_t - 1/[\eta]_0 = k''t$ for atactic (32) (square) and isotactic (33) poly(methacrylic acid).

experimental photolysis rate constants, as expected from Eq. (4). They
are of an order of magnitude 10^{-3}. Those for the atactic acid were not
determined but appear to be similar.

The peak values of the spectra for isotactic acid are given in Fig. 9.
This curve can be considered as a spectrophotometric titration curve; a
pK value of about 8 is indicated, in agreement with the value obtained

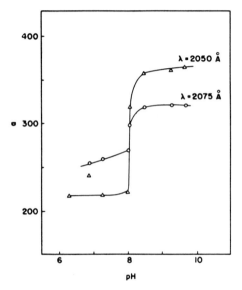

Fig. 9. Monomeric unit molar absorptivity a [(monomeric unit mole)$^{-1}$ cm^{-1} 1] as a
function of pH: (○), $\lambda = 2075$ Å, (△) $\lambda = 2050$ Å for fraction A-1 (33).

from intrinsic viscosity measurements. The maxima at 2070 Å increase
linearly with irradiation time for isotactic PMA, but they decrease linearly
with time for the atactic acid.

It can be shown for either acid that the photolysis rate constants do not
decrease in direct proportion to the increase in degree of dissociation,
α' or $(1 - \alpha')$. The experimental rate constants in either case can be
expressed by a relationship as follows:

$$k_{\exp} = \frac{K'}{K'' - (1 - \alpha')} \tag{46}$$

where K' and K'' are characteristic constants for the acids.

For the atactic acid, the chain scission reaction may be pictured as follows: The primary reaction consists of severing a side group:

$$\underset{\underset{\overset{|}{\text{OH}}}{\overset{|}{\text{C=O}}}{\overset{\overset{\text{CH}_3}{|}}{\sim\text{C}}}\underset{\overset{|}{\text{H}}}{\overset{\overset{\text{H}}{|}}{\text{C}\sim}} \xrightarrow{h\nu} \underset{\overset{|}{\text{H}}}{\overset{\overset{\text{CH}_3}{|}}{\sim\text{C}}}\underset{\overset{|}{\text{H}}}{\overset{\overset{\text{H}}{|}}{\text{C}\sim}} + \cdot\text{COOH}$$

This primary reaction leads then to the actual rupture of main-chain links:

$$\underset{}{\overset{\text{CH}_3}{\sim\text{C}}}\,\underset{\overset{|}{\text{H}}}{\overset{\overset{\text{H}}{|}}{\text{C}}}\,\underset{\overset{|}{\text{COOH}}}{\overset{\overset{\text{CH}_3}{|}}{\text{C}\sim}} \rightarrow \underset{\overset{|}{\text{H}}}{\overset{\overset{\text{CH}_3}{|}}{\sim\text{C}}}\!=\!\overset{\text{H}}{\text{C}} + \underset{\overset{|}{\text{COOH}}}{\overset{\overset{\text{CH}_3}{|}}{\sim\text{C}\cdot}}$$

In the case of the isotactic acid, there is opportunity for hydrogen bonding:

$$\sim\!\text{C}\!-\!\text{C}\!-\!-\!\text{C}\!-\!\text{C}\!-\!-\!\text{C}\!\sim \xrightarrow{h\nu} \sim\!\text{C}\!-\!\text{C}\!-\!-\!\text{C}\!-\!\text{C}\!-\!-\!\text{C}\!\sim + \cdot\text{COOH}$$

$$\downarrow$$

$$\sim\!\text{C}\!-\!\text{C}\!=\!\text{CH}_2 + \text{C}\!-\!-\!-\!\text{C}\!\sim$$

As the degree of dissociation increases with pH, the number of hydrogen bonded structures will decrease. It can be assumed either that the rate of breaking bonds is directly proportional to the number of these ring structures or that the ring structures are more susceptible to photolysis than the unattached side groups. Either process can be formulated. In the first instance, the chain scission equation becomes:

$$\frac{1}{DP_{n,t}} - \frac{1}{DP_0} = k'\frac{[n']_0}{[n]_0}t = k_{\exp}t = \frac{K't}{K'' - (1 - \alpha')} \qquad (47)$$

where $[n]_0$ is the initial concentration of main-chain links (almost equal to the polymer concentration) and $[n']_0$ is the initial concentration of susceptible groups; k' is dependent on pH. The alternative formulation is as follows:

$$\frac{1}{DP_{n,t}} - \frac{1}{DP_0} = k_{exp}t = \{(1 - \alpha'')k_1 + \alpha''k_2\}t = \frac{K't}{K''t(1 - \alpha')} \quad (48)$$

k_1 and k_2 are rate constants dependent on pH. α'' is the fraction of ring structures which have opened up.

These kinetic schemes fit the experimental results. The decrease of k_{exp} with increasing pH values is believed to be a consequence of the change of chain conformation as a function of pH values. The polymer molecules are progressively stretched as the degree of dissociation is increased. As a matter of fact, the reciprocal experimental rate constants plotted as a function of the fractional root-mean-square end-to-end distances give straight lines.

As already mentioned above, the maxima at 2070 Å of the absorption spectra increase linearly with time of irradiation for the isotactic acid, while the corresponding maxima for the atactic acid decrease. These changes cannot be due directly to the chain scission reaction, as the latter is chemically such a very minor, although important, reaction. Products of chain scission cannot be detected (or only with great difficulty) in the ultraviolet spectra for moderate degrees of degradation. The changes may either be due to a subsequent reaction such as formation of monomer in a depropagation step or it may be due to a completely independent reaction of the side groups. Calculation shows that monomer formation is not an unreasonable assumption, but no attempt has as yet been made to determine it experimentally.

Reactions of the side groups of the isotactic acid may consist of stripping a number of these groups from the polymer chain, producing acid and conjugated double bonds. This would increase the extinction. The reaction for atactic acid must be different as the extinction decreases. A tentative reaction scheme would be as follows:

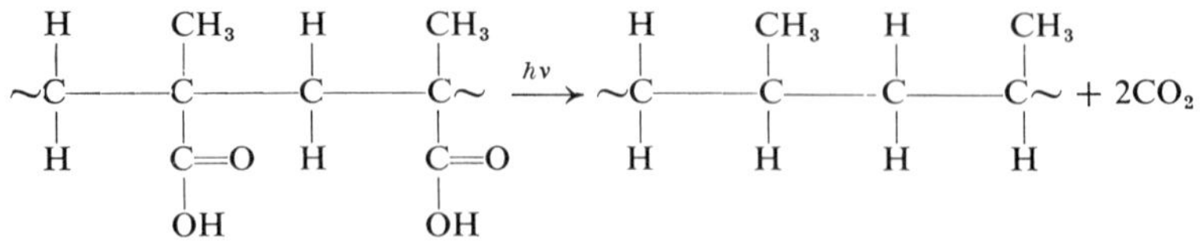

In this case, the extinction would decrease as the number of carboxyl groups is decreased. Here again no attempt has as yet been made to find CO_2.

Photolysis of isotactic poly(methacrylic acid) in aqueous solutions at pH 7.38 (phosphate buffer) in the presence of small amounts of Cu^{2+} ions was studied by Jellinek and Lipovac (34). Complex formation takes place with probably two acid groups per Cu^{2+} ion. The light source was the same as for the previous studies, a low-pressure mercury lamp ($\lambda = 2537$ Å; $I_0 = 5.3 \times 10^{16}$ quanta sec^{-1} 20 ml^{-1}). The photolysis of the complex is very

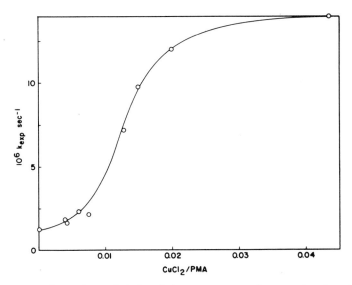

Fig. 10. Over-all experimental chain scission rate constant k_{exp} as a function of molar ratio of $CuCl_2/PMA$; fraction A-1, ($DP_0 = 33440$), pH = 7.35, $\lambda = 2537$ Å; incident light intensity $I_0 = 5.3 \times 10^{16}$ quanta sec^{-1} (20 ml)$^{-1}$ (34).

rapid. The extinction of the absorption maximum at 2070 Å increased with irradiation time. The chain scission rate constants of a fractionated sample as a function of the molar ratio Cu^{2+}/PMA [total moles of Cu^{2+} in solution (bound or unbound)/total monomeric unit moles of PMA in solution] are shown in Fig. 10. The rate constants increase very rapidly with increase in this ratio, reaching eventually a plateau when the rate constants have become about 12 times larger than those in the absence of Cu^{2+} ions. The rate constants were obtained from Eq. (2) after converting viscosity-average chain lengths to number-average chain lengths by means of the random theory of breaking links; this was done for PMA in the absence of Cu^{2+}. Actually, the intrinsic viscosity decreases linearly with increasing Cu^{2+}/PMA ratio, indicating that the degree of coiling increases with the amount of Cu²⁺ ions complexed with the chains. The rate constants for the photolysis increase with the degree of coiling. In absence of Cu²⁺ ions, it was found that the rate constants increased with decreasing pH values or also with increasing coiling of the chains.

Gardner et al. (*34a*) found indications that mixtures of isotactic and syndiotactic poly(methyl methacrylate) (in the form of films) were more stable than the individual polymers when exposed to light of wavelength 2537 Å. This is believed to be due to the formation of stereocomplexes between the two polyisomers. Similar results were obtained on exposure to high-energy electrons (*34b*).

V. OXIDATIVE DEGRADATION

The oxidation of hydrocarbons comprises a large field. As far as unsaturated and saturated polymers are concerned, there are several reviews and books available (*35*). The processes are quite complex and have by no means been elucidated in all their details. Only a few general remarks can be made here as far as the fundamental background is concerned.

The general mechanism on which the oxidation process is based is one originally proposed by Bolland and other workers (*35,35a,36*). There is uncertainty about the initiation reaction. Hydroperoxides are produced, which react with various species and also decompose, leading to branching chain reactions, which can, in principle, be propagated either by a steady state process or become degenerate (nonsteady). Termination reactions are of second order. It is scarcely to be expected that this kinetic scheme is applicable to all oxidation processes of unsaturated or saturated hydrocarbons. As a matter of fact, the mechanism has to be modified for each polymer; however, the principal features of the Bolland mechanism are preserved. Under certain circumstances, of course, diffusion phenomena become rate determining for some of the steps, especially for second-order termination of polymer radicals; in the same category belong cage effects for steps which include decomposition reactions. Thus the possibility for variations of this free-radical mechanism is very large and each polymer has to be studied carefully under the prevailing experimental conditions and from several points of view (oxygen uptake, peroxide formation, production of volatiles, chain scissioning, cross-linking, spectroscopic determination of groups such as $C{=}O$, action of inhibitors, etc.) before a probable mechanism can be formulated. For stereoregular polymers, the extent of crystallinity has quite a marked influence on rates of oxidation as long as the temperature remains below the softening point.

The general Bolland mechanism is as follows:

Initiation

Production of radicals, e.g.,

1. $RH \rightarrow R\cdot + (H\cdot)$ rate $= v_i$

Propagation

2. $R\cdot + O_2 \rightarrow RO_2\cdot$ k_2
3. $RO_2\cdot + RH \rightarrow ROOH + R\cdot$ k_3
4. $ROOH \rightarrow RO\cdot + HO\cdot$ k_4

Chain branching

5. $RO\cdot + RH \rightarrow ROH + R\cdot$ k_5
6. $HO\cdot + RH \rightarrow HOH + R\cdot$ k_6

Termination

7. $RO_2\cdot + RO_2\cdot$ ⎫ k_7
8. $RO_2\cdot + R\cdot$ ⎬ usually inert k_8
9. $R\cdot + R\cdot$ ⎭   products k_9

or

Inhibition

10. $ROO\cdot + AH \rightarrow ROOH + A\cdot$ k_{10}
11. $RO\cdot + AH \rightarrow ROH + A\cdot$ k_{11}
12. $HO\cdot + AH \rightarrow HOH + A\cdot$ k_{12}

RH stands for a polymer molecule and AH for an inhibitor molecule. The radicals in the chain branching steps can also be inhibited. If only steps 1, 2, 3, 7, 8, and 9 are operative, and steady state conditions prevail, the rate of oxygen consumption or hydroperoxide formation becomes:

$$-\frac{d[O_2]}{dt} = \frac{d[ROOH]}{dt} = \frac{k_2 k_3 [RH][O_2] v_i^{1/2}}{2k_2^2 k_7 [O_2]^2 + k_2 k_3 k_8 [O_2][RH] + 2k_3^2 k_9 [RH]^2}$$

(49)

For relatively high $[O_2]$ concentrations, Eq. (49) leads to:

$$-\frac{d[O_2]}{dt} = \frac{d[ROOH]}{dt} = k_3 [RH]\left(\frac{v_i}{2k_7}\right)^{1/2}$$

(50)

At very low oxygen concentrations, Eq. (49) reduces to:

$$-\frac{d[O_2]}{dt} = \frac{d[ROOH]}{dt} = v_i^{1/2} k_2 k_9^{-1/2} [O_2]$$

(51)

If step 10 replaces steps 7, 8, and 9, the inhibited rate of oxygen consumption at high oxygen concentration becomes:

$$-d[O_2]/dt = v_i k_3 [RH]/n k_{10}[AH] \tag{52}$$

where n is the number of chains stopped by one inhibitor molecule. Combination of Eqs. (50) and (52) gives:

$$\frac{(d[O_2]/dt)_{\text{inhibited}}}{(d[O_2]/dt)^2_{\text{uninhibited}}} = 2k_7/(n k_3 k_{10}[RH][AH]) \tag{53}$$

Similarly, if the termination reactions are replaced by step 11, one obtains for high concentration of oxygen:

$$\frac{(d[O_2]/dt)_{\text{inhibited}}}{(d[O_2]/dt)^2_{\text{uninhibited}}} = 2k_1 k_7 [O_2]/(n k_3^2 k_{11}[AH][RH]^2) \tag{54}$$

The oxidative degradation of polypropylene has attracted much attention in recent years, not only in this country, but also to a large extent in Russia. A book edited by Neiman (37) contains an appreciable amount of material on oxidative degradation, including oxidation of isotactic polypropylene. Often it is not clearly indicated whether a particular discussion pertains to stereoregular polymers or not. Miller et al. (38) studied the oxidation of polypropylene in a static apparatus with initial pressures of oxygen of 500 mm Hg over a temperature range from 120 to 150°C. The authors do not state explicitly whether the polymer was stereoregular; however, it was prepared at low pressure and had a molecular weight of 2×10^5. The oxygen absorption curves showed pronounced induction periods decreasing with increasing temperatures. Addition of hydroperoxide shortened the induction periods. When an inhibitor such as diphenylolpropane was added to the polymer, the induction periods increased in direct proportion to the inhibitor concentration. A number of volatile reaction products were formed during oxidative degradation, such as H_2O, CH_2O, CH_3CHO, and CO_2. The time at which the hydroperoxide concentration reached its maximum was the same as that for the maximum rate of oxygen consumption, whereas this was not the case for the formation of aldehydes.

It was shown by infrared spectra that the polymer initially contained a small number of $C{=}O$ groups, which increased appreciably during the reaction. The energy of activation for oxygen consumption is 22 kcal/mole.

These authors proposed the following mechanism:

$$
\begin{array}{ccc}
& CH_3 & & CH_3 \\
& | & & | \\
R-CH_2-C-CH_2-R' \rightarrow & R-CH_2-\overset{\cdot}{C} & CH_2-R' \\
& | & & | \qquad | \\
& O-O\cdot & & O-\!-\!-O
\end{array}
$$

Chain scission occurs either by

$$
\begin{array}{cc}
CH_3 & CH_3 \\
| & | \\
R-CH_2-\overset{\cdot}{C} \quad CH_2-R' \rightarrow R-CH_2-\overset{\cdot}{C} + \cdot OCH_2-R' \\
| \qquad | & | \\
O-\!-\!-O & O\cdot
\end{array}
$$

$$\downarrow$$

$$
R-CH_2-\underset{\underset{O}{\parallel}}{C}-CH_3 + CH_2O + \cdot R'
$$

Or

$$
\begin{array}{cccc}
CH_3 & CH_3 & CH_3 & CH_3 \\
| & | & | & | \\
R-C-CH_2-\overset{\cdot}{C} \quad CH_2-R' \rightarrow R-C-CH_2-CH \quad CH_2R' \rightarrow \\
| \qquad\qquad | \qquad | & | \qquad\qquad | \qquad | \\
H \qquad\qquad O-\!-\!-O & O-\!-\!-O
\end{array}
$$

$$
\begin{array}{cc}
CH_3 & CH_3 \\
| & | \\
R-\underset{\cdot}{C}-CH_2-CH + \cdot OCH_2R' \rightarrow \\
& | \\
& O\cdot
\end{array}
$$

$$
\begin{array}{c}
CH_3 \\
| \\
RC\!=\!CH_2 + CH_3CHO + CH_2O + R'\cdot
\end{array}
$$

It was ascertained that 0.1 % of the tertiary hydrogen atoms were transformed into hydroperoxide groups. A kinetic analysis was not attempted in this paper.

Isotactic polypropylene (MW 4×10^5) was investigated by Rysavy et al. (39) over a temperature range from 120 to 150°C at an oxygen pressure of 1 atm. Reproducible results could be obtained only by absorbing the volatile products with KOH. The oxygen uptake for the polymer films (0.1 mm thick) was diffusion controlled. It ceased when 0.73 moles of oxygen were absorbed for each monomeric unit mole. Soon after the maximum rate had been reached, the rate of oxidation became slower than the rate of diffusion of oxygen into the polymer. The logarithm of the maximum rate was a linear function of the reciprocal absolute temperature and gave an energy of activation of 29 kcal/mole in contrast to 22 kcal/mole found by Miller et al. (38) and 27 kcal/mole reported by Hawkins et al. (40). These latter authors oxidized atactic polypropylene films (0.256 mm thick). Oxidation of these films was not diffusion controlled, which is surprising in view of the findings by the Russian workers, who used films 0.1 mm thick. The temperature range was 60° to 140°C. The logarithm of the induction period as a function of $1/T$ yielded an energy of activation of about 27 kcal/mole, as was stated above. The isotactic sample remained crystalline during oxidation, while the atactic polymer was amorphous throughout the reaction.

Oxidative degradation of polypropylene was also studied by Pudov et al. (41). Films 40 μ thick were degraded over a temperature range from 90 to 140°C. Volatiles such as water, formaldehyde, acetaldehyde, acetone, hydrogen, peroxides, carbon monoxide, and carbon dioxide were formed. The formation of C=O groups and OH groups in the polymer were followed by infrared spectra. The rate of oxygen uptake reached a maximum when 15% of the structural units in the polymer were oxidized, assuming that one oxygen molecule is needed for each structural unit.

The experimental rate of oxygen absorption v_{O_2}, obeyed the following relationship:

$$v_{O_2} = a[ROOH]^{1/2} + b[ROOH] \tag{55}$$

where a and b are experimental rate constants and [ROOH] is the concentration of hydroperoxide groups. The rates of volatile formation were directly dependent on the rate of hydroperoxide formation; e.g., the rate of water formation was directly proportional to the hydroperoxide concentration. This indicates that peroxide is the primary oxidation product, whereas the other products are produced by the decomposition of the hydroperoxide groups, i.e., $ROOH + RH \rightarrow RO\cdot + H_2O + R\cdot$.

Any addition of a compound, such as an antioxidant, which has a weaker bond than the R—H bond, will lead to preferred reaction with ROOH. The energy of activation of ROOH decomposition is 25 kcal/mole, whereas in the presence of antioxidants, e.g., N—H bonds (e.g., N-cyclo-hexyl-N'-penyl-p-phenylene diamine), it is only 13 kcal/mole.

The mechanism formulated by Pudov and co-workers is a variation of Bolland's scheme. [See also Semenov (42) and Bateman et al. (43).]

Initiation:	$RH + O_2 \rightarrow R\cdot + HO_2\cdot$	v_i
Propagation:	$R\cdot + O_2 \rightarrow ROO\cdot$	k_1
	$ROO\cdot + RH \rightarrow ROOH + R\cdot$	k_2
Branching		
chain:	$ROOH + RH \rightarrow RO\cdot + H_2O + R \rightarrow 2R\cdot$	k_4
Termination:	$ROO\cdot + ROO\cdot \rightarrow$ inactive products	k_3

Application of the steady state method, noting that the oxygen consumption is given by $v_{O_2} = k_1[O]_2[R\cdot]$, leads to the following rate equation;

$$v_{O_2} = k_2 \frac{(2k_4)^{1/2}}{k_3^{1/2}}[RH]^{3/2}[ROOH]^{1/2} + 2k_4[RH][ROOH] \qquad (56)$$

This equation can also be written:

$$\frac{v_{O_2}}{[RH][ROOH]} = 2k_4 + k_2\frac{2k_4[RH]^{1/2}}{k_3[ROOH]^{1/2}} \qquad (57)$$

Plotting

$$(v_{O_2}/[ROOH]) \text{ vs. } [ROOH]^{-1/2}$$

and

$$(v_{O_2}/[ROOH]^{1/2}) \text{ vs. } [ROOH]^{1/2}$$

gives good straight lines in accordance with Eqs. (55), (56), and (57).

The effect of inhibitors on isotactic polypropylene was studied by Slyapnikov et al. (44). Two phenolic inhibitors were used: I: 2,6-di-tert-octyl-4-methylphenol; and II: 2,2'-methylene-bis(4-methyl-6-tert-octyl-4-butylphenol). The oxidation was carried out over a range of temperatures from 170 to 210°C with I and 190 to 210°C with II. A linear dependence of the induction period on inhibitor concentration could not be established. The composition of oxidation products during the induction period remained constant, but the chain length decreased considerably; the rate of decrease in chain length increased with inhibitor concentration. When both inhibitors were present in the polymer, the induction period was shortened appreciably.

Kinetic schemes are given in Neiman's book (37) for the action of inhibitors. The inhibitor HA is assumed to react with hydroperoxide radicals. In the case of polypropylene;

$$\text{ROO}\cdot + \text{HA} \rightarrow \text{inactive products} \qquad k_5$$

Semenov (42) discussed such reactions and introduced the concept of "critical" inhibitor concentration. It follows from the solution of the kinetic scheme that as long as (37)

$$[AH] > \frac{k_2}{k_5}[RH]$$

the oxidation can be treated by the steady state method, whereas for the case where

$$[AH] < \frac{k_2}{k_5}[RH]$$

a nonsteady state (degenerate branching) will prevail. At the point of the reaction, where

$$[AH]_{cr} = \frac{k_2}{k_5} [RH]$$

the critical inhibitor concentration $[AH]_{cr}$ has been reached; above this concentration, a steady state is operative; below it the process becomes nonsteady. The same results can also be obtained starting with the following rate equation:

$$\frac{d[n]}{dt} = v_i + \varphi[n] - k[n][x] \tag{58}$$

where $[n]$ is the concentration of radicals at time t, v_i the rate of initiation, φ a constant ($\varphi[n]$ is actually the branching rate), $[x]$ the inhibitor concentration, and $k[n][x]$ the inhibition rate. It can be seen that if $k[x] < \varphi$, the reaction will be autoaccelerated, but if $k[x] > \varphi$, a steady state will prevail. An example is propylene inhibited by phenyl-β-naphthylamine.

For theories which have been developed for cases where the antioxidants not only terminate but also initiate chains, a paper by Slyapnikov et al. (44; Part II), should be consulted. The oxidation of linear isotactic polypropylene was studied in the presence of inhibitors I or II, discussed above, and of dicetyl sulfide. The latter compound decomposes hydroperoxides without formation of active products.

Oxidation of isotactic polypropylene over a range of temperatures from 125 to 150°C was investigated by Stivala et al. (45) by following the change in area under the infrared carbonyl band (5.6 to 5.8 μ). The oxygen content was varied by adding N_2 and keeping the system at a pressure of one atmosphere. The original polymer showed a small carbonyl content. Films, 2.5 μ thick, were oxidized. When the oxidation was carried out on 7-μ films the reaction became diffusion controlled. The oxidation showed an initial induction period, whose duration depended on temperature and oxygen concentration. The logarithm of the maximum rates for the increase in carbonyl content was a linear function of $1/T$, yielding an energy of activation for oxidation of 22 ± 1 kcal/mole. A linear relationship was also obtained between the logarithm of the reciprocal of the induction periods and $1/T$, giving an activation energy of 31 ± kcal/mole. Weight losses were small; after $2\frac{1}{2}$ hr at 140°C and with 89% vol. % O_2, the weight loss was 3.7%. The expression $\ln[(\rho_m - \rho)/\rho_m]$, where ρ_m is the maximum rate and ρ a rate not too near ρ_m, plotted vs. time gave straight lines.

The experimental results can be accounted for by a mechanism elaborated by Cullis and Hinshelwood (46) for the low temperature oxidation of higher paraffins. It originates from Semenov's (*42*) slow chain branching theory (steady state condition). The sequence of the steps is different than that in Ref. (*45*), but the subscripts for the k values have not been altered.

Initiation

$$RH + O_2 \rightarrow R\cdot + HO_2\cdot \qquad\qquad v_i$$

Propagation

$$R\cdot + O_2 \rightarrow RO_2\cdot \qquad\qquad k_2$$
$$RO_2\cdot + RH \rightarrow ROOR + H\cdot \qquad\qquad k_3$$

or

$$\rightarrow ROOH + R\cdot$$

Chain branching

$$ROOR \rightarrow 2RO\cdot \qquad\qquad k_5$$
$$R'\cdot + RH \rightarrow R\cdot + R'H \qquad\qquad k_8$$

Various reactions

$$ROOR \rightarrow \text{inactive nonvolatile products} \qquad\qquad k_6$$
$$\text{(chain rupture)}$$
$$RO\cdot \rightarrow R'\cdot + \text{volatile products} \qquad\qquad k_7$$
$$\text{(e.g., CO, CO}_2\text{, H}_2\text{O; R'}\cdot$$
$$\text{is a fairly stable radical)}$$

Termination

$$RO_2\cdot + RH \rightarrow \text{inactive products} \qquad\qquad k_4$$
$$R\cdot' + O_2 \rightarrow \text{less reactive products} \qquad\qquad k_9$$

Step k_7 was assumed to follow immediately after steps k_4 and k_5. Oxygen reacts at random with tertiary hydrogen atoms. Nevertheless, the concentration of these tertiary atoms remains practically constant during the process. A termination such as $R\cdot + R\cdot \rightarrow R\text{—}R$ has not been formulated because the medium has a very high viscosity, but the same objection can be raised to step k_4, which remained in the scheme; cage effects are to be expected but have not been considered.

The reaction scheme proposed by Pudov et al. (*41*), described above, shows some similarities with the one under discussion. Thus the initiation reactions are the same in both cases, as are the propagation reactions. Steps k_5 and k_8 actually produce the same chain carriers as the branching reaction formulated by Pudov et al. Termination in the Russian scheme is by $ROO\cdot + ROO\cdot$, a step which does not appear in the original scheme formulated by Cullis and Hinshelwood.

The rate of carbonyl formation, applying steady state kinetics, is then given by:

$$\rho = \frac{[k_3 k_6 v_i (1 - e^{-At})/(k_3 + k_4)(k_5 + k_6)]}{1 - [2k_3 k_5/(k_3 + k_4)(k_5 + k_6)]\{k_8[RH]/(k_8[RH] + k_9[O_2])\}}$$

$$= k_6[ROOR] \tag{59}$$

where A is given by:

$$A = (k_5 + k_6) \frac{2k_3 k_5 k_8[RH]}{(k_3 + k_4)(k_8[RH] + k_9[O_2])} \tag{60}$$

The maximum rate ρ_m is

$$\rho_m = \frac{C_1 v_i}{1 - \{C_2[RH]/(C_2[RH] + C_3[O_2])\}} = \frac{K_1[O_2]}{1 - \{K_2/(K_3 + [O_2])\}} \tag{61}$$

Equation (61) is in very good agreement with the experimental results. At_m is nearly constant. For very small $[O_2]$ concentrations, Eq. (61) reduces to:

$$\rho_m = \frac{K_1 K_3[O_2]}{K_3 - K_2} \tag{62}$$

For large $[O_2]$ concentrations, when $[O_2] \gg K_3 - K_2$, it reduces to:

$$\rho_m = K_1 K_3 + K_1[O_2] \tag{63}$$

Furthermore, Eqs. (59) and (61) lead to:

$$\rho = \frac{\rho_m(1 - e^{-At})}{1 - e^{-At}m} \tag{64}$$

which in logarithmic form, provided $\rho \ll \rho_m$, is

$$-\ln \frac{\rho_m - \rho}{\rho_m} = At \tag{65}$$

Equation (65) is also obeyed by the experimental results. An equation of the form:

$$\frac{1}{\Theta} = K[O_2] \tag{66}$$

can also be derived from the reaction scheme, where Θ is the induction period and K a constant. This equation is also satisfactorily obeyed by the experimental data. Thus, the proposed reaction scheme accounts well for the experimental results. The differences between the present findings and those of the Russian workers may be due to the different types of parameters which have been measured. In the present case, the change in carbonyl content was followed, whereas the Russian workers measured oxygen uptake, peroxide, and volatile formation.

In a recent communication (47), the same authors reported measurements on the infrared band due to hydroperoxide (2.8 μ to 3.0 μ). The rate for hydroperoxide formation could be expressed by;

$$\rho_{HP} = \text{constant } [O_2]e^{-At} \qquad (67)$$

A has the same meaning as before. Hence, a straight line should be obtained by plotting log ρ_{HP} against time, for constant oxygen concentration. This was actually the case up to about 0.8 hr at 150°C. The data based on measurements of C=O absorptions showed a similar trend. The deviation from the straight line is attributed to morphological changes during oxidation. A value of $A = 0.021$ was derived at constant $[O_2]$ from both carbonyl and hydroperoxide measurements, carried out under similar conditions.

The same authors made some additional comments on their oxidation studies during a symposium on Degradation Reactions (48). They discussed papers by Bevilacqua et al. (49) and Matveeva et al. (50), dealing with oxidation products of isotactic polypropylene, where it is stated that formic acid, acetic acid, esters, unsaturated material, formaldehyde, acetaldehyde, water, CO, CO_2, H_2, peroxide, and acetone are formed during oxidation. These authors formulated reactions to explain these observations, some of which were quite similar to the ones suggested by Stivala et al. From Arrhenius plots, they obtained $E_8 - E_9 \simeq 6$ kcal/mole and $E_i + E_6 - E_5 \simeq 18$ kcal/mole; the subscripts correspond to the steps of the reaction scheme indicated by the subscripts of the rate constants. Furthermore, they obtained $E_i + E_6 \simeq 51$ kcal/mole and $E_5 \simeq 33$ kcal/mole for the decomposition of ROOR: The latter value compares favorably with a value of 33 kcal/mole given by Stannett and Mesrobian (51) for the decomposition of acrylic hydroperoxide.

The rate of formation of volatile products according to the scheme by Stivala et al. (45) is given by:

$$\rho_{vp} = K(1 - e^{-At})/A \qquad (68)$$

Differentiating Eq. (68) with respect to time and taking logarithms gives

$$\ln \rho_{vp}' = \ln S - At \qquad (69)$$

where

$$\rho_{vp}' = [d(\rho_{pv})/dt].$$

Hence, a linear relationship should exist between ln ρ_{vp}' and t. Equation (69) was followed by the data of the Russian workers (37).

A general critical review of the Bolland mechanism was recently published by Hawkins (52).

The work on oxidation of isotactic polypropylene, discussed above, does not present a consistent picture but contains a variety of features, some even of a contradictory nature. This is probably due to different histories of the samples such as variations in the polymerization processes, different molecular weights, a variety of abnormal structures or alien groups, etc. One point which emerges with some certainty is that the degree of crystallinity influences the oxidation process. This is one of the causes of the difference in the oxidation of atactic compared to isotactic polypropylene. Furthermore, as pointed out above, the amorphous regions in the isotactic case are preferentially attacked by oxygen and the polymer actually becomes more crystalline on moderate oxidation than it was initially. This is true provided, of course, that the oxidation is carried out below the softening point.

Many disturbing factors can be excluded if degradation reactions are carried out in solution and an additional parameter, the concentration, is gained. The influence of diffusion can be minimized in solution and, of course, morphological changes have no influence. Thus differences in the oxidation of isotactic and atactic polymers are more likely to be due to actual differences in structure.

Oxidation of isotactic and atactic polypropylene, polybutene-1, and linear and branched polyethylene in solution was studied by Dulog et al. (53). The autoxidation was followed by uptake of oxygen. The polymers were prepared using a Ziegler–Natta catalyst and carefully purified. The samples were separated into ether-soluble and ether-insoluble fractions. Thus, atactic (ether-soluble) and isotactic (ether-insoluble) fractions were obtained. Polymer in solutions of trichlorobenzene was oxidized. The solutions were prepared under nitrogen and measurements were started 10 min after introduction into the reaction vessel, when temperature equilibrium was reached. Apparently it was assumed that very little oxidation took place during the initial period; however, it is quite obvious from plots of oxygen uptake vs. time that appreciable oxygen consumption took place during this initial stage. Thus the initial part of the reaction had been missed, amounting in some cases from 30 to 50% of the total oxygen consumed. Thus it is not known whether there are induction periods in this reaction. Whether chain rupture took place was not investigated. The range of temperatures investigated for polypropylene was 120 to 140°C; for polybutene-1 and polyethylene, 150 and 176°C. These temperatures were arranged so that about 0.015 moles of oxygen were consumed for each monomeric unit mole of polymer in 1 to 3 hr. The measurements were discontinued before degradation products started interfering with the reaction. It was found that all ether-soluble or atactic samples gave curves for the rate of oxygen consumption in moles per second vs. reaction time, whereas the ether-insoluble or isotactic samples gave straight line relationships. The oxygen concentrations were expressed in moles/l in the solutions. If the rates of oxygen consumption were plotted against the square root of oxygen consumption, curves were obtained for the isotactic polymers and straight lines for the atactic samples.

Thus the total rate of oxygen consumption for isotactic polymer is given by:

$$v_{\text{iso}} = K_b[O_2] = \frac{d[\text{ROOH}]}{dt} \tag{70}$$

and for atactic polymer by:

$$v_{\text{at}} = K_m[O_2]^{1/2} = \frac{d[\text{ROOH}]}{dt} \tag{71}$$

Equation (70) pertains to a steady state chain reaction, where the initiation and termination reactions are of second order. For any steady state process, the rate of initiation equals the rate of termination. The authors did not elaborate the mechanism but state that for second-order initiation and second-order termination, the rate of oxygen consumption is given by:

$$v_{O_2} = K_b[\text{ROOH}] \tag{72}$$

and for first-order initiation and second-order termination by:

$$v_{O_2} = K_m[\text{ROOH}]^{1/2} \tag{73}$$

These equations have not been verified directly, as hydroperoxide concentrations were not determined.

These authors (54) also investigated syndiotactic polypropylene in the same manner. It behaved like the atactic polymer, as was to be expected. The rate of oxygen uptake was also given by Eq. (71). The energy of activation for syndiotactic polypropylene is 7 kcal/mole higher than that for the isotactic polymer.

A nonbranching chain reaction can be formulated to account for Eqs. (72) and (73). As soon as a few hydroperoxide groups have been formed, they start decomposing as follows [see also Bolland and Gee (36)].

Initiation: $2ROOH \rightarrow 2R\cdot + ?$ k_1

Propagation: $R\cdot + O_2 \rightarrow RO_2\cdot$ k_2

$RO_2\cdot + RH \rightarrow ROOH + R\cdot$ k_3

Termination: $2RO_2\cdot \rightarrow$ stable products k_4

Practically all the oxygen is consumed in the propagation reaction k_2, hence the total oxygen consumption is given by:

$$v_{O_2} = k_2[R\cdot][O_2] \tag{74}$$

Under steady state conditions, the rate of initiation must equal that of termination, hence:

$$k_1[ROOH]^2 = k_4[RO_2\cdot]^2 \tag{75}$$

Furthermore:

$$+\frac{d[R\cdot]}{dt} = k_1[ROOH]^2 - k_2[R\cdot][O_2] + k_3[RO_2\cdot][RH] = 0 \tag{76}$$

Therefore:

$$[R\cdot] = \frac{k_1[ROOH]^2 + k_3[RO_2\cdot][RH]}{k_2[O_2]} \tag{77}$$

$$v_{O_2} = k_1[ROOH]^2 + k_3\left(\frac{k_1}{k_4}\right)^{1/2}[ROOH][RH] \tag{78}$$

The oxygen consumption due to initiation is negligible; furthermore, for stages of oxidation where decomposition products are still negligible, [RH] is constant. Hence, v_{O_2} becomes

$$v_{O_2} = K_b[ROOH] \tag{79}$$

If the initiation is first order with respect to hydroperoxide, but termination is of second order, it can be shown very easily that Eq. (73) is obtained. It is not unlikely that in the very beginning the oxidation of the isotactic polymers is also first order.

The explanation given by the authors for the difference in the rate of oxidation in the two polymer isomers is as follows. Models show that the peroxide radical fits so well into the structure of an isotactic molecule that it can come very near to the nearest tertiary hydrogen atom. Thus, a hydrogen peroxide radical group can be formed easily;

```
    CH₃  H    CH₃   H    H   CH₃
    |    |    |     |    |    |
~C——C————C————C————C————C~
    |    |    |     |    |    |
    H    H    O——O·  H    H    H
```

This could easily lead to a zip reaction, forming a number of hydroperoxide groups in a row, which can then interact and decompose.

Such spatial arrangements are not possible for atactic and syndiotactic polymers and tertiary hydrogen atoms will react statistically.

The over-all energies of activation reflect these spatial considerations. Thus for polypropylene one obtains: isotactic, 20 kcal/mole; atactic and syndiotactic, 27 kcal/mole. For polybutene-1 one obtains: isotactic, 28 kcal/mole; atactic, 36 kcal/mole. For polyethylene one obtains: ether-insoluble, 36 kcal/mole; ether-soluble, 37 kcal/mole. Polyethylenes of different molecular weights show the same energy of activation; this indicates that the differences for the atactic and isotactic polymers are not due to differences in the molecular weights of the samples. According to Bateman (35), second-order hydrogen peroxide decomposition is favored at temperatures around 80°C, whereas first-order decomposition is prevalent above 130°C.

A paper by Tobolsky et al. (55) on the oxidation of atactic polypropylene with benzoyl peroxide as initiator is noteworthy. The data suggest that the rate-determining step for chain scission is a bimolecular reaction of peroxy radicals. A paper by Natta et al. (56) is also of interest in this connection.

Some work on the oxidative degradation of isotactic polystyrene (based on changes in IR spectra) has been reported recently by Beschell et al. (56a).

VI. DEGRADATION BY HIGH ENERGY RADIATION

Considerable work has been done on the high energy irradiation of atactic and isotactic polypropylene. Several studies have been carried out by Black and Lyons (57), Waddington (58), and Gupta (59).

A paper by Black and Lyons (60) gives a detailed account of the irradiation of polypropylene made by a Ziegler catalyst at low pressure. Polypropylene takes an intermediate position between polyisobutene, which degrades by chain scissioning, and polyethylene, which cross-links on exposure to high energy irradiation. Films 0.1 to 0.25 mm thick were exposed to γ-rays of a ⁶⁰Co source of about 16 Ci and also to electrons of a 0.4-kW beam from a 2-MeV Van de Graaf generator. The polymer was shown to have, initially, a random distribution of chain lengths ($M_w/M_n = 2$). Intrinsic viscosities were measured in tetrahydronaphthalene solutions at 135°C. The amount of unsaturation was determined and infrared spectra were taken after electron irradiation.

A very rapid decrease in molecular weight was observed initially, which slowed down as the polymer was irradiated further. Insoluble gel was obtained after a dose of 50 Mrad. Thus up to a dose of about 40 Mrad, molecular weights were measured by intrinsic viscosities. The changes in the number-average molecular weights obtained from the viscosity data were then evaluated according to the random theory of breaking links. Above 40 Mrad, swelling and solubility measurements were carried out.

For a chain scission reaction, which is of a purely random nature, Eq. (2) holds with k_{ir} given by Eq. (5). Equation (2) can also be expressed in terms of molecular weights:

$$\frac{S'}{N_A} = \frac{s}{M_0} = \frac{1}{\bar{M}_r} - \frac{1}{M_0} = \frac{k_{ir}t}{M_1} = \frac{r't}{E_d N_A} = \frac{r}{E_d N_A} \tag{80}$$

where S' is the average number of broken links for each gram of polymer; and M_0, $\bar{M}_r$, and M_1 are the initial molecular weight, the molecular weight after radiation dose r, and the monomer molecular weight, respectively.

Thus ($1/M_r$) plotted vs. r should give a straight line. According to the authors, this is not the case, but ($1/M_r$) is proportional to $r^{1/2}$. This relationship was derived from a double logarithmic plot. Close inspection of the experimental results, however, show a distinct change of slope at $r \simeq 5$ Mrad, which becomes quite noticeable by plotting ($1/M_r$) against r. This means that ($1/M_r$) increases with r up to about 5 Mrad according to a square root relationship, but eventually the plot ($1/M_r$) vs. r becomes strictly linear between about 10 to 30 Mrad. This result indicates that in the region from 0 to 5 Mrad random scission is predominant. Above this dose, random scission and cross-linking also take place simultaneously, but compensating each other so that a linear relationship is obtained.

The authors base their conclusions on a square root relationship between molecular weight and dose, including doses larger than 5 Mrad.

According to a theory by Flory and Rehner (61), the swelling ratio (weight of swollen gel/dry weight) vs. logarithm of ($r - r_g$), where r_g is the radiation dose per gram needed for gel formation, should give a straight line with slope $-5/3$, provided that cross-linking is directly proportional to the radiation dose. For $r_g = 50$ Mrad, this seems to be the case. However, the accuracy of the experiments is not sufficient to establish this relationship with certainty. The sol fraction was plotted according to the Charlesby–Pinner relationship [Eq. (23)], which was followed by the experimental data.

Infrared spectra showed an increase in vinylidene unsaturation. Approximately one vinylidene double bond was produced for each bond fracture; this agrees with the following disproportionation reaction:

$$\sim\underset{\substack{|\\H}}{\overset{\substack{CH_3\\|}}{CH}}\!-\!\underset{\substack{|\\H}}{\overset{\substack{H\\|}}{C}}\cdot\;+\;\cdot\underset{\substack{|\\H}}{\overset{\substack{CH_3\\|}}{C}}\!-\!\underset{\substack{|\\H}}{\overset{\substack{H\\|}}{C}}\!\sim\;\rightarrow\;\sim\overset{\substack{CH_2\\||}}{C}\!-\!CH_3\;+\;H_2C\!-\!\underset{\substack{|\\H}}{\overset{\substack{CH_3\;H\\|\quad|}}{C}}\!\sim$$

However, additional chemical evidence showed that the total unsaturation has double the value of that for the vinylidene unsaturation.

The kinetics given by the authors are based on very approximate rate equations and are open to doubt; they will, at best, only be valid for the very initial stages of the degradation process. The proposed mechanism for chain scission is as follows:

$$R\!-\!\left[\underset{\substack{|\\H}}{\overset{\substack{CH_3\\|}}{C}}\!-\!\underset{\substack{|\\H}}{\overset{\substack{H\\|}}{C}}\right]_n\!\!-\!R'\;\rightarrow\;R\!-\!\left[\underset{\substack{|\\H}}{\overset{\substack{CH_3\\|}}{C}}\!-\!\underset{\substack{|\\H}}{\overset{\substack{H\\|}}{C}}\right]_n^{*}\!\!-\!R'$$

$$R\!-\!\left[\underset{\substack{|\\H}}{\overset{\substack{CH_3\\|}}{C}}\!-\!\underset{\substack{|\\H}}{\overset{\substack{H\\|}}{C}}\right]_{n-1}\!\!\!-\!\underset{\substack{|\\H}}{\overset{\substack{CH_3\\|}}{C}}\!=\!\underset{\substack{|\\H}}{\overset{\substack{H\\|}}{C}}\;+\;R'H$$

Schnabel and Dole (*62*) carried out extensive studies on the irradiation of atactic and isotactic polypropylene at room temperature by γ-rays from a ^{60}Co source (dose rate, 0.1 Mrad hr^{-1}, in vacuo). These workers also found about equal amounts of cross-linking and chain rupture. Two isotactic samples, in the form of flakes and films, respectively, and one atactic sample were investigated. The intrinsic viscosities, measured in decalin solutions at 135°C were 5.3, 3.77, and 2.19 g/dl for the isotactic flake, isotactic film, and atactic samples, respectively. The corresponding weight-average molecular weights were 8.04×10^5, 1.08×10^5, and 2.66×10^5 in the same order as above. Evolved gas was analyzed in a mass spectrometer. Gel measurements were performed by extracting the sol fraction. The main gaseous products were H_2 and CH_4. The G values for H_2 and CH_4 and total gas formation for a dose of 11.4×10^{20} eV g^{-1} were, for instance, $G(H_2) = 2.78$, $G(CH_4) = 0.072$, and $G(\text{total gas}) = 2.85$, respectively.

Gel data could be expressed by the Charlesby–Pinner relation, Eq. (23). This equation is valid for doses larger than those needed to reach the gel point. It appears from the experimental results that $G(S)/2G(X) \simeq 0.45$ for the atactic polymer and 0.745 for the isotactic samples. Separate evaluation of $G(S)$ and $G(X)$ is somewhat uncertain because the initial size distributions were not random. Equation (23) is well obeyed in spite of the fact that $M_w/M_n = 5$ instead of 2 (random), but even starting with such a wide distribution, two bond ruptures in each original chain will reduce M_w/M_n from 5 to a value not far from 2.7.

The evolution of hydrogen gas is somewhat smaller for the atactic than for the isotactic polymers. There may be some head-to-head structures in the atactic samples. This would reduce the yield of hydrogen. CH_4 is probably formed by breaking off CH_3 side groups from the main chains. CH_4 evolution in isotactic propylene is smaller than in the atactic polymer. This may be due to some enhanced cage effect in the isotactic sample as this is more crystalline than the atactic polymer.

The authors also attempted to reach some conclusions as to the magnitude of $G(S)$ and $G(X)$ values by considering the change in the ratio $M_w/M_n = b$ during degradation. As already pointed out above, these calculations have some uncertainties as various assumptions have to be made. Nevertheless, it can be calculated that for $X = [M_n G(S)_r/100 N_A] = 1$, b has been reduced from 5 to 2.68, where the relevant relationship is as follows:

$$b = \frac{2(1 + x)}{x}\left[1 - \frac{1}{x}\left(1 - \frac{1}{(1 + x/\beta)^\beta}\right)\right] \tag{81}$$

where $\beta = [1/(b_0 - 1)]$ represents the width of the initial molecular size distribution and X is described by the relationship given above. The term r is expressed in eV g^{-1}.

Keyser et al. (63) investigated the intrinsic viscosities of isotactic and atactic polypropylene as a function of irradiation time. The isotactic samples were the same as those used previously; the atactic sample was different ($[\eta] = 1.57$, $M_w = 1.77 \times 10^5$). The method of irradiation was the same as before. The initial decrease in $[\eta]$ was quite pronounced.

The intrinsic viscosities could be expressed by the following relationship:

$$\ln \frac{[\eta]_r}{[\eta]_0} = Ar^{1/2} + \frac{Br}{2} \tag{82}$$

$B = 0$ for the atactic fraction, but was -8×10^{-24} g/eV for the isotactic polymer. These results were plotted by the present author in the form of

$1/[\eta]_r$ vs. $r^{1/2}$; fairly good straight lines were obtained. This is understandable since Eq. (82) can be expressed with good approximation by:

$$\frac{1}{\overline{M}_{n,r}} - \frac{1}{\overline{M}_{n,0}} = A'r^{1/2} + \frac{Br}{2} \tag{83}$$

This is shown below. As $[\eta]_r = K\overline{M}_{n,r}^\alpha$, one can write for Eq. (82);

$$-\ln\frac{1}{K\overline{M}_{n,r}^\alpha} + \ln\frac{1}{K\overline{M}_{n,0}^\alpha} = Ar^{1/2} + \frac{Br}{2}$$

or

$$-\ln\frac{1}{\overline{M}_{n,r}} + \ln\frac{1}{\overline{M}_{n,0}} = \frac{A}{\alpha}r^{1/2} + \frac{Br}{2\alpha}$$

$(1/\overline{M}_{n,r})$ and $(1/\overline{M}_{n,0})$ are small numbers, hence

$$\ln\frac{1}{\overline{M}_{n,r}} \cong 2\frac{\dfrac{1}{\overline{M}_{n,r}} - 1}{\dfrac{1}{\overline{M}_{n,r}} + 1} \quad\text{and}\quad \ln\frac{1}{\overline{M}_{n,0}} = 2\frac{\dfrac{1}{\overline{M}_{n,0}} - 1}{\dfrac{1}{\overline{M}_{n,0}} + 1}.$$

This procedure leads finally to:

$$\frac{1}{\overline{M}_{n,r}} - \frac{1}{\overline{M}_{n,0}} = \frac{Ar^{1/2}}{4\alpha} - \frac{B}{8\alpha} \tag{84}$$

Equation (84) agrees well with that found by Black and Lyons (60) and shows that appreciable chain scission takes place.

When $(1/[\eta]_r)$ is plotted against r, fairly good straight lines are obtained up to 0.6 Mrad for atactic polypropylene and up to 1 Mrad for isotactic polypropylene. Past these doses, the slopes of the straight lines decrease and continue eventually as straight lines. The slopes for the atactic and isotactic polymers are similar.

According to the authors, there are two sets of results, which is hard to understand theoretically: (1) the sharp initial drop in $[\eta]_r$ and (2) the proportionality between $\ln([\eta]_r/[\eta]_0)$ and (radiation dose)$^{1/2}$. This relationship was also found for poly(1-pentene) and poly(1-hexene) (64) and for copolymers of α-methylstyrene and styrene (65). The decrease in $[\eta]_r$ is believed by Dole and co-workers to be due to main link fracture, formation of branch points or inter- and intramolecular cross-linking and decrease in the K constant of the Mark–Houwink equation, brought about by changes in the size distributions. Many of these difficulties arise because the initial distribution was not random ($M_w/M_n = 2$), but $M_w/M_n = 5$. Hence any explanation for the initial reaction is subject to doubt. The authors were puzzled by the "fact" that the slope of ln ($[\eta]_r/[\eta]_0$) was constant; they rather expected it to change. They remarked that there may be a fortuitous cancellation of various effects. However, this seems to be unlikely. It is quite likely that main-chain link rupture is the overriding effect for quite a large range of the radiation, as was also assumed by Black and Lyons (60). It is also noteworthy that Eq. (84) held for a radiation dose up to 30 Mrad in the case studied by Black and Lyons, whereas in the case investigated by Dole et al. the gel point was reached at a dose of 10 to 15 Mrad.

Kondo and Dole (66) have continued the work on the effect of γ-radiation on atactic and isotactic polypropylene. Irradiation was carried out in the presence of N_2O gas. This gas is known to increase the amount of cross-linking in polyethylene at the expense of chain rupture. In polypropylene, however, both cross-linking and chain rupture were increased in the presence of N_2O. The atactic sample had molecular weights of $M_w \cong 7.72 \times 10^4$ and $M_n \cong 1.4 \times 10^4$ and was in powder form. The isotactic sample had $M_w \cong 5.24 \times 10^5$, $M_n \cong 0.78 \times 10^5$ and $M_w \cong 2.0 \times 10^5$, $M_n \cong 0.77 \times 10^5$; the isotactic samples were in the form of films.

The ^{60}Co cell (1288 Ci) for these experiments was appreciably stronger than that used by Black and Lyons (60). The dose rate was 4.64×10^{19} eV g^{-1} hr^{-1} or 0.742 Mrad hr^{-1}; exposures were carried out at 35°C in vacuum or in the presence of 60 or 74 cm Hg of N_2O. The samples were annealed before viscosity measurements were made by heating just below the softening point in order to destroy radicals.

The sol fractions could again be expressed by the Charlesby–Pinner relationship [Eq. (23)], in spite of the fact that the initial distributions were not random. Intrinsic viscosities were measured in tetralin solutions at 135°C with some antioxidant added. Thermal degradation under these conditions was negligible. The results are given in Fig. 11. The results for the atactic sample cannot be evaluated, as the initial molecular weight of the sample was quite small and the experimental errors were relatively large.

The isotactic sample, irradiated in vacuum, approximately obeys Eq. (82); the results can also be plotted as $1/[\eta]_r$ vs. dose, as already pointed out above. A rapid linear increase of $[\eta]_r^{-1}$ with radiation dose occurs but eventually the slope changes and the plot continues as a straight line. At a dose of about 2 Mrad, the slope becomes zero. The finite slopes for the case in vacuum and that in the presence of N_2O are not much different.

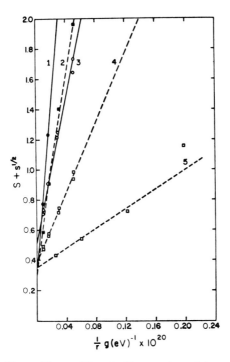

Fig. 11. Charlesby–Pinner Plots: (1) and (3), atactic and isotactic polypropylene, respectively, under vacuum (samples 3 and 2); (2) atactic in 60 cm N_2O; (4) and (5) isotactic (samples 2 and 1) in 60 cm N_2O (66).

Evolved gases were analyzed in a mass spectrometer. Some of the ratios of various G values in the presence of N_2O to those in vacuum are given in Table 3. $G(H_2)$ and $G(CH_4)$ were reduced by almost the same proportion in the presence of N_2O. N_2O most likely acts as an electron scavenger. According to a general mechanism by Dyne (67) for the radiolysis of

TABLE 3

	H_2	CH_4	X, cross-linking	S, chain scission
Isotactic polypropylene				
Sample 1	—	—	1.61	1.29
Sample 2	0.77	0.81	2.01	1.43
Atactic polypropylene	—	—	1.48	1.29

aliphatic hydrocarbons, a reactive species $A*$ is formed first, which then leads to evolution of gases such as H_2 and CH_4. The kinetic scheme is as follows:

$$A-\left[\begin{array}{l}\rightarrow A* \\ \rightarrow A^+ + e^-\end{array}\right. \tag{A}$$

$$A^+ + e^- \rightarrow A* \tag{B}$$

The electron is actually assumed to be trapped in the neighborhood of A^+ (ca. 100 Å away). If N_2O reacts with the electron, the formation of $A*$ is diminished and with it the amounts of H_2 and CH_4, since the following reactions can take place:

$$A*-\left[\begin{array}{l}\rightarrow (X)H + \text{products} \\ \rightarrow \ \ H_2 + \text{products}\end{array}\right. \tag{C}$$

$$(X)H + A \rightarrow H_2 + \text{products} \tag{D}$$

Kondo and Dole (66) suggest that the initial rapid decrease in intrinsic viscosity is due to weak links in the polymer structure, such as a few head-to-head configurations. Recent experimental confirmation of this assumption was given by Bailey et al. (68), who pyrolyzed polypropylene and found that propane was evolved during the very initial stages of the reaction. This gas can only be formed from head-to-head structures in the polymer. Actually, Kondo and Dole express the following opinion, especially in view of the fact that the Charlesby–Pinner relationship [Eq. (23)] holds: "Thus we imagine the polymer first to be degraded to give this distribution (this refers to the random distribution) and then to be cross-linked to produce gel." This statement agrees with the curves obtained when plotting $1/[\eta]_r$ against the irradiation dose for the isotactic sample investigated by Kondo and Dole. (The atactic sample cannot be evaluated in this way, because, as already pointed out, its initial molecular weight was too small and the molecular weight changes are of the same magnitude as the experimental errors.) The initial part with relatively larger slopes up to about 0.5 to 1 Mrad can be assigned to degradation of weak links. The straight lines with the smaller slopes are due to chain scissioning of normal links. This holds up to about 4 to 5 Mrad (or less in the presence of N_2O). The further slowing down of the reaction in its later stages can be related to that part of the radiolysis where cross-linking becomes predominant. The mechanism proposed by Kondo and Dole is as follows:

$$\sim CH_2 - \underset{\underset{CH_3^+}{|}}{CH}\sim \quad \rightarrow \sim CH_2 - \underset{\underset{CH_2\cdot}{|}}{\overset{+}{C}}\sim + H_2$$

$$\sim \overset{+}{CH_2}\sim + \sim CH_2 \sim \rightarrow \sim CH_3^+ \sim + \sim \dot{C}H \sim$$

$$\sim \overset{+}{CH_3}\sim + e^- \quad \rightarrow \sim \dot{C}H \sim + H_2$$

N_2O interferes as follows:

$$N_2O + e^- \rightarrow N_2O^-$$

$$N_2O^- + \sim \overset{+}{CH_2} \rightarrow N_2 + OH\cdot + \sim \dot{C}H\sim$$

$$OH\cdot + \sim CH_2 \sim \rightarrow \sim \dot{C}H \sim + H_2O$$

$\sim \dot{C}H \sim$ can either lead to cross-linking or chain rupture. $\cdot CH_3$ radicals may be produced directly from side chains leading eventually to some production of CH_4. A much higher rate of irradiation was used by Dole et al. than by Black and Lyons (60).

Fischer and Hellwege (69) measured the ESR spectra of isotactic (stretched and unstretched) and atactic polypropylene irradiated with X-rays up to radiation doses of 0.1 to 0.6 Mrad. The temperature during irradiation was 77°K and the samples were under vacuum. The spectra were first measured at 120°K; they changed on heating in the range 190 to 270°K for unstretched isotactic samples. However, they did not change further on heating from 270 to 340°K. The spectra obtained by heating the samples from 270 to 340°K were also directly obtained by irradiation at room temperature. The spectra for the high-temperature range were assigned to a different radical than those obtained at lower temperatures. They could be changed reversibly by repeated heating and cooling of the polymer. The atactic polymer behaved somewhat differently. The same spectra as for isotactic polypropylene were obtained at 77°K and on heating from 230 to 270°K. However, above 270°K, the radical concentration became negligible which means that the spectrum disappeared. The radical spectrum obtained at the elevated temperatures was transformed in the presence of air into a typical peroxide radical spectrum.

The spectrum of the isotactic polymer determined at 120°K, after being stretched to about seven to eight times its original length and irradiated at 77°K, was independent of the angle between the direction of the magnetic field and the axis of stretching. In contrast, samples irradiated at room temperature showed pronounced changes in their spectra on rotation in

the magnetic field. Tsvetkov et al. (70) proposed the following radical for
the spectrum obtained at low temperatures:

$$
\sim CH_2 - \overset{\displaystyle H}{\underset{\displaystyle CH_3}{\overset{|}{\underset{|}{C}}}} - CH_2 - \overset{\displaystyle \cdot}{\underset{\displaystyle CH_3}{\overset{|}{\underset{|}{C}}}} - CH_2 - \overset{\displaystyle H}{\underset{\displaystyle CH_3}{\overset{|}{\underset{|}{C}}}} \sim
$$

However, Libby et al. (71) suggested a different radical;

$$
\sim CH_2 - \overset{\displaystyle H}{\underset{\displaystyle CH_3}{\overset{|}{\underset{|}{C}}}} - CH_2 - \overset{\displaystyle \cdot}{\underset{\displaystyle H}{\overset{|}{\underset{|}{C}}}} - CH_2 - \overset{\displaystyle H}{\underset{\displaystyle CH_3}{\overset{|}{\underset{|}{C}}}} \sim
$$

Hellwege and Fischer favor the first formulation. Both types of radicals
are actually in agreement with the gas analysis results for irradiated polypropylene reported by Dole and co-workers. The formation of the first
would lead to H_2 and that of the second to CH_4 evolution. The spectrum
taken at room temperature was assigned to a resonance stabilized radical
as follows:

$$
\sim CH_2 - \overset{\displaystyle H}{\underset{\displaystyle CH_3}{\overset{|}{\underset{|}{C}}}} - \overset{\displaystyle H}{\overset{|}{C}} = \overset{\displaystyle H}{\overset{|}{C}} - \overset{\displaystyle \cdot}{\underset{\displaystyle H}{\overset{}{C}}} - \overset{\displaystyle H}{\underset{\displaystyle CH_3}{\overset{|}{\underset{|}{C}}}} \sim
$$

A similar radical was found during the irradiation of polyethylene by
various Russian workers (72).

Dynamic properties of polymers can be influenced by irradiation.
Young's modulus and the damping factor were investigated by Baccaredda
et al. (73) for isotactic polystyrene, isotactic polypropylene, and *trans*-1,4-
polybutadiene as a function of irradiation from an atomic pile. The fact
that isotactic polypropylene cross-linked and that main-chain links were
broken was reflected in the change of these properties. Thus Young's
modulus first decreased, passed through a minimum, and increased again
at higher doses of irradiation. Apparently, a reduction in crystallinity and
a certain plasticizing action also occurred due to chain rupture. At higher
doses, cross-linking prevailed. On the whole, all these changes of the
mechanical properties were relatively small.

Polystyrene was scarcely affected by this radiation as far as the mechanical parameters were concerned. This is due to the protective action of the
phenyl groups; moreover, room temperature is far below the glass-transition temperature of this polymer.

Some experiments on high energy irradiation of isotactic polybutene-1 were carried out by Rubin et al. (74). The hexagonal and tetragonal modifications were exposed at −196°C in vacuo to γ-rays. The dose was 1 Mrad. Radicals trapped in the polymer were determined by ESR spectra. Apparently, these radicals are preferentially trapped in crystalline regions. The radical produced from the hexagonal form was assigned to the following structures, which are similar to those formulated for polypropylene:

$$\sim \underset{\underset{\text{H}}{|}}{\overset{\overset{\text{H}}{|}}{\text{C}}} - \underset{\underset{\cdot}{|}}{\overset{\overset{\text{C}_2\text{H}_5}{|}}{\text{C}}} - \underset{\underset{\text{H}}{|}}{\overset{\overset{\text{H}}{|}}{\text{C}}} - \text{H} \quad \text{or} \quad \sim \underset{\underset{\text{H}}{|}}{\overset{\overset{\text{C}_2\text{H}_5}{|}}{\text{C}}} - \text{CH}_2 - \underset{\underset{\cdot}{|}}{\overset{\overset{\text{CH}_3}{|}}{\text{C}}} - \underset{\underset{\text{H}}{|}}{\overset{\overset{\text{H}}{|}}{\text{C}}} \sim$$

The radical obtained from the tetragonal polymer could not be identified. As the degree of crystallinity of the two modifications was not much different, the type of radicals produced must also be, to some extent, dependent on the different crystal structures of the polymers.

VII. CONCLUSION

As far as the limited data allow any general conclusions to be drawn concerning the degradation of stereoregular polymers, it appears that the main differences in the results obtained for the degradation of atactic and the corresponding stereoregular polymers are, in fact, not due to stereoregularity. They are, rather, due to the mode of polymerization producing different end groups, a few abnormal structures in the molecule, and various degrees of crystallinity.

The differences to be expected due to the actual stereoregular structures will be small (e.g., small differences in energy of activation for the depropagation step for some thermal degradation reactions) and will be obscured by other effects. Morphology plays an important role in oxidative degradation below the crystalline melting point. Amorphous regions are preferentially attacked by oxygen. The differences of the corresponding atactic and stereoregular polymers on exposure to high energy radiation are also small as far as structure is concerned, except for effects due to morphology or mode of preparation.

More pronounced differences due to structure become apparent for degradation in solution. Thus photolysis of water-soluble polyacids, such as poly(methacrylic acid), show differences due to different acid strength (pK values) of the atactic and isotactic polymeric acids. The pK values are directly influenced by the structures of the molecules. Also, appreciable differences have been found for oxidation in solution (e.g., polypropylene) as the oxygen molecule fits better into one of the structures (isotactic) than into the other.

Generally, it can be stated that very careful and accurate experiments will have to be performed under rigorously controlled conditions in order to find, with any certainty, the small differences in degradation reactions directly caused by variations in stereoregular structure.

ACKNOWLEDGMENTS

Thanks are due for grants received from the following agencies; they made this work possible: U.S. Army Research Office, Durham (CRD-ID-AA-5463-C) and Public Health Service, Division of Water Pollution (1 ROl-WP00791-02) and Division of Air Pollution (1 ROL-AP00486-01).

REFERENCES

1. H. H. G. Jellinek, *Degradation of Vinyl Polymers*, Academic Press, New York, 1955; N. Grassie, *Chemistry of High Polymer Degradation Processes*, Wiley (Interscience), New York, 1956.
2. H. H. G. Jellinek and S. Y. Fok, *Makromol. Chem.*, **104**, 18 (1967).
3. N. Grassie, in *Encyclopedia of Polymer Science and Technology*, Vol. 4, Wiley, New York, 1966, pp. 647–712.
4. H. H. G. Jellinek, in *Encyclopedia of Polymer Science and Technology*, Vol. 4, Wiley, New York, 1966, pp. 740–793.
5. A. Charlesby and S. H. Pinner, *Proc. Roy. Soc. (London)*, **A249**, 367 (1959).
6. A. Charlesby, *Atomic Radiation and Polymers*, Pergamon Press, New York, 1960; A. Chapiro, *High Polymers*, Vol. XV, Wiley (Interscience), New York, 1962.
7. H. H. G. Jellinek and M. D. Luh, *J. Phys. Chem.*, **70**, 3672 (1966).
8. H. H. G. Jellinek and J. E. Clark, *Can. J. Chem.*, **41**, 355 (1953).
9. N. Grassie and H. W. Melville, *Proc. Roy. Soc. (London)*, **A199**, 1, 14, 22, 39, 949 (1949); N. Grassie and E. Vance, *Trans. Faraday Soc.*, **49**, 184 (1953); A. Brockhaus and E. Jenkel, *Makromol. Chem.*, **18–19**, 262 (1956); S. L. Madorsky, *J. Polymer Sci.*, **11**, 491 (1953); S. Bywater, *J. Phys. Chem.*, **57**, 879 (1953); M. Gordon, *J. Phys. Chem.*, **64**, 19 (1960); S. Bywater and P. E. Block, *J. Phys. Chem.*, **69**, 1967 (1965); S. E. Bresler et al., *Colloid J. U.S.S.R. English Transl.*, **20**, 381 (1958); J. R. McCallum, *Makromol. Chem.*, **82**, 137 (1965); H. H. G. Jellinek and J. E. Clark, *Can. J. Chem.*, **41**, 355 (1963); J. E. Clark and H. H. G. Jellinek, *J. Polymer Sci.*, **A3**, 1171 (1965).
10. H. H. G. Jellinek and M. D. Luh, *Makromol. Chem.*, to be published.
11. V. E. Hart, *J. Res. Natl. Bur. Std.*, **56**, 67 (1956).
12. J. C. Bevington, *Radical Polymerization*, Academic Press, New York, 1961, p. 73.
13. S. L. Madorsky and S. Straus, *J. Polymer Sci.*, **36**, 183 (1959).
14. A. Nakajima, F. Hamada, and T. Shimizu, *Makromol. Chem.*, **90**, 229 (1966).
15. H. Wesslau, *Makromol. Chem.*, **20**, 111 (1956).

16. I. Hameda, *Chem. High Polymers Japan*, *69*, 402 (1961).

17. H. H. G. Jellinek, *Trans. Faraday Soc.*, **40**(6), 1 (1944); **44**, 345 (1948); H. H. G. Jellinek, *J. Polymer Sci.*, **3**, 850 (1948); **4**, 1, 13 (1949); *Degradation of Polystyrene*, Chapter 13, ACS Monograph on Styrene No. 115, 1952; see also Ref. *1*.

18. N. Grassie and W. W. Kerr, *Trans. Faraday Soc.*, **53**, 234 (1957); **55**, 1050 (1959).

19. G. G. Cameron and N. Grassie, *Makromol. Chem.*, **51**, 130 (1962); **53**, 72 (1962).

20. L. A. Wall, *Pyrolysis in Analytical Chemistry of Polymers*, Part II (G. M. Kline, ed.), Wiley (Interscience), New York, 1962, Chapter V; L. A. Wall, S. Straus, J. H. Flynn, and D. McIntyre, report to NASA, *The Thermal Degradation of Polystyrene*.

21. F. Danusso and G. Moraglio, *J. Polymer Sci.*, **24**, 161 (1957).

22. M. Matsumoto, *Chem. High Polymers Japan*, **6**, 36 (1949).

23. D. W. Brown and L. A. Wall, *J. Phys. Chem.*, **62**, 848 (1958).

24. N. Grassie and H. W. Melville, *Proc. Roy. Soc. (London)*, **A199**, 1 (1949).

25. H. H. G. Jellinek and H. Kachi, *J. Polymer Sci.*, 1966; *IUPAC Meeting, Tokyo and Kyoto*, 1966.

26. S. L. Madorsky, *J. Polymer Sci.*, **9**, 133 (1952); **11**, 491 (1953).

27. D. H. Grant, E. Vance, and S. Bywater, *Trans. Faraday Soc.*, **56**, 1697 (1960). See also J. M. G. Cowie and S. Bywater, *J. Polymer Sci.*, **54**, 221 (1961).

28. D. Braun and G. Heufer, *Makromol. Chem.*, **79**, 98 (1964).

29. J. V. Schooten and P. W. O. Wijga, *SCI Monograph No. 13*, 432 (1961).

30. T. E. Davis, R. L. Tobias, and E. B. Peterli, *J. Polymer Sci.*, **56**, 485 (1962).

31. J. B. Kinsinger, paper presented at *132nd Meeting of the ACS, New York, 1957*.

32. H. H. G. Jellinek and H. Chou, *Can. J. Chem.*, **42**, 522 (1964).

33. H. H. G. Jellinek and S. N. Lipovac, *J. Macromol. Chem.*, **1**, 773 (1966).

34. H. H. G. Jellinek and S. N. Lipovac, *IUPAC Meeting, Brussels, 1967*, to be published in *J. Polymer Sci.*

34a. D. G. Gardner and G. A. Henry, *Polymer Letters*, **5**, 101 (1967).

34b. D. G. Gardner, G. A. Henry, and D. Ward, *Energy Transfer in Radiation Processes* (G. Phillips, ed.), Elsevier, Amsterdam, 1966.

35. J. L. Bolland, *Quart. Rev. (London)*, **3**, 1 (1949); L. Bateman, *Quart. Rev. (London)*, **8**, 147 (1954); W. O. Lundberg (ed.), *Autoxidation and Antioxidants*, Wiley (Interscience), New York, Vol. 1, 1961; Vol. 2, 1962; G. S. Scott, *Atmospheric Oxidation and Antioxidants*, Elsevier, Amsterdam, 1965. W. L. Hawkins and F. H. Winslow, in *Chemical Reactions of Polymers*, Vol. 19 (E. M. Fettes, ed.), Wiley (Interscience), New York, 1964, Chap. 20; see also Vol. 20 (R. A. V. Raff and K. W. Doak, eds.), Wiley (Interscience), New York, 1964–1965; see also Refs. *1* and *3*.

35a. L. Reich and S. S. Stivala, *Rev. Macromol. Chem.*, **1**, 249 (1966). The review appeared after this chapter was written. It contains material relevant to stereoregular polymers.

36. J. L. Bolland and G. Gee, *Trans. Faraday Soc.*, **42**, 236, 244 (1946).

37. M. B. Neiman (ed.), *Aging and Stabilization of Polymers* (translation), Consultants Bureau, New York, 1965. Original in Russian, 1964.

38. V. B. Miller, M. B. Neiman, V. S. Pudov, and L. I. Lafer, *Vysokomolekul. Soedin.*, **1**(11), 1696 (1959).

39. D. Rysavy, L. Balaban, V. Slavik, and J. Ruza, *Vysokomolekul. Soedin.*, **3**(7), 110 (1961).

40. W. L. Hawkins, W. Matreysak, and F. H. Winslow, *J. Polymer Sci.*, **41**, 1 (1959).
41. V. S. Pudov, B. A. Gromov, M. B. Neiman, and E. G. Sklyarova, *Neftekhimiya*, **3**, 743 (1963); V. S. Pudov and M. B. Neiman, *Neftekhimiya*, **3**, 750 (1963); see also Ref. *37*, Chap. I.
42. N. N. Semenov, *Some Problems in Chemical Kinetics and Reactivity*, Vol. 2, Princeton Univ. Press, Princeton, N.J., 1959, pp. 264, 271; see also N. N. Semenov, *Chemical Kinetics and Chain Reactions*, Oxford Univ. Press, Fair Lawn, N.J., 1935.
43. L. Bateman et al., *Discussions Faraday Soc.*, **14**, 190 (1953).
44. Yu. A. Slyapnikov, V. B. Miller, M. B. Neiman, and Ye. S. Torsuyeva, Part I, *Vysokomolekul. Soedin.*, **4**(8), 1228 (1960); Part II, **5**(10), 1507 (1963).
45. S. S. Stivala, L. Reich, and P. G. Kelleher, *Makromol. Chem.*, **59**, 28 (1963).
46. C. F. Cullis and C. N. Hinshelwood, *Discussions Faraday Soc.*, **2**, 117 (1947).
47. L. Reich and S. S. Stivala, *J. Polymer Sci.*, **B3**, 227 (1965).
48. S. S. Stivala and L. Reich, *Polymer Eng. Sci.*, **5**(9), 179 (1965).
49. E. M. Bevilacqua, E. S. English, and J. S. Gall, *J. Appl. Polymer Sci.*, **8**, 1691 (1964).
50. E. N. Matveeva, S. S. Khinkis, A. I. Isvetkova, and V. A. Balandina, *Soviet Plastics English Transl.*, **4**, (1964).
51. V. Stannett and R. B. Mesrobian, *Discussions Faraday Soc.*, **14**, 242 (1953).
52. W. L. Hawkins, *Polymer Eng. Sci.*, **5**(3), 196 (1965).
53. L. Dulog, E. Radlmann, and W. Kern, *Makromol. Chem.*, **60**, 1 (1963).
54. L. Dulog, E. Radlmann, and W. Kern, *Makromol. Chem.*, **79**, 67 (1964).
55. A. V. Tobolsky, P. M. Norling, N. H. Frick, and H. Yu, *J. Am. Chem. Soc.*, **86**, 3925 (1964).
56. G. Natta, E. Beati, and F. Severini, *J. Polymer Sci.*, **34**, 685 (1959).
56a. H. C. Beschell and L. H. Smiley, *J. Polymer Sci.*, **A1**(5), 1635 (1967).
57. R. M. Black and B. J. Lyons, *Nature*, **180**, 1346 (1957).
58. F. B. Waddington, *J. Polymer Sci.*, **31**, 221 (1958).
59. R. P. Gupta, *Kolloid-Z.*, **174**, 74 (1961).
60. R. M. Black and B. J. Lyons, *Proc. Roy. Soc.* (*London*), **A253**, 322 (1959).
61. P. Flory and J. Rehner, *J. Chem. Phys.*, **11**, 521 (1943).
62. W. Schnabel and M. Dole, *J. Phys. Chem.*, **67**, 295 (1963).
63. R. W. Keyser, B. Clegg, and M. Dole, *J. Phys. Chem.*, **67**, 300 (1963).
64. G. D. Cooper and A. R. Gilbert, *J. Polymer Sci.*, **38**, 275 (1959).
65. A. M. Kotliar, *J. Polymer Sci.*, **55**, 71 (1961).
66. M. Kondo and M. Dole, *J. Phys. Chem.*, **70**, 883 (1966).
67. P. J. Dyne, *Can. J. Chem.*, **43**, 1080 (1965).
68. W. J. Bailey, C. Liotta, and D. Fung, *Tech. Rept. AFML-TR-65-100*, April 1965.
69. H. Fischer and K. H. Hellwege, *J. Polymer Sci.*, **56**, 33 (1962).
70. Yu. D. Tsvetkov, Yu. N. Malin, and V. V. Voevodsku, *Vysokomolekul. Soedin.*, **1**, 1805 (1959).
71. D. Libby, M. G. Ormerod, and A. Charlesby, *Polymer*, **1**, 212 (1960).
72. A. G. Kiselev, M. A. Malkulskin, and Yu. S. Lazurkin, *Vysokomolekul. Soedin.*, **2**, 1678 (1960).
73. M. Baccaredda, E. Butta, and V. Frosini, *J. Appl. Polymer Sci.*, **10**, 399 (1966).
74. I. D. Rubin and L. M. Huber, *J. Polymer Sci.*, **B4**, 337 (1966).

Author Index

Numbers in parentheses are reference numbers and indicate that an author's work is referred to although his name is not cited in the text. Numbers in italics show the page on which the complete reference is listed.

Subject Index

A

Acetaldehyde–*n*-butyraldehyde copolymers, isomorphism in, 54, 55
Acetals, equilibrium hydrolysis, 362
Acetic polyaldehyde, isotactic, chain model, 36
Acrylic acid–acrylamide copolymers, microtacticity effects on reactions, 348, 350–351
Acrylic acid–ethyl ethacrylate copolymers, microtacticity effects on reactions, 343
Acrylic acid–methacrylic copolymers, microtacticity effects on reactions, 335–359
Acrylic acid–methyl acrylate copolymers, microtacticity effects on reactions, 346
Acrylic polymers, microtacticity effects on reactions, 335–359
Aldehydes, polymers, *see* Polyaldehydes
1-Alkyl butadienes, optically active polymers from, 193
Alkyl β-chlorovinyl ethers, polymerization, NMR studies, 123
α-Angelica-lactone, polymerization, 199
Atomic nuclei, properties, 62–63
Autohesion of stereoregular polymers, 228
Automata theories of hereditary tactic copolymerization, 305–331

B

Bernoullian statistical process in polymerization, 83–84
Biopolymers, NMR studies, 135
Bolland mechanism of polymer oxidation, 404–405

Bond orientation effect on conformation, 15
Bulk density of stereoregular polymers, 240
Butadiene–1,3-pentadiene copolymers, isomorphism in, 56
cis-Butene-2–ethylene copolymer, chain repetition groups, 12
configuration, 9
n-Butyraldehyde–acetaldehyde copolymers, isomorphism in, 54, 55

C

Carbohydrates, NMR studies, 135
Central Dogma of hereditary information, 308, 326
Chain conformation, crystallinity and, 1–60
line repetition groups and, 11, 12, 13
types, 11
unperturbed type, 21–27
"Characteristic ratio," of macromolecules in solution, 252–261
Charlesby-Pinner relationship in polymer degradation, 378, 422, 423
Cis-trans isomerism, *see* Geometric isomerism
Conformation, energetic factors determining, 15
equivalence principle of, 10
internal energy of, principle 10, 15–18
as function of internal rotation angles 18–21
ordered, of solid-state linear macromolecules, 244–249
of polymers in solution, 243–244, 249–261
"characteristic ratio," 252–253
principle of minimum internal conformational energy, 10

449

Polyvinylcyclohexane, isotactic, chain-conformation data, 30
  chain packing, 45
Poly(vinyl ethers), optical activity, 203, 205
Poly(vinyl ethyl ether), NMR studies, 122
Poly(vinyl fluorides), PMR studies, 121, 122
Poly(vinyl formate), NMR studies, 122
Polyvinylidine, conformation in solid state, 244
Poly(vinylidene chloride-*co*-isobutylene), NMR studies, 134
Poly(vinylidene fluorides), NMR studies, 121, 122
Poly(vinylidene fluoride-*co*-hexafluoropropylene), NMR studies, 134
Poly(vinyl isobutyl ethers), isotactic, chain-conformation data, 30
  physical properties, 214
Poly(vinyl isopropyl ether), isotactic, chain-conformation data, 30
  NMR studies, 122
Poly(vinyl methyl ethers) isotactic, chain-conformation data, 30
  chain packing, 44
  NMR studies, 120–122
Poly(vinylnaphthalene), chain packing, 41
  NMR studies, 122
  in solution, properties, 276–277
Poly(2-vinylnaphthalene), NMR studies, 122
Poly(2-vinylpyridine), NMR studies, 122
Poly(vinyl trifluoroacetate), 364
  NMR studies, 122
Principle of minimum internal conformational energy, 10, 15–18
Propylene, polymerization, *cis*-opening, 163–167
  NMR studies, 123
Propylene oxide–citraconic anhydride copolymers, NMR studies, 130–131, 132, 133
Propylene oxide–maleic anhydride copolymers, NMR studies, 130
Proteins, 287

in solution, properties, 278
synthesis, 289

R

Racemic mixture, 193
Radiation degradation of stereoregular polymers, 417–427
Random degradation, 371
  kinetics, 372–375
Resole-type resins, NMR studies, 132
Resolution, 193
RNA, messenger, 290, 307
  synthesis, 289
  transfer type, 290
  types, 307
Rubber, natural, chain packing, 45

S

Screws, tetragonal packing, 38
Silk fibroin, conformation, 297
Solution, stereoregular polymers in, properties, 243–285
Sorption isotherms of stereoregular polymers, 228
Specific heats of stereoregular polymers, 228–231
Stereoregular polymers, chain conformation, 9–36
  data on, 31–36
  configuration, 1–9
  crystallinity determination, 46–51
  degradation, 371–430
  isomorphism in, 53–56
  mode of packing, 36–46
    of cylindrical chains, 37–40
    of lattice-containing chains, 41–46
    principles, 36–37
  optically active, *see* Optically active stereoregular polymers
  paracrystalline forms, 51–53
  physical properties, 213–241
  in solution, properties, 243–285
complex formation, 272–275
  second virial coefficient, 261–265
  solvent effects, 268–272
  thermodynamic parameters